Spirituality and Mental Health

A handbook for
service users,
carers and staff
wishing to bring a
spiritual dimension to
mental health services

Pavilion

Edited by Peter Gilbert

Spirituality and Mental Health

A handbook for service users, carers and staff wishing to bring a spiritual dimension to mental health services

© Peter Gilbert 2011

Published by:
Pavilion Publishing and Media Ltd
Rayford House
School Road
Hove
BN3 5HX
Tel: +44 (0) 1273 434943
Fax: +44 (0) 1273 227308
Email: info@pavpub.com
Web: www.pavpub.com

First published 2011. Reprinted 2012

A catalogue record of this book is available from the British Library.

ISBN: 978-1-908066-00-8

Pavilion is the leading publisher and provider of professional development products and services for workers in the health, social care, education and community safety sectors. We believe that everyone has the right to fulfil their potential and we strive to supply products and services that help raise standards, promote best practice and support continuing professional development.

Pavilion editors: Kerry Boettcher and Catherine Ansell-Jones, Pavilion
Cover design: Emma Garbutt, Pavilion
Page design: Katherine Jones, Pavilion
Printing: Ashford Press

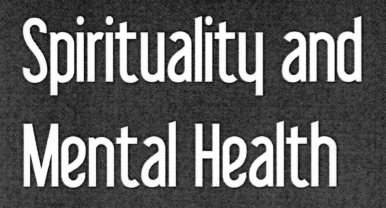

Spirituality and Mental Health

A handbook for
service users,
carers and staff
wishing to bring a
spiritual dimension to
mental health services

Pavilion

Edited by Peter Gilbert

Contents

Contributors

Peter Gilbert is Emeritus professor of social work and spirituality at Staffordshire University, and visiting professor with the University of Worcester and previously Birmingham and Solihull NHS Foundation Trust. Peter was the NIMHE project lead on spirituality from its inception to 2008, and now works with the National Spirituality and Mental Health Forum. From 2008 to 2010 he was chair of the National Development Team for Inclusion. A former director of social services for Worcestershire, Peter is a registered social worker with 13 years of direct practice. Between 2003 and 2006 he was NIMHE/SCIE fellow in social care with Professor Nick Gould, and is now a member of the NMHDU's Equalities Programme Board. He was very involved in partnership working in both Staffordshire as director of operations, and Worcestershire as director, initiating service user, carer and advocacy fora. In the 1980s he specialised in learning disability and mental health, publishing several books on working with people with learning disabilities and their families (including *Managing to Care*, with Terry Scragg, 1992). Having experienced an episode of depression in 2000/1 Peter is very committed to a holistic and person-centred approach, and the integration of personal experience. Peter is signed up to ensuring the integration of theory with practice, and as such has served on several national groups such as the former CSCI Mental Health Improvement Board, and the Social Perspectives Network. Peter is an associate member of ADASS and ADSS (Cymru), and wrote the national ADSS/NIMHE guidance on the integration of mental health services. In 2008 he published Guidelines on Spirituality for Staff in Acute Care Services (Staffordshire University) for NIMHE/CSIP. He is national facilitator for the National Social Care Strategic Network. Peter published *Leadership: Being effective and remaining human*, in 2005, and he and his co-editors published *Spirituality, Values and Mental Health: Jewels for the journey* in 2007. He co-authored a SCIE position paper on leadership and personalisation in 2009. His latest publications are *Social Work and Mental Health: The value of everything* (with colleagues) in 2010; a leadership development pack with Dr Neil Thompson; editing a special edition of *Mental Health, Religion and Culture*; co-editing a special edition of *The International Journal of Leadership in Public Services* (June, 2010, with Professor Bill Fulford) and a chapter on his experience of mental illness in Basset and Stickley's (2010) *Voices of Experience: Narratives of survival and mental health*.

Sarajane Aris is a consultant clinical psychologist and head of clinical psychology services for the past seven years. She has worked for mental health service within the NHS for over 30 years. She is currently head of clinical psychology for the city division, Derbyshire Mental Healthcare Services NHS Trust. She is also an associate for the Healthcare Commission. She founded the Transpersonal Network for Clinical and Counselling Psychologists and Therapists in the UK following the foundation of the transpersonal section within the British Psychological Society in 1997. She has been involved in organisational change and development work for Avon and Wiltshire Partnership NHS Trust and other organisations since 1991. She has worked as an adviser and consultant to the Cancer Help Centre, Bristol for a number of years. She has contributed chapters for books on consciousness and spirituality in mental health. She has recently co-written a book on counselling and helping with Professor Richard Velleman. This includes a chapter on spirituality and helping. Her life is informed by the principles of love, wisdom and compassion, and she seeks to live her life guided by a wish to serve for the greater good.

Ben Bano has been a social worker for 38 years and was director of older people's services in East Kent Mental Health Partnership Trust from 2002 to 2005. In 2005 Ben founded Telos Training Ltd (www.telostraining. co.uk) with a focus on a whole person approach to care and has delivered a range of training workshops in meeting the spiritual needs of people with dementia and their carers. Ben also delivers leadership training for local authority managers. He is involved in pastoral work with people with dementia in his parish and at the older people's wards at St Martins Hospital, Canterbury. In 2009 he produced a DVD on spirituality and dementia 'It's still ME, Lord...' as well as an online learning resource for Caritas Social Action Network, and facilitated a series of follow-up workshops across England. Ben is also a visiting lecturer at Canterbury Christchurch University.

Joanna Barber is a qualified medical doctor, with a research degree from Oxford University, who is a long-term mental health service user. She is also a semi-professional violinist with a diploma from Birmingham Conservatoire. She has worked as a volunteer for the Birmingham and Solihull Mental Health Foundation Trust for 12 years. Initially, this was as a therapeutic musician and befriender, playing live music for elderly mental health service users. More recently, she has become involved in mental health research in the Trust, particularly in the field of spirituality and mental health. She has written a handbook of spiritual care in mental illness, which is soon to be used for clinical staff training in spiritual care. She has recently planned a large research project to test the value of improved spiritual care on rate and degree of recovery from mental illness.

Susan Mary Benbow is an old age psychiatrist and family therapist. She is professor of mental health and ageing at the Centre for Ageing and Mental Health, Staffordshire University, and director of Older Mind Matters Ltd. She worked as consultant old age psychiatrist in Central Manchester, then Wolverhampton (2001–2009). She led the development of a national work programme as National Institute for Mental Health England fellow in ageing and mental health (2003–2006) and served as elected chair of the faculty of old age psychiatry (2002–2006). Dr Benbow regularly reviews books and papers, is invited to present at regional, national and international meetings, is associate editor for *International Psychogeriatrics*, and is a partner/clinical adviser to a number of research projects. Her research interests are broad and include spirituality in relation to dementia. Recently, she has been working on user and carer participation and how staff can learn from users and carers.

Julian Bowers was ordained as an Anglican priest in 1972, following theological training in Edinburgh. Periods of church ministry followed in Wiltshire, Bristol, Somerset and London and he also worked for nearly five years as a school chaplain in Sri Lanka. He has had a long-term interest in mental health as well as in the interface of psychology and spirituality. He holds a theology degree and has completed a course in psychodynamic counselling at Birkbeck College and a Master's in Psychoanalytic Theory mainly from a clinical perspective at Goldsmiths College. He has been head of chaplaincy at St Andrew's Healthcare since 2004 where he teaches mindfulness-based stress reduction to a wide range of staff and healthcare professionals. He is an honorary canon of Peterborough Cathedral.

Sarah Carr is a senior research analyst at the Social Care Institute for Excellence who is managing a major work stream on the personalisation of adult social care services. She has worked for the National Institute for Social Work, Oxleas NHS Trust and at the Sainsbury Centre for Mental Health in research and information roles. Sarah is also an honorary fellow at the Faculty of Health, Staffordshire University and a fellow of the Royal Society of Arts. She holds both Bachelor's and Master's degrees in Theology. Sarah has had a number of voluntary sector social care jobs including residential support worker at a farm hostel for homeless people in Edinburgh, worker at a rehabilitation project for young women sex workers, and an HIV and AIDS awareness trainer in Manchester. She has been a trustee at PACE (London's leading charity promoting the mental health and emotional well-being of the lesbian, gay, bisexual and transgender (LGBT) community), and a member of INVOLVE, the national advisory group, funded by the Department of Health, which aims to promote and support active public involvement in NHS, public health and social care research. She now is a trustee of NDTi, an executive committee member of the Social Perspectives Network (SPN) and a member of the Personalised Care in Mental Health Research Group, based at the Institute of Psychiatry. Sarah is a long-term user of mental health services and has written on her own experiences as well as general mental health practice and policy, service user empowerment and participation, and LGBT equality issues.

Janice Clarke is a senior lecturer at the Institute of Health and Society, University of Worcester. After nursing for many years in a broad range of specialities including elderly care, intensive care, cardiology and in many nursing homes, she has led a variety of post-registration programmes for health care workers. She now leads a Master's degree in Advancing Practice in Health Care and delivers mentorship programmes for the NHS. She is on the executive committee for the British Association for the Study of Spirituality and the editorial board of Practical Theology. She has published in a variety of health care journals on aspects of spiritual health care and her particular interests include interpretations of spirituality in health care literature, attitudes to religion, incorporating the body in spiritual care and creating a critical and practical approach to spiritual care for nursing. She has spoken at conferences in the UK and the US about a holistic model of spiritual care which includes the physical body.

Sarah Eagger is an honorary senior clinical lecturer at the Department of Psychological Medicine, Imperial College and consultant psychiatrist for older adults in north London. She is on the executive board and was chair (2005–2009) of the Spirituality and Psychiatry Special Interest Group of the Royal College of Psychiatrists. She also chairs the Spirituality and Faith Committee in her mental health trust and is a trustee and now co-chair of the National Forum for Spirituality and Mental Health. Her particular interests include training doctors in assessing patients' spiritual needs. She is the co-ordinating editor of a facilitators' manual for healthcare professionals, *Values in Healthcare: A spiritual approach*, published in 2004, and contributed to the edited work *Spirituality and Psychiatry*, published by the Royal College in 2009. Dr Eagger is especially interested in the spiritual aspect of the holistic model, and has practised and taught meditation in various NHS settings for many years. She has also spoken on aspects of consciousness and spirituality at numerous national and international conferences.

Joy Gauci is senior lecturer at the University of Worcester, having designed and led a Master's in Social Work over the past three years and currently leads on the development of an international Master's in Social Work and Community Studies. Joy has practised as a community social worker for 20 years, working with adults experiencing emotional and cognitive transition and trauma. Joy undertook a Master's in Applied Philosophy for Social Work Practice (2000) to explore and develop a distinct approach based on 'strengths' or capacity based work with survivors. Joy lectures in key areas relating to social work and social welfare, including skills in community work with vulnerable adults, safeguarding, philosophy and ethics, statutory law and policy for social work practice. Joy's research, publications and conference presentations have explored and promoted the concept of meaningful engagement in relationship based practice. Joy has worked closely with service users as colleagues in teaching and practice and has developed a consultancy and training partnership with third sector provision (Community First Worcestershire, 2007–2010) to promote a participatory model of relationship based practice for community development initiatives. Joy is interested in the international translation and validity of this approach and is currently engaged in a collaborative research and practice initiative stemming out of a partnership agreement between the Universities of Worcester and Perm State University, Northern Russia. Joy holds a practice educator and mentorship award for Social Work and has constructed a reflective practice contract for social work students engaged in reflection about their professional development (MASW Programme, University of Worcester, 2009). The contract echoes Joy's professional interest in a distinct model of professional engagement based on the shared theme of professional and service user engagement in capacity building. This chapter explores the potential alignment between this 'reflective consciousness' and spirituality – a theme that has been central to Joy's social work practice and broader life journey.

Paul Gilbert is professor of clinical psychology at the University of Derby and consultant psychologist at Derbyshire Mental Health Services NHS Trust. He has a visiting professorship at the University of Fribourg (Switzerland) and University of Coimbria (Portugal). He has been a fellow of the British Psychological Society since 1993. He was committee member and then president of the International Society for Evolutionary Approaches to Psychopathology (1992) and a committee member and past president of the British Association for Behavioural and Cognitive Psychotherapy (2001–2004). He was also on the British Government's Advisory committee NICE (National Institute for Clinical Excellence) for the Depression Guideline (2002–2004). He has authored over 100 academic papers and book chapters and authored/edited 16 books. He has researched and written extensively in the areas of mood disorder, social anxiety and psychosis. Throughout his 30-year career he has focused on evolutionary mechanisms underpinning vulnerabilities to psychological problems with a specific focus on attachment and social ranking systems. Twenty years ago he began to explore the value of developing compassion, especially self-compassion, for people from troubled backgrounds, who have high shame and self-criticism. With his patients, and from a variety of influences from standard psychotherapies, Buddhism and other compassion focused practices he has developed an approach to therapy called compassion focused therapy. To help advance compassionate approaches to psychological and other human problems he established a charity called The Compassionate Mind Foundation (www.compassionatemind.co.uk). The mission statement is 'promoting well-being through the scientific understanding and application of compassion'. His recent books include: *The Compassionate Mind*; *Overcoming Depression: A self-help guide using cognitive behavioral techniques* (2009); *Compassion: Conceptualisations, research and use in psychotherapy* (2005) and *Psychotherapy and Counselling for Depression* (2007). Paul has recently developed a series of self-help talks 'Overcoming Depression: Talks with your therapist' (available from Amazon).

Andrew Goodhead is a British Methodist minister. He is presently spiritual care lead at St Christopher's Hospice, Sydenham, London. He has served as a circuit minister and superintendent minister in circuits in England and Scotland. Andrew began work at St Christopher's Hospice in 2005 and has a responsibility for the pastoral and spiritual care of patients and their families. He is also engaged in teaching spiritual care and spirituality to other healthcare professionals and tutor on the hospice's 'Multi-Professional Week' and runs the annual study week for hospice and hospital chaplains on end of life care.

Arthur Hawes retired as archdeacon of Lincoln and a canon of Lincoln Cathedral in September 2008. His parish ministry began in 1968 when he was appointed curate of St John's, Kidderminster. Here he founded KARE – the Kidderminster Association for Rehousing in Emergency. From 1976–1992 he was rector of Attlebridge, Alderford and Swannington and chaplain to the Norwich acute psychiatric services. He then moved to be the team rector of St Faith's, Gaywood in King's Lynn. Mental health has always featured in his ministry and it began in 1971 when he was founder chairman of the North Worcestershire Association for Mental Health, following postgraduate work at Birmingham University. From 1976 to 1992 he was chaplain for the acute psychiatric units in Norwich, and from 1986 to 1995 he was a Mental Health Act commissioner where he led visiting teams to both Broadmoor and Rampton hospitals and chaired the Section 57 group of the Commission. In 1995 he was appointed chair of the Church of England's Mental Health Advisory Group and, as a member of the Mission and Public Affairs Council, he has presented two debates in the General Synod of the Church of England on mental health issues, which are available on the Church of England website. The first debate included the launch of the parish pack – *Promoting Mental Health: A resource for spiritual and pastoral care*. In 1996 he was appointed a jubilee patron of MIND, and in 1999 was a member of MIND's National Reference Group. From 1998–2006 he was a non-executive director of the Mental Health Trust in Lincolnshire. His particular responsibilities were to chair the Mental Health Act Sub-Committee of the Trust and to have a responsibility for managers' appeals and renewals. From 2003–2007 he was a member of the NHS Confederation Mental Health Policy Committee and from 2003 to 2005 was chairman of the East Midlands NIMHE Regional Development Centre. In 2007 he was invited to become a member of the Criminal Justice Mental Health Research Group at Lincoln University, chaired by Professor Charlie Brooker. In 2006–2008 he was appointed Mental Health Act adviser to the Lincolnshire Partnership Trust. From 2003 onwards he has been a member of the National Spirituality and Mental Health Forum. He is now co-chairman of the Forum with Dr Sarah Eagger. He has published many occasional papers and edited the book *The Anne French Memorial Lectures*.

Margaret Holloway is a qualified social worker and professor of social work at the University of Hull, having previously worked at the Universities of Sheffield and Manchester. She has acted as social care lead with the National End of Life Care Programme since October 2009. She has specialised in practice, teaching and research in the field of death, dying and bereavement and the health and social care interface since 1983. Over the years she has lectured on various topics associated with the understanding of death, dying and bereavement to audiences ranging from sociology undergraduates and social work students to pastoral carers, doctors and palliative care nurses. From 1989–1992 she also acted as consultant to an Anglican diocesan bereavement counselling scheme as well as setting up and supervising a local bereavement support service. In recent years Professor Holloway has concentrated her interests on care of older people, particularly at the end of life, and trans-cultural aspects. She is a founder member of the British Association for the Study of Spirituality (BASS) and particularly interested in exploring models of spiritual care, which are appropriate in contemporary health and social care contexts in the UK. Recent research includes a study of spirituality in contemporary funerals, funded by the Arts and Humanities Research Council.

Tanya Kennard-Campbell is the managing director and founder of Freemind Well-being, a thriving community interest company, whose aim is to raise awareness of the need to provide simple, yet effective education and understanding about what creates and maintains emotional health and well-being. Tanya began her career as a registered mental health nurse in 1991, mainly out of a desire to understand what creates mental distress and how to recover from it. As her career developed, she was fascinated by the resiliency and courage of many patients and families despite the low levels of hope felt by clinicians and patients alike. She became a 'recovery trainer' alongside a number of 'psychiatric survivors/consumers' and it was at this point that she felt her career finally began, in pointing people toward lasting personal change. In this role she helped develop the New Zealand Recovery Plan and trained over 750 multidisciplinary staff members on how to assist in their consumers' recovery, as well as influence general system change. After her return to the United Kingdom in 2003, she started her consultancy work out of frustration at the lack of change in practice since she left over 10 years ago. She was shocked that most clinicians or service users hadn't heard of the word 'recovery'. Around this time she became a principle based facilitator, and had begun to use this simple understanding in her work with clients with acute psychosis. One of her roles through her consultancy business was in the then, National Institute for Mental Health in England (later CSIP), where she created a series of resources, such as the *Whole Life* workbook, including the Whole Life Recovery Plan, DVD and the *Playing It Forward* well-being resource.

Qaisra Khan is an experienced public sector professional who has performed a number of roles ranging from local councillor, social services inspector to care co-ordinator. She has worked as spiritual and cultural care co-ordinator at Oxleas NHS Foundation Trust since November 2004. She has been a visiting lecturer at St Mary's University College, Twickenham for over 10 years, lectured on the University of Greenwich Dark Empire course for three years, and recently did a session on mental health awareness for the Muslim Spiritual Care Provision in the NHS, a project of the Muslim Council of Britain. Recently, she received a long service award for being a school governor for over 10 years. Her education includes a Master's degree in Islamic Cultures and Societies, School of African and Oriental Studies, University of London and a BA (joint honours) in history and archaeology, St David's University College, University of Wales. The BA involved a year doing Christian theology. Publications include public inspection reports, contributions to the Runnymede Trust journal, *Life in the Day*, a recovery journal by Pier Professional and MCT magazine for multicultural teaching.

Wilf McSherry was appointed professor in dignity of care for older people in August 2008; a shared role between Staffordshire University and Shrewsbury and Telford Hospital NHS Trust. He has had a career in nursing; working as a registered nurse within acute hospital care. His interest in the spiritual dimension developed alongside a realisation that this aspect of care was neglected and forgotten by some healthcare professionals. He has published several books and many articles addressing different aspects of the spiritual dimension such as educational issues, and spiritual assessment. He completed his doctoral studies at Leeds Metropolitan University in May 2005 researching *The Meaning of Spirituality and Spiritual Care: An investigation of healthcare professionals, patients and public's perceptions*. Prior to being appointed to his current role, Wilf was a senior lecturer in nursing at the University of Hull where he was also instrumental in creating with colleagues the Centre for Spirituality Studies of which he was the director. Wilf is currently one of the vice presidents of BASS (British Association for The Study of Spirituality).

Rob Merchant is a gerontologist and priest. He was deputy director of the Centre for Ageing and Mental Health at Staffordshire University until 2009. He is currently rector of seven parishes in rural Gloucestershire and co-chair of the newly established Centre for Faith, Values and Science in Healthcare at the University of Gloucestershire.

Jacqui Miller's professional background is in mental health social work. She is also trained in human resource development and service improvement. She previously worked as an education, development and training manager. This work involved leading practice development for social work, nursing and allied health professionals. Jacqui has worked as a programme lead on race equality in mental health for the West Midlands. Her current role is working as a programme specialist for improving access to psychological therapies at a regional level. This role has a key responsibility for ensuring that all primary care trusts commission appropriate talking therapies for those suffering with anxiety and depression. Jacqui is also a lay minister within the Church of God of Prophecy and works as a regional women's ministry leader. She has a passion to encourage people with a healing word, especially those suffering with mental ill health. She is also a carer for members of her family suffering with mental ill health and believes that spirituality is key in enhancing the recovery journey.

Katja Milner is a spirituality healthcare worker with Nottinghamshire Healthcare NHS Trust. This is a pioneering new role within the NHS and involves promoting the importance of people's spirituality, religion and belief in mental health care and recovery, and includes the development of spiritual interventions and staff training. She has completed a degree in psychology and a postgraduate certificate in psychological therapies and has worked in various mental health contexts, including forensic, primary care and psychiatric research. Katja also has a longstanding interest in a broad range of spiritual approaches and has completed training in shamanic and spiritual healing.

Ivor Moody has been the vice dean and canon pastor of Chelmsford Cathedral since April 2010. Previously, he was chaplain of Anglia Ruskin University (Chelmsford campus), where he taught about the concept and role of spirituality to students of various academic disciplines, but most notably nursing students from the faculty of health and social care. He has had articles published in several theological journals on spirituality and chaplaincy on the higher education campus, most recently in *Discourse, Learning and Teaching in Philosophical and Religious Studies*, published by the Higher Education Academy (2010), with an article examining the importance of establishing cross-curricular links between concepts of spirituality and aspects of the secular curriculum. He is chair of Essex Mind and Spirit, a community voluntary organisation dedicated to raising awareness of the importance of spirituality in the understanding of and recovery from mental ill health among service carers and service users, and is a member of the National Spirituality and Mental Health Forum. He is also chair of the Mid-Essex Inter-faith Forum.

Bernard Moss is Emeritus professor of social work education and spirituality at Staffordshire University where he has worked for 17 years educating and training social work students. He played a key role in developing the Centre for Spirituality and Health at the University, and has published widely in this field. His teaching excellence was recognised by the Higher Education Academy in 2004 with the awarding of a National Teaching Fellowship and subsequently with prestigious senior fellow status. His publications include *Religion and Spirituality* (1995); *Values* (2007) both published by Russell House Publishing; *Communication Skills for Health and Social Care* (2009) published by Sage, and *Spirituality and Social Work* (2010) co-authored with Professor Margaret Holloway, published by Palgrave Macmillan.

Rebecca Nye has been an academic researcher, speaker, author and consultant on children's spirituality since 1994. She has held research posts at Birmingham, Nottingham, Cambridge and Anglia Ruskin Universities. Originally pursuing this area as a psychologist, the professional contexts for her work also includes advocacy and training for schools and faith communities across the UK and internationally. Her current teaching is focused on postgraduate students in this field in Cambridge, Chester and for the Open University. She conducted a landmark research study of children's spirituality (*The Spirit of the Child* (2nd ed), 2006, Jessica Kingsley), and between 1996–2004 developed the psychology and christianity programme at the Faculty of Divinity, University of Cambridge (*Psychology for Christian Ministry*, 2002, Routledge). Her most recent book, *Children's Spirituality: What it is and why it matters* (Church House Publishing) was published in 2009.

Madeleine Parkes is a research assistant at Birmingham and Solihull Mental Health NHS Foundation Trust. She is currently working closely with Dr Joanna Barber, a service user, to design, test and develop a number of spiritual care interventions for service users from a variety of different faith (or no faith) backgrounds, diagnoses, ages and ethnicities. The aim of the research programme is to robustly test the effectiveness of spiritual care for service users' recovery, using scientific methodology. Madeleine completed her undergraduate degree in theology and religious studies at the University of Birmingham in June 2008, and explored the psychology of religious symbols in her dissertation. Personal interests in eastern philosophy and new age spiritualities has led her to advocate in a diverse and all-encompassing concept of spirituality, and in her volunteer work and training as a person-centred counsellor, she finds that clients express their spirituality in a variety of ways that can be beneficial to their emotional well-being. Publications include articles for *Mental Health, Religion and Culture* and *The International Journal of Leadership in Public Services.*

Malcolm Payne is policy and development adviser, St Christopher's Hospice, having previously been director of psycho-social and spiritual care at the Hospice, and visiting/honorary professor at Kingston and Opole Universities. He has broad experience of social work and has been a consultant in teamwork and team development in local government, health and social care organisations. Among more than 300 publications are his books *Modern Social Work Theory* (3rd ed, 2005), *What is Professional Social Work?* (2nd ed, 2006), *Social Care Practice in Context* (2009) and *Social Work in End of Life and Palliative Care* (2009, with Margaret Reith).

Barbara Pointon was a principal lecturer in music at Homerton College, Cambridge but took early retirement to care for her husband who was diagnosed at 51 with Alzheimer's disease – a 16-year journey, documented in Paul Watson's film 'Malcolm and Barbara ... Love's Farewell' (ITV, 2007). She campaigns for a better understanding of people with dementia and their carers, receiving an MBE in 2006 for her work, and is an ambassador for the Alzheimer's Society and a patron of Dementia UK (Admiral Nursing). She is a member of the Standing Commission on Carers, the Care Quality Commission's Carers Advisory Board, the Department of Health's Programme Board for Personal Health Budgets and two Ministerial advisory groups for dementia. She has contributed to several health and social care books, journals, websites and DVDs, and having helped to shape the national Dementia, End of Life and Carers' Strategies, she is now actively involved in their implementation, including the training of health and social care workforces and family carers in enlightened dementia support and care from diagnosis to death.

Julian Raffay is currently employed by Sheffield Health and Social Care NHS Foundation Trust where he has been working for two-and-a-half years as chaplain team leader, mainly in an acute adult mental health setting. He is interested in demonstrating to staff how including spirituality as part of healthcare can make their work more effective, more rewarding, and safer. He has a degree in psychology with management science from the University of Stirling (1984), as well as a degree in theology from the University of Durham (1989). Julian is currently in the second year of a Master's in Chaplaincy (healthcare) at the University of Cardiff. He has worked as a nursing assistant at the Intensive Psychiatric Care Unit in Edinburgh. Later, he worked as assistant chaplain in Derby, while also taking on responsibilities as a carer. Julian is ordained in the Church of England and has worked in a number of parishes in Leeds, Derby, and Sheffield, serving a total of 14 years in parish ministry. Currently, he is a trustee of Sheffield Mental Health Citizen's Advice Bureau and has set up a mental health working team of the Diocesan Faith and Justice Board. He is also collaborating on developing an assessment tool for looking at the spiritual strengths and needs of people with learning disabilities. Julian recently had an article accepted for publication in the journal *Mental Health, Religion and Culture* entitled 'Training the workforce in spiritual care'.

Kate Read is the West Midlands development director for the charity Dementia UK and also a senior lecturer in the Association for Dementia Studies at the University of Worcester. For many years Kate worked in the local authority as a social worker, manager and commissioner of services for older people. From 2000 to 2005 she was the executive director of Dementia Plus, which was the dementia services development centre for the West Midlands. Subsequently, she taught social work at Staffordshire University before moving to Worcester in November 2009. Kate's areas of interest and expertise include social care for people with dementia and their families, service user and carer involvement, commissioning, family care, intermediate care and service development. She has collaborated on a range of research projects following these interests and has written a number of articles and chapters exploring the experience and needs of people with dementia and their families.

Peter Richmond was born in Portsmouth in 1954. He grew up in Bromley and in Bedfordshire. He is an NHS chaplaincy team leader working for Kent and Medway NHS and Social Care Partnership Trust. He is an Anglican, ordained in 1980. The first part of his ministry combined parish and educational posts in the Midlands. At the turn of the millennium, he moved to Somerset where his role was a split between parish, mental health chaplaincy and clergy vocations adviser. In 2003 he became a whole time mental health chaplain in East Kent. His professional qualifications are in agriculture, theology and religious education, his MSc is in public health and health promotion. Peter is a musician and singer. He believes that spiritual care must connect to each person individually, as music might, respecting the choices that people make. He is a proponent of group working for spiritual care, complementing the more usual one-to-one approach. He is convinced that more effective spiritual care occurs when it is normal to share such responsibilities with regular staff as well as with patients and carers. He believes in including volunteers in the spiritual care team, as well as working closely with faith community leaders.

Ranjit Senghera is a programme specialist with NHS West Midlands Strategic Health Authority (SHA) and is currently working on learning disabilities health and mental health agendas for the region. Her previous roles with the West Midlands Regional Development Centre (RDC) and SHA included: leading on the equality and human rights agenda within the RDC; leading on equalities projects with regional mental health commissioners and working with the wider strategic health authority as an equality champion for the RDC. Ranjit is trained as a regional coach with NHS West Midlands and provides coaching and mentoring to key individuals in the region in developing talent and leadership potential in the NHS. Ranjit's focus as the race equality regional lead for NHS West Midlands RDC (a role which she previously carried out for NIMHE West Midlands) continues to be working strategically with key stakeholders and communities across the West Midlands to implement the Delivering Race Equality (DRE) Action Plan. Ranjit has been working with the National DRE central team, serving as interim deputy director, leading on areas such as DRE mainstreaming, the National DRE Ambassadors Programme and the National DRE Review. She has been instrumental in ensuring that DRE is implemented through national and regional work. Ranjit previously worked for Birmingham and Solihull Mental Health Trust as mental health promotion manager/standard one lead for mental health promotion. She has extensive background in working in the mainstream voluntary sector and specifically the black and Asian community voluntary sector. A social researcher by training, Ranjit has authored and co-authored a number of key programmes and projects across the country concerned with race equality and health services for BME communities. Ranjit works on the belief of developing effective capacity and community ownership with all communities, to improve the quality of health and social care services for all.

Hári Sewell is founder and director of HS Consultancy and is a former executive director of health and social care in the NHS. He is a writer and speaker in his specialist area of ethnicity, race and culture in mental health. Hári is honorary Senior Visiting Fellow at University of Central Lancashire and also at Buckinghamshire New University. He has worked as an expert panellist with the Department of Health and the Royal College of Psychiatrists. Hári is joint editor of the *Journal Ethnicity and Inequalities in Health and Social Care* and is on the editorial board of Journal of Integrated Care. He was the founder and chair of the national Social Care Strategic Network (Mental Health) until November 2010. Hári was part of the Marmot Review of Health Inequalities post 2010. His book *Working with Ethnicity Race and Culture in Mental Health: A handbook for practitioners* was published in October 2008.

John Swinton holds the chair in practical theology and pastoral care at the University of Aberdeen, Scotland, United Kingdom. He is also an honorary professor at Aberdeen's Centre for Advanced Studies in Nursing. Professor Swinton worked for 16 years as a registered nurse specialising in psychiatry and learning disabilities. He also worked for a number of years as a hospital chaplain and a community mental health chaplain. Professor Swinton's areas of research include mental health studies, the relationship between spirituality and health and the theology of disability. In 2004 he founded the Centre for Spirituality, Health and Disability at the University of Aberdeen (www.abdn.ac.uk/cshad). The centre has a dual focus on a) the relationship between theology, spirituality and contemporary healthcare practices and b) the theology of disability. It is a multidisciplinary project that aims to enable researchers, practitioners and educators to work together to develop innovative and creative research projects and teaching initiatives.

Steve Wharmby works as a senior occupational therapist for the states of Jersey, Channel Isles. Since qualifying at the University of Wales, College of Medicine he has experienced a variety of settings in Wales, England, the Isle of Man and Jersey, including inpatients, community mental health, eating disorders, rehabilitation and assertive outreach. Steve has obtained further qualifications in management studies and relaxation therapy, and recently participated in the Jersey Focus Partnership Programme, led by Professor Peter Gilbert, aimed at promoting service-user involvement as being central to service development and provision.

Andrew Wilson is joint team leader of the Spiritual and Pastoral Care Service within the South London and Maudsley NHS Foundation Trust. The Trust works across four London boroughs. Andrew was ordained in Southwark Diocese in 1971, and worked for 18 years in South London parishes until he was appointed as community mental health chaplain in Croydon in 1989. The Community Care Bill, which came into effect the following year underlined the need to create effective links between mental health services and the local faith communities and agencies, and this has remained the focus of his work ever since. From the outset he has always worked closely with the local Association for Pastoral Care in Mental Health of which he is a trustee, and which has established a large volunteer team which provides four drop-in centres and a number of creative and well-being groups. With MIND in Croydon and the Association for Pastoral Care in Mental Health (APCMH), Andrew was involved in the ground breaking video 'Hard to Believe', which addresses the need to respect and support the religious, spiritual and cultural needs of mental health service users. Recently, with funding from his Trust, he has worked with APCMH to produce a pilot training scheme where Trust staff work alongside people from local faith groups and support agencies to learn from each other, and to produce practical projects which further awareness both within the clinical setting and within community groups, creating effective working links between them. Andrew works as a therapist, and spiritual director, and sees support and training for clergy, pastoral workers and faith leaders as a vital part of his work. He was made an honorary canon of Southwark Cathedral in 2005.

Chapter 1

Understanding mental health and spirituality

Peter Gilbert

Spirituality and mental illness

'Siddra' was born into a second generation Pakistani family who were Muslim. Her parents adhered to the Five Pillars of Islam (the profession of faith; the five daily prayers; almsgiving; fasting; pilgrimage to Mecca) and were also keen that their children should integrate themselves into UK society, be as well educated as possible, and gain rewarding careers.

'Siddra' went to university, got a good degree and went into medicine. As a third year medical student she became stressed, anxious and then depressed. In her turmoil she questioned herself about her illness. Was it:

▶ purely biological

▶ a result of a stressful environment

▶ abandonment by Allah (God)

▶ an identity crisis; was she caught between two cultures, and was her scientific training a help or a hindrance in this crisis?

A sympathetic and skilled GP, an Imam trained in mental health, and her family supported 'Siddra', and she eventually recovered and qualified as a doctor.

In *The Dark Threads*, Jean Davison writes of her existential crisis as a teenager from a Christian family in the 1970s:

'As a teenager I wanted badly to find a meaning, a purpose, a pattern, a God. To think as I started doing then, that there might be none of these things, was hard for me to take. Over the years I have learnt to live with ambiguities, uncertainty, a possibility of never knowing. But it seems that "something" of my leanings towards spirituality never left me' (Davison, 2009).

Davison sought advice from a GP who was unsympathetic; and then from a psychiatrist who she felt would offer her listening time, but instead admitted her to High Royds psychiatric hospital near Bradford. There, she received a diagnosis of schizophrenia (which appears then, and in retrospect, to be inappropriate), as well as major tranquilisers and electroconvulsive therapy. Eventually she moved out of the system and created a fulfilling career for herself in working with those also experiencing mental distress.

Her yearnings for a spiritual dimension never left Davison and towards the end of the book she quotes a poem by Benjamin Franklin:

'Not 'til the loom is silent
And the shuttles cease to fly,
Will God unroll a canvas
And explain the reason why
The dark threads are as needful
In the Weaver's skilful hand
As the threads of gold and silver
In the pattern He (sic) has planned' (In: Davison, 2009).

One doesn't need a specific religious faith to feel that we have an 'inner spirit' and value, a motivating force and life meaning, and purpose which shapes our lives (see Gilbert *et al*, 2010, chapter 9).

Reflection exercise

What do you feel gives your life meaning and purpose?

How do you see your identity? Who do you think you are?

Definitions of mental health

The World Health Organization states clearly that *'there is no health without mental health'* (see Friedli, 2009). The connection between mental and physical health is increasingly recognised, as is the sense that in a knowledge-based society, mental well-being is essential for economic prosperity as well as social cohesion.

One way of looking at mental health is as follows:

'Essentially about how we think and feel about ourselves and about others and how we interpret the world around us ... it also affects our capacity to cope with change and transitions such as life events ... Mental health may be central to all health and well-being.' (Rankin, 2005)

A whole person approach

To work with people in an effective and cost-effective way we need to connect with the whole person in the context of their whole life. This includes their family, social groups, community, housing, employment and leisure time etc (see Gilbert, 2010). Figure 1 illustrates the aspects which should be considered when working with someone with mental health problems.

Figure 1: Looking at the whole person

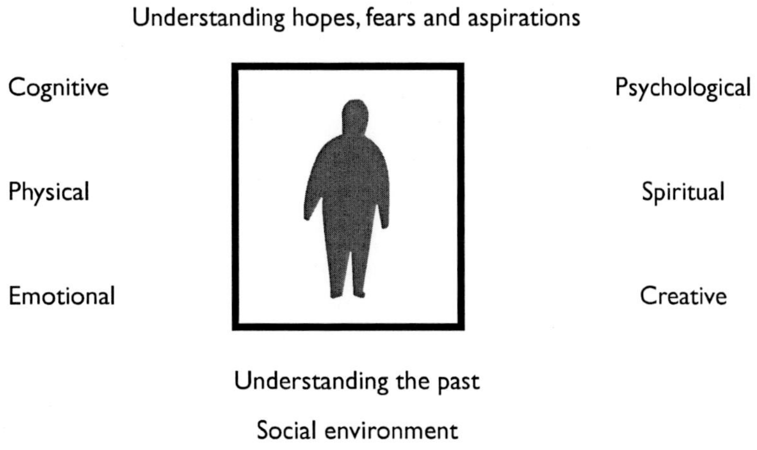

Understanding hopes, fears and aspirations

Cognitive   Psychological

Physical   Spiritual

Emotional   Creative

Understanding the past

Social environment

> **Reflection exercise**
>
> When you experience mental distress, what elements from figures 1 and 2 do you feel are most relevant to your experience?
>
> What are your hopes for the future?
>
> What approaches do you take to ensure your well-being?

Models of mental illness

Andrew McCulloch summarises a number of possible models of mental illness (McCulloch, 2006).

▶ Biological models that are concerned with the biological and chemical basis of mental illness – this is fundamentally what we refer to as the 'medical model', although many doctors use a more integrative approach.

▶ Social or psychological models that are concerned with life events, family dynamics and belief systems or thinking style. This also encapsulates social models of disability that focus on how society reacts to the disabled individual.

▶ Intuitive or spiritual explanations that see the mind as a battleground for conflicting forces: the conscious versus the unconscious, good versus evil, etc.

▶ Existential belief, which views mental illness as another valid form of human existence – this is rare.

Quite often these models will interact, meaning that a life event may cause a chemical imbalance which requires a range of approaches, including social, spiritual, medical and cognitive. Sometimes there will be a range of different perspectives eg. the voices an individual hears could be seen as a psychotic illness, demonic possession, or as the Hearing Voices Network (see Romme *et al*, 2009 and Jane Taylor in Gilbert *et al*, 2010, p5–8) would argue, another dimension of the human experience (see figure 2).

Figure 2: Diverse perspectives of mental well-being and ill-health

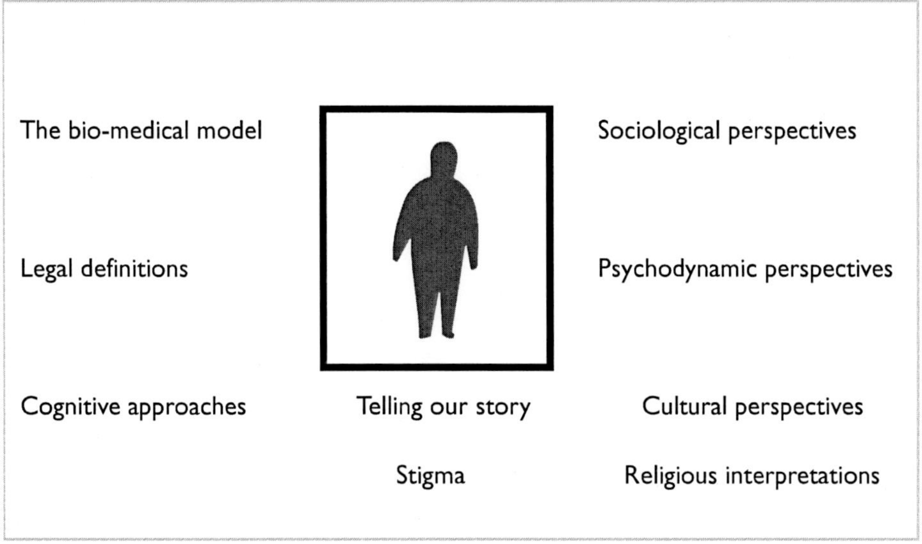

The bio-medical model

Sociological perspectives

Legal definitions

Psychodynamic perspectives

Cognitive approaches

Telling our story

Cultural perspectives

Stigma

Religious interpretations

(First published in Gilbert *et al* (2010) *Social Work and Mental Health: The value of everything* (2nd edition) and reproduced with permission from Russell House Publishing)

Stigma and prevalence

Despite the fact that prominent individuals, such as Stephen Fry and Alastair Campbell, and medical practitioners such as Cathy Wield and Liz Miller, have spoken publically about their episodes of mental distress, there is still a great deal of stigma generally, and this may be exacerbated in some cultural communities. The esteemed scientist, Dr Lewis Wolpert, who wrote about his depression in the very moving *Malignant Sadness* (Wolpert, 2006) says that nearly everybody he speaks to has some experience of mental distress, either directly or through a close relative or friend. They talk to him about it, because they know he has been through a similar experience.

It is often said that one in four people experience an episode of mental ill-health at one time in their lives, and issues such as the recession and associated unemployment, demographic change and stigma and discrimination can all have an effect on those experiencing mental ill-health. For instance suicide rates, having dropped steadily over the past 10 years, have seen a rise since the credit crunch and subsequent economic and social disruption (see Gilbert, 2010; The NHS Confederation, 2009).

Discovering the spirit

The idea that human beings have an inner spirit is prevalent in all philosophical and religious traditions. In the West we base a great deal of our scientific and medical advances on the wisdom of the ancient Greeks. The philosopher Plato (circa 428–348 BCE) stated that: *'As you ought not to cure the eyes without the head, or the head without the body; so neither ought you to attempt to cure the body without the soul, because the part can never be well unless the whole be well.'* (Phaedo, quoted in Ross, 1997, p1)

Embryologist, Lewis Wolpert, while describing himself as 'a hard line materialist', uses spiritual and religious language in his description of depression: *'If we had a soul – and as a hard line materialist I do not believe we do – a useful metaphor for depression could be 'soul loss' due to extreme sadness. The body and mind emptied of the soul lose interest in almost everything except themselves. The idea of the wandering soul is widely accepted across numerous cultures, and the adjective 'empty' is viewed across most cultures as negative. The metaphor captures the way in which we experience our own existence. Our 'soul' is our inner essence, something distinctively different from the hard material world in which we live. Lose it and we are depressed – cut-off, alone.'* (Wolpert, 2006)

In the Hindu religion, the Bhagavad Gita talks about *'that which pervades the entire body with consciousness, you should know to be indestructible. No one is able to destroy that imperishable soul'* (BG, 2.17) and *'the soul can never be cut to pieces by any weapon, nor burned by fire, nor moistened by water, nor withered by the wind. This individual soul is unbreakable and insoluble, and can be neither burned nor dried. He (sic) is everlasting.'* (BG, 2.23–25)

Sometimes the words 'spirit' and 'soul' are used interchangeably. In the Jewish faith, however, these are distinct. The soul (nephesh) is God given but a relatively passive entity. The spirit (ru'ach), however, means both breath and spirit and denotes not just life, but invigorated life. Rabbi Dove uses the analogy of the craftsman making glass through blowing into the molten liquid so that gradually the form takes shape through the action of the maker's breath (see Gilbert and Kalaga, 2007). For Muslims, Allah is said in the Qur'an to breathe Allah's ruh into each human being. The Oxford English Dictionary defines spirit as our 'animating or life-giving force' and it is evident that mental health services which don't work with an individual's animating or life-giving force cannot really be either effective, or indeed cost-effective.

As the UK becomes more multicultural, and many people live their lives across several cultures (see Gilbert *et al*, 2010, p119–120), understanding varied and perhaps interlocking modes of spirituality will become increasingly important (see Coyte *et al*, 2007; Fung *et al*, 2009).

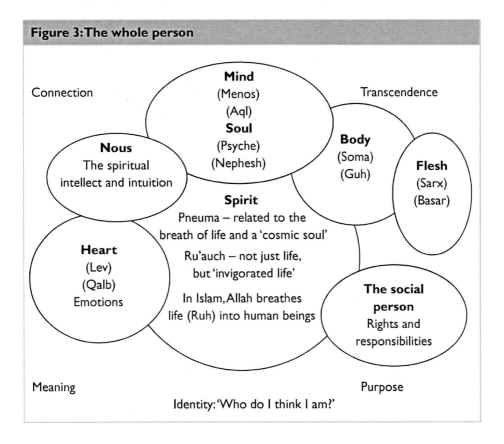

Figure 3: The whole person

One way of looking at the interaction of mind, body and spirit, through various philosophical and religious traditions, is detailed in figure 3. It is important to note that again all philosophical traditions, whether religious or not, have a strong sense of social responsibility, so that the citizen has responsibilities as well as rights, and a duty to minister to the needs of those less fortunate than themselves.

Some commentators have asserted that the word 'spirituality' is relatively recent. Ursula King (2009) on the other hand traces it back to the early part of the fifth century CE, and it gradually developed in its use as a counterpoint to 'materiality', and so continues to this day as a counterpoint to the obsession with material goods and consumerism (see Coyte *et al*, 2007).

The Royal College of Psychiatrists defines spirituality as: *'Spirituality is a distinctive, potentially creative and universal dimension of human experience arising both within the inner subjective awareness of individuals and within communities, social groups and traditions. It may be experienced as relationship with that which is intimately "inner", immanent and personal, within the self and others, and/or as a relationship with that which is wholly "other", transcendent and beyond the self. It is experienced as being of fundamental or ultimate importance and is thus concerned with matters of meaning and purpose in life, truth and values.'* (Cook *et al*, 2009, p4)

Religious belief

As the UK becomes a society of many cultures, religious faith is likely to become increasingly important.

The word 'religion' derives from a Latin word meaning 'binding obligation', and this demonstrates how much it is to do with a sense of community and social cohesion. It stems back to a time when it was vital that people knew who you were and what to expect from you, and the sense of social solidarity and obligation.

Religion encompasses most, if not all, of the aspects described in definitions of spirituality, usually in the context of belief in, and possibly a personal relationship with, a transcendent being or beings, and with a meta-narrative which seeks to explain origins of the world and those living in it, and the questions which face human beings around life, suffering, death, and re-awakening in this world or another.

Religion can provide a 'world view', which is acted out in narrative, doctrine, symbols, rites, rituals, sacraments and gatherings; and the promotion of ties of mutual obligation. It creates a framework within which people seek to understand and interpret and make sense of themselves, their lives and daily experiences.

Faith communities can be welcoming, integrative and supportive; while some others can be exclusive and stigmatising of people experiencing mental ill-health.

The benefits and disadvantages of spirituality and religion

As we have seen, spirituality relates to a person's inner spirit, and therefore intensely to their experience of being human, their meaning and purpose in life; their human quest; what makes them tick; what keeps us well when life throws its challenges at us. It may also be related to a belief in a personal god, a cosmic life force, and/or an organised religious grouping. A Sikh, Christian, Muslim, Jew, Hindu etc. may feel as close to God while walking in the hills as worshipping in their gurdwara, church, mosque, synagogue or temple.

Case study 1

Anna is a practising Roman Catholic, married to David, who was brought up in the Jewish faith but hasn't practised for some time. Despite the different cultural traditions, the mutual respect between the religious traditions has been helpful to both Anna and David as the marriage progressed. When David developed a bipolar condition, however, his behaviour in relationships with his wife and children, and in his handling of money, became unpredictable.

The community team offers the family positive support, but now there is an increasing range of spiritual and cultural issues as both their two teenage children struggle to respond to the pressures they face of growing up, and coping with their father's illness, and their mother's anxiety.

David is giving indications that this mental health crisis is also a spiritual one for him, and that he may need to re-explore aspects of his original faith.

Question
How can the cultural and spiritual aspects of this family best be attended to?

(Taken from Gilbert (2008) *Guidelines on Spirituality for Staff in Acute Care Services*)

The downside of being in a society which is increasingly individualised, atomistic and consumerist can be that individuals are often locked within the confines of their own hearts, not reaching out to others in compassion (suffering with) and social solidarity. It can all be about 'me'.

The advantages of belonging to an organised religion are:

▶ feeling that a benevolent and more powerful entity is looking after you

▶ a sense of 'divine empathy'

▶ the provision of specific coping resources, not least through the signs, symbols, rituals and narratives which faith communities provide to give a framework for life

▶ the generation of positive emotions, eg. love and forgiveness, which fit strongly with the Foresight research into mental well-being, which shows that altruism or giving is a major element in a person's mental well-being (Foresight, 2008)

▶ a sense of belonging

▶ trust in God and in the faith community.

(see Swinton, 2001 and Sims, 2009, and chapter 2 of this book)

The downside of religion again stems from its original meaning. Organised religion can be:

▶ over-controlling, and a straightjacket rather than a framework

▶ overly paternalistic, repressive and homophobic

▶ some of the earliest religions seem to have been female-led, but the priesthoods we know today tend to be male-dominated

▶ overly concerned with the needs of the organisation and not the individual or group.

(see figure 4)

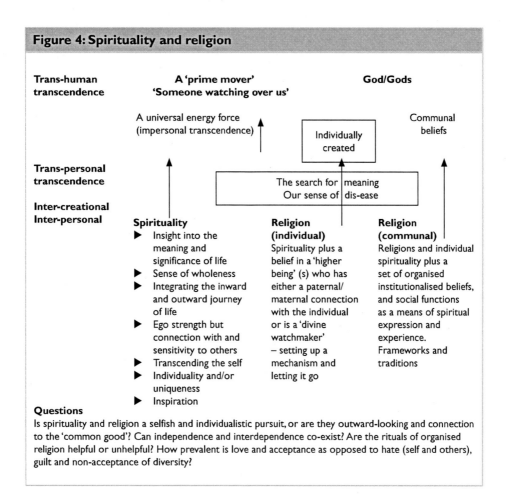

Figure 4: Spirituality and religion

Trans-human transcendence — A 'prime mover' 'Someone watching over us' — God/Gods

A universal energy force (impersonal transcendence)

Individually created

Communal beliefs

Trans-personal transcendence

Inter-creational Inter-personal

The search for meaning
Our sense of dis-ease

Spirituality
▶ Insight into the meaning and significance of life
▶ Sense of wholeness
▶ Integrating the inward and outward journey of life
▶ Ego strength but connection with and sensitivity to others
▶ Transcending the self
▶ Individuality and/or uniqueness
▶ Inspiration

Religion (individual)
Spirituality plus a belief in a 'higher being' (s) who has either a paternal/maternal connection with the individual or is a 'divine watchmaker' – setting up a mechanism and letting it go

Religion (communal)
Religions and individual spirituality plus a set of organised institutionalised beliefs, and social functions as a means of spiritual expression and experience. Frameworks and traditions

Questions
Is spirituality and religion a selfish and individualistic pursuit, or are they outward-looking and connection to the 'common good'? Can independence and interdependence co-exist? Are the rituals of organised religion helpful or unhelpful? How prevalent is love and acceptance as opposed to hate (self and others), guilt and non-acceptance of diversity?

Some of the saddest people are those who adhere to all the religious rituals, but seem to have no inner spirit, and very little ability to walk in the shoes of the original founder of the religion or philosophy. The efficacy of religion depends on the degree in which it is well integrated into people's lives, and on the manner in which people extend that belief system and framework into all aspects of their lives to the benefit of others.

Dignity in care

The scandal at Mid Staffordshire Hospital, detailed in the Healthcare Commission report of March 2009 and the subsequent Robert Francis QC enquiry of February 2010, highlighted the tragedy of unnecessary deaths and an underlying routine lack of care.

'In the trusts' drive to become a foundation trust, it appears to have lost sight of its real priorities ... and did not properly consider the effect of reductions in staff on the quality of care.' (Healthcare Commission, 2009, p11)

'The care of patients was unacceptable.' (Healthcare Commission, 2009, p6)

'The trust did not have an open culture where concerns were welcomed'. (Healthcare Commission, 2009, p9)

Both reports demonstrate that when a healthcare organisation loses its way and concentrates on an inappropriate business model, while neglecting its primary function of treatment and care, people suffer.

To create and sustain a service which centres on:

▶ people's personal, family and group needs

▶ an individual's 'animating and life-giving force'

▶ people's dignity

▶ the underlying culture and identity of each individual.

Leadership with integrity of spirit needs to be developed at all levels. Leadership is all about setting a value-based direction, with others, towards a better future; creating the right culture; bringing the necessary resources to bear to meet the goals; and developing people (Gilbert, 2005a; Goffee & Jones, 2006; Gilbert & Fulford, 2010).

If those managing an organisation are inauthentic and robotic, and don't develop and nurture their staff, then it is unlikely that those staff, in their turn, will be able to work with service users and carers to empower them and provide dignity in care.

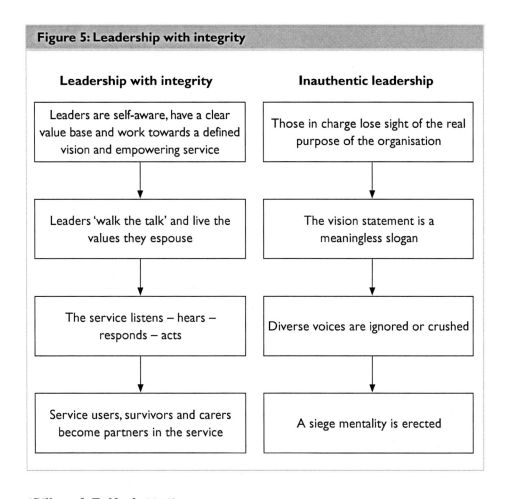

Figure 5: Leadership with integrity

Leadership with integrity	Inauthentic leadership
Leaders are self-aware, have a clear value base and work towards a defined vision and empowering service	Those in charge lose sight of the real purpose of the organisation
Leaders 'walk the talk' and live the values they espouse	The vision statement is a meaningless slogan
The service listens – hears – responds – acts	Diverse voices are ignored or crushed
Service users, survivors and carers become partners in the service	A siege mentality is erected

(Gilbert & Fulford, 2010)

Who am I? Who are you?

Professor Kamlesh Patel, former Chair of the Mental Health Act Commission, spoke clearly about identity: *'If you don't know who I am, how are you going to provide a package of care for me to deliver something? When you do not know how important my religion is to me, what language I speak, where I am coming from, how are you going to help me cope with my mental illness? And that is what I am trying to get over to people; the first step is about identity. It is absolutely fundamental to the package of care we offer an individual'* (Mulholland, 2005, p5).

We never entirely know who someone is, or indeed perhaps even who we are. People will often say to me that they have had a particular experience, either positive or negative, or have undertaken some further awareness training: the Myers-Briggs type indicator, the Enneagram, a meditation course etc, and it has told them things about themselves that they didn't fully realise. For my own part, I found a residential course on the Enneagram (Hampson, 2005) extremely enlightening about a number of facets of my character and how I operate under pressure. Some of my characteristics are in many ways quite contradictory eg. the obsessive push for outcomes and achievement, with a desire to care and look after people. Sometimes they conflict – quite markedly!

It is one of the strange dimensions of mental health services that so many people operating in a professional capacity seem to have real difficulty in acknowledging that they have experienced mental distress, or perhaps a diagnosed mental illness. This is in some ways in contrast with when I was teaching nursing students working in the field of learning disability, who would quite often mention that they had a sibling with a learning disability, or had contact with people with learning disabilities at an early age and that this had formed part of their motivation to undertake this professional caring role. The Director of the National Mental Health Development Unit, Dr Ian McPherson, interviewed in the *Society Guardian*, spoke about his experience of depression, and being an inpatient at a child and adolescent unit *'within a large Victorian psychiatric hospital on the outskirts of Glasgow'* (O'Hara, 2009). He recalls that *'being in hospital was a strange experience – not particularly bad, but nor was it remotely therapeutic'* (O'Hara, 2009).

When he came into mental health services as a practising psychologist, then as a manager and subsequently also as a trainer, he thought: *'probably slightly naively, that having had experience (of depression), it would actually be something I could bring with me as well as my training. I quickly got the message – subtly and less subtly – that even in what is a fairly liberal profession there was an implicit distinction between people who are patients and people who are professionals'* (O'Hara, 2009).

McPherson now believes that things are changing, and that people are more prepared to disclose elements of their experience, and stand on 'common ground' with those who use the service and their carers. While saying that his own illness *'gives no unique insight'* into mental health conditions in general, McPherson feels that what it has done is *'allow me to understand what it feels like*' to be seen as separate or '*that person over there with a mental illness*' (O'Hara, 2009).

The strengths and needs of service users and carers, and assessment are topics covered in chapters 4, 5 and 10.

Exploring your own spirituality

To really engage with other people's spirituality we need to engage further with our own. This isn't always easy, as it is not something we are used to doing. Recently, an Antarctic explorer spoke about how in the first week of her trip she tended to think about things at home that she had left undone; in the second week her thoughts became more orientated to serious issues; and in the third week she began to engage with issues such as the meaning of life.

At Staffordshire University, we invited social work students across the three years to join together in a small seminar group to explore the issues of spirituality, and asked them to bring in an item which had spiritual importance. One person brought a small statue of the Buddha which they had purchased in Thailand; another brought a picture of herself, her husband and her child, her husband had died suddenly at an early age, leaving her a single mum so this was a particularly moving image; another spoke of her husband who was currently serving in a war zone; another with a religious affiliation brought a copy of their scripture; and another brought pictures of his voluntary work.

Some items had a very deep emotional impact, others less so, but they were all important to the person bringing them, and were all treated with immense respect by the other participants. This safe environment enabled people to really explore their spirituality and listen to other people's with respect. Organisations need to create opportunities where people can use exercises, such as the reflection exercises in this chapter, to explore experience, identity and spirituality.

Please use figure 6 to consider aspects of your identity and spirituality.

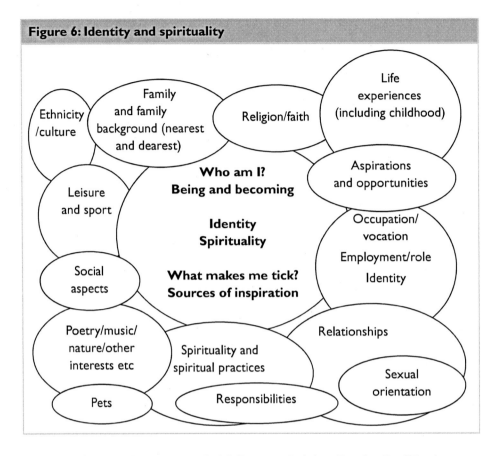

Figure 6: Identity and spirituality

(Adapted from Gilbert (2008) *Guidelines on Spirituality for Staff in Acute Care Services*, p9.)

Creating space isn't easy in a busy environment, but is absolutely necessary to allow staff to engage with their own humanity, those of others, and with the human spirit of the whole organisation (see Aris and Gilbert, 2007).

Speaking from experience

When I experienced an episode of life-threatening depression 10 years ago, I drew on a range of spiritual, physical, medical and communal approaches to survive and recover (see Gilbert, 2010). My inner spirit has much to do with 'connection' and I found that depression disconnected or 'unplugged' me from myself, other people and God. I found the following helped me to 'reconnect' with my inner spirit.

- ▶ A GP who really listened attentively, gave me a measure of control over how I dealt with my illness, and prescribed the right medication for me.

- ▶ A friend who absorbed my extreme anger and sadness. As a society we are not very good at coping with and responding positively to strong feelings.

- ▶ My running club where I received communal support and the physical and spiritual benefits of running (Gilbert, 2005b).

- ▶ A friend who had been through a similar experience and offered wise counsel and support.

- ▶ Counselling to help me understand how past and present experiences were impacting on me.

- ▶ A place of spiritual 'asylum', the Benedictine Abbey at Worth in Sussex, where I didn't have to 'do' anything. I could sit in the choir stalls and the monastic community uplifted me through their prayers.

- ▶ Valued friends and colleagues who offered me employment, and valued me through their expressed faith in me.

Real 'recovery' took some time – about a year later I was off medication and back in work. Running along a beach next to Bamburgh castle in Northumbria, and looking across to the Holy Island of Lindisfarne, I experienced an epiphany which gave me confidence of moving forward in a sense of positive discovery and recovery.

Languages of love

Talking to a service user before the multi-faith conference in 2006, he remarked that what service users want from professionals and services is 'love'. The Royal College of Psychiatrists' recent book echoes this theme when the authors say:

'... as we meet on the path of life, there is one medicine constantly at our disposal that even comes free. This is the power of love, lending hope, giving comfort and helping bring peace to the troubled mind' (Powell in Cook, Powell and Sims, 2009 (Eds), pXVIII)

Love isn't an easy word to unpack, but inspection reports, surveys and feedback from user groups across a range of care situations, state that people desire loving attention to their humanity, identity, dignity as individuals, cultural context and practices, and innate spirituality. It is sometimes particularly difficult to demonstrate love to those who have been in a professional caring role, and then need care themselves (see case study 2).

Case study 2

Jenny had worked as a mental health nurse in both community and acute residential settings for 12 years, before she experienced an episode of acute mental disorder, following a period of stress at work.

Although in a mental health setting, and in a trust which spoke of the importance of 'experts by experience', and sharing experience, Jenny had noticed that, in a recent survey within the trust, very few people had felt able to indicate experience of mental ill health; and the prevailing culture was to: 'grin and bear it'. Trying to hide her symptoms, Jenny became increasingly manic, creating problems for herself, her family, her colleagues and service users, and eventually arrived at her GP's surgery in such a state, that she needed to access secondary care services – which caused her distress and the feeling of being stigmatised. For Jenny, being a mental health nurse had become a way of life, believing passionately in the need to care for others in distress, so when she became ill it was as though her whole life and identity was falling apart.

Now back at work, Jenny has found supportive colleagues and managers. She has been able to accept this experience and see it as valuable, and she has integrated the experience into her working life.

Questions

Does this sound like an experience you recognise?

How accepting is your organisation of the experience of mental ill health among staff?

How could Jenny have been supported initially?

Do you feel able to speak about your negative as well as your positive experiences?

(Taken from Gilbert (2008) *Guidelines on Spirituality for Staff in Acute Care Service*, p18–19.)

Figure 7: The five languages of love

Language

The method of human communication, either spoken or written, consisting of the use of words in an agreed way.

It is said that there are five languages of love:

► time
► words
► touch
► gifts
► acts of service.

However, language is sometimes difficult, country to country, or even the use and understanding of language from region to region within the same country.

What is precious, valuable, acceptable; difficult to appreciate or accept in one language might be quite different in another.

Many people find it hard to accept verbal compliments, but may find a small gift an affirmation which they can accept without a problem.

Some professions may use different languages eg. nurses, especially in physical care, may be using a great deal of touch. Social workers and psychiatrists may be using words more often. Care workers, acts of service.

How do we understand and use these different languages?

For different people, love and care will be expressed, acceptable and accepted in different ways. For some, a few appreciative words may have profound meaning; but for others it will be very difficult to accept any measure of appreciation, as they feel they don't deserve it. For others, touch is very reassuring, and this is often the feedback we receive from people who are dying and feel isolated, alone and afraid; but for others touch is invasive or culturally unacceptable. An expression of empathy can be very subtle, sometimes the sharing of the feeling through a look or even mutual tears (see Gilbert, 2010) may establish a common bond of humanity which pulls us through the crisis.

Recently I went to my GP, who was professional, a good listener, human, humorous and gave me a sense of hope. As she had made me feel better I sent her a card expressing my thanks. Neither her care nor my thanks was very complicated, nor did it take much time, and if she had been less human and less effective then it would have probably taken just as much surgery time. So why is it that we find being human so hard to do? It's not that difficult – is it?

Conclusion

Spirituality, in whatever form it takes, is a vital dimension of our humanity. As disillusionment with robotic and mechanistic forms of care has set in, and our society has become more multifaceted and multicultural, spirituality is becoming of increasing importance in health and social care.

The subsequent chapters will explore this in a range of ways which are intended to be helpful for those who use services, informal carers, frontline staff, managers and policy makers.

References

Aris SJ & Gilbert P (2007) Organisation health: engaging the heart of the organisation. In: ME Coyte, P Gilbert & V Nicholls (Eds) *Spirituality, Values and Mental Health: Jewels for the journey*. London: Jessica Kingsley.

Bhaktivedenta AC (trans) *Bhagavad Gita*. Los Angeles: Bhaktivedenta Trust.

Cook C, Powell A & Sims A (Eds) (2009) *Spirituality and Psychiatry*. London: RCPsych.

Coyte ME, Gilbert P & Nicholls V (Eds) (2007) *Spirituality, Values and Mental Health: Jewels for the Journey*. London: Jessica Kingsley.

Davison J (2009) *The Dark Threads*. Glamorgan: Accent Press.

Foresight (2008) *Mental Capital and Well-being*. London: Foresight.

Francis R QC/The Mid Staffordshire NHS Foundation Trust Inquiry (2010) *Independent Inquiry into Care Provided by Mid Staffordshire NHS Foundation Trust*. London: DH.

Friedli L (2009) *Mental Health, Resilience and Inequalities*. Denmark: WHO with NIHME, CPAG, FPH and the Mental Health Foundation.

Fung LA, Bhugra D & Jones PB (2009) Ethnicity and mental health: the example of schizophrenia and related psychoses in migrant populations in the western world, *Psychiatry* **8** (9) 335–341.

Gilbert P (2005a) *Leadership: Being effective and remaining human*. Lyme Regis: Russell House Publishing.

Gilbert P (2005b) Keep up your spirits. *Openmind* **135** 6–8.

Gilbert P (2008) *Guidelines on Spirituality for Staff in Acute Care Services*. Staffordshire University: NIMHE/CSIP.

Gilbert P (2010) The bridge of sighs and the bridge of love: a personal pilgrimage. In: T Bassett & T Stickley (Eds) *Voices of Experience: Narratives of survival and mental health*. Oxford: Blackwell/Wiley.

Gilbert P with Bates P, Carr S, Clark M, Gould N & Slay G (2010) *Social Work and Mental Health: The value of everything* (2nd edition). Lyme Regis: Russell House Publishing.

Gilbert P & Fulford KWM (2010) Bringing the spirit and values back into public services. *The International Journal of Leadership in Public Services* **6** (2).

Gilbert P & Kalaga H (2007) Nurturing Heart and Spirit: Papers from the multi-faith symposium. Stafford: Staffordshire University.

Goffee R & Jones G (2006) *Why Should Anyone be Led by You?: What it takes to be an authentic leader*. Boston: Harvard Business School.

Hampson M (2005) *Head Versus Heart: And our gut reactions, the 21st century enneagram*. Ropley: O Books.

O'Hara M (2009) Voice of experience. *Society Guardian*, 24th June, p5.

Healthcare Commission (2009) *Investigation into Mid Staffordshire NHS Foundation Trust*. London: Commission for Healthcare Audit and Inspection.

King U (2009) *The Search for Spirituality: Our global quest for meaning and fulfilment*. Norwich: Canterbury Press.

McCulloch A (2006) Understanding mental health and mental illness. In: C Jackson C & K Hill (Eds) *Mental Health Today: A handbook*. Brighton: Pavilion/Mental Health Foundation.

Mulholland H (2005) Counting on change. *The Guardian*, 7th December, p5.

NHS Confederation (2009) *Fact Sheet: Key facts and trends in mental health*. London: NHSC.

Rankin J (2005) *Mental Health in the Mainstream*. London: IPPR/Rethink.

Romme M, Escher S, Dillon J, Corstens D & Morris M (2009) *Living with Voices: 50 stories of recovery*. Ross-On-Wye: PCSS.

Ross L (1997) *Nurses' Perceptions of Spiritual Care*. Aldershot: Averbury.

Sims A (2009) *Is Faith Delusion?: Why religion is good for your health*. London: Continuum.

Swinton J (2001) *Spirituality in Mental Health Care: Rediscovering a 'forgotten' dimension*. London: Jessica Kingsley.

Wolpert L (2006) *Malignant Sadness: The anatomy of depression* (3rd edition). London: Faber & Faber.

Chapter 2

Researching spirituality: evidence and practice

John Swinton and Madeleine Parkes

'I think it was a combination of my GP, the medication and my spiritual life ... I think it was the spiritual element that was the glue that held it all together.' (Mental Health Foundation, 2002b, p24)

The importance of religion and spirituality for healthy human development has been noted across the healthcare disciplines (Hill & Pargament, 2003). There is a growing body of evidence that indicates that a focus on religion and spirituality can have a positive impact on the way a patient perceives and experiences illness and can be beneficial in terms of mental and physical health (Leshner *et al*, 2006; Coward & Kahn, 2005; Bauer-Wu & Farran, 2005). Overall, the evidence suggests that religion and spirituality can be:

▶ positively associated with quality of life (Brady & Cella *et al*, 1999)

▶ that this association is unique (ie. cannot be subsumed to psychological processes) (Pargament, 1997)

▶ has clinical utility within the development of optimal quality of life for patients (Brady & Peterman *et al*, 1999).

While the evidence is not unambiguous, a generally positive correlation seems reasonably convincing. However, researching religion and spirituality is far from straightforward. In this chapter we will highlight some of the main issues that people researching this area will encounter, and point towards some possible ways forward that might allow spirituality and religion to find a valid and validated place within health and social care practices.

What is research?

A helpful place to begin our exploration is with the question: what is research? It is useful to notice that research is not just something that professional researchers do. All of us are constantly doing research in our everyday lives. We just don't notice it! Any activity that involves gathering and processing data and information and facts to improve knowledge can count as research. Going through a catalogue to check out alternative sofas that you might want to purchase, reading a book, surfing the internet – these are all forms of research. We are all researchers by nature! But, of course, research in its more formal academic and professional sense is considerably more complicated, although not qualitatively different from our everyday research activities.

Webster's dictionary describes research as:

'Studious inquiry or examination; especially: investigation or experimentation aimed at the discovery and interpretation of facts, revision of accepted theories or laws in the light of new facts, or practical application of such new or revised theories or laws.' (Merriam-Webster Collegiate Dictionary, 10th edition)

This definition is quite complicated, but, for current purposes, we will highlight three key points that are of importance for the purposes of this chapter:

1. Research has to do with studious enquiry. It is a concentrated activity designed to explore in-depth a particular context or situation with a view to developing deeper and sometimes changed understandings of what is actually going on. In healthcare settings, such concentrated enquiry can involve statistics, and testing new interventions in a systematic way. An example of this mode of enquiry would be clinical trials, such as those testing the effectiveness of a new drug. Here the research might involve giving one group of people a new drug, and other groups of people an alternative drug or a placebo ie. an inert substance that the person believes is the same drug as others in the trial, but which in fact has no properties that could be beneficial to their condition. The focus here is on improving clinical efficacy. By measuring which one is most effective using assessments that may record numbers and require complex analysis using statistical software packages, the efficacy of the drug can be assessed. Similarly, one might carry out a review of existing studies and

publications (literature reviews) to help the researcher or the research team identify gaps in knowledge around a subject area. Qualitative studies will concentrate on listening to stories and developing deep understandings about people's experiences in order that such understanding can inform the delivery of care. The key thing is that such studious enquiry is intended to take our everyday observations about the world and make them more concrete, deep and significant for the ongoing task of healing, caring and supporting others.

2. Research is discovery and interpretation. Most of us simply go through our lives without really noticing what is going on. Much of what goes on around us simply passes us by because we rarely take the time to slow down and notice it. The research process is designed to enable us to slow down and notice things in new ways. Research has to do with making the familiar strange. For example, most of us rarely think about our bodies until something goes wrong with them. Then, that which is for the most part unnoticed becomes everything. We suddenly realise how dependant we are on our bodies, how they hold us in the world and how much of our interaction with the world is determined by the shape, texture and function of our bodily aspects. When we notice these things, we begin to see the world slightly differently and encounter it in fresh ways. Research functions in a similar way. As we engage with the methods and perspectives of the research process, we are allowed to see and to develop new understandings of our day-to-day lives. (Swinton & Mowat, 2006)

3. Research challenges us to see the world differently and in seeing things differently, begin to reflect on how we might change our practices in response. As the cadence of our understanding deepens, so our practices will shift and change in rhythm with our expanding knowledge. Research thus opens our minds to possibilities that would not otherwise be available to us; this 'revelation' will inevitably bring us to a place where we have to explore the practical application of our new theory. That being so, contrary to common stereotypes, good research is never sterile and esoteric; it is always (or at least should always be) action oriented and transformative.

In summary, research helps us to understand our present situation more fully, while at the same time challenging us to move beyond the expectations of our current boundaries. It is therefore an invaluable tool for reflection, knowledge development, change and transformation.

Why is research important in the NHS and clinical settings?

For the reasons outlined so far, research is important in the NHS and within clinical settings to establish the suitability of an intervention or service and to improve our understanding and practices of care. The NHS has an 'evidence-based culture', that is, it is an organisation that requires empirical evidence to demonstrate the validity of a need or solution to a problem or issue. For this reason, even something as fluid, apparently esoteric and deeply personal as spirituality is required to have some form of evidence base to support its development and acceptance. This is what makes researching spirituality more than a little tricky! How can you measure or assess the health value of something that has no obvious observable shape or form beyond people's personal expressions? The quotation at the start of the chapter indicates that patients often want their spiritual needs met. But how can we show the efficacy of spirituality in an evidence-based culture?

Religion and spirituality

One of the difficulties in researching spirituality is that the concept is rather vague. Much of the research that has been done thus far has emerged from the United States and has focused on religion rather than the more generic term 'spirituality', which is common parlance in health and social literature in the United Kingdom. As this is the case, we will need to begin by trying to clarify our terms. We need to distinguish between 'religiousness' and 'spirituality'.

Religiousness is defined as participation in the particular beliefs, rituals and activities of traditional religion. It can serve as a nurturer or channel for spirituality, but is not necessarily synonymous with it. Spirituality is more basic than religiousness. Spirituality relates to the way in which people understand and live their lives in view of their core beliefs and values and their perception of ultimate meaning (see also chapter 1). Religion is relatively easy to measure as it relates to specific things that individuals and groups of people do, the consequences of which can be measured and their health benefits measured against an assumed norm. For example, some studies have measured the significance of religion according to the amount of times a person attends church each month, or the number of times a day they pray (Meisenhelder & Chandler, 2000; Reyes-Ortiz *et al*, 2007). Such behaviours are relatively easy to quantify and thus more suited to a clinical research study that seeks to determine the pattern between religious adherence and mental well-being. What is often not addressed in such studies is what attending religious services and performing religious actions actually means to the person on a deeper, spiritual level. This raises some important methodological questions, as Richard Sloan somewhat ironically put it: '*Anyone who believes that sitting in church makes you a Christian must also believe that sitting in a garage makes you a car!*' (Sloan, 2008). The meaning behind religious practices is as important as simply noticing that engagement in them may or may not be correlated with health.

It is nonetheless encouraging to note from the studies carried out in the USA that, despite these possible methodological shortcomings, people who are more religious, (that is, express their religion through regularly attending a religious institution) belong to a religious community and participate in religious practices, are generally more likely to have better resistance to mental illness, and to make a faster recovery if they do become unwell (Koenig *et al*, 2001). Some general observations will help make this point. Between 65–85% of the studies featured in Koenig *et al's* (2001) collection show a positive correlation between religious adherence and:

▶ increased hope and optimism

▶ a sense of purpose and meaning

▶ increased self-esteem

▶ less depression

▶ fewer suicides

▶ less substance abuse and dependency

▶ less psychosis and fewer psychotic tendencies.

The reasons why this might be the case, include:

▶ the social element of religious belonging – knowing people care for you, and having people do practical things to help you

▶ the promotion of positive self-perception – God/the Divine cares for me; I am a child of God

► the provision of specific coping resources – symbols, rituals and narratives that faith communities provide to give a framework for life

► the generation of positive emotions – for example, love and forgiveness

► encouraging people to be 'outward looking' – caring for others, the community and the environment helps people stay connected to the life around them and encourages a sense of purpose.

Researching spirituality

Researching spirituality in its more generic forms is more complicated. This mode of spirituality is much less clearly defined tending to relate to what people think and feel rather than necessarily what they actually do. Religion, of course, has to do with thought and feeling, but the studies looking at religion tend to focus on actions rather than the subtleties of specific beliefs and feelings. Within the more recently developed models of spirituality it is suggested that everyone has their own personal spirituality and that this relates to such things as meaning, purpose, hope, love and for some, God. However, measuring love is no easy task. Spirituality is therefore much more difficult to capture scientifically and more complicated in terms of developing an evidence base.

Qualitative research

One way we might deal with this problem is through the use of qualitative research. Qualitative research comprises the collecting, analyzing and interpreting of data relating to the observation of behaviour and the recording of verbal expressions of specific experiences, with a view to developing a rich and deep understanding of those experiences. Quantitative research (see below) refers to counting and measuring things; qualitative research relates to the meanings, concepts, definitions, characteristics, metaphors, symbols, and descriptions of things. Qualitative research brings about understanding and transformation by revealing hidden meanings and perspectives and allowing these new meanings to resonate constructively with current assumptions. It looks at lived experience and the meanings people use to make sense of their experiences. As such it is particularly suitable for accessing the spiritual aspects of people's experience (see Basset & Stickley, 2010).

Qualitative research focuses on the unique significance of the individual's experience. Quantitative research looks for generalisations; qualitative research assumes that that which is unique to the individual has deep meaning and significance (Swinton & Mowat, 2006). Within such an approach, the search is not for general definitions of spirituality that will apply to all people in all circumstances. Rather, the focus is on how this particular person is understanding spirituality. If a person names an action or feeling as real and spiritual, that is to be respected and believed.

This is not to suggest that spirituality is 'nothing but what people say it is?'. There may well be general forms of spirituality that all people encounter to greater or lesser degrees. The point from a qualitative perspective is that the uniqueness of the particular understanding of spirituality is significant for knowledge and practice. We have already indicated that spirituality is a diverse concept with various different meanings. In a cultural context wherein religion is not the only spiritual language available for use, people will use other forms of language to express the sacred and the spiritual. A helpful way to think about this is by reflecting on the term 'sanctification'. To sanctify something is to set it apart for a spiritual purpose; to make it holy. In a religious context the practice of sanctification comes via the rituals and practices of religious communities. However, the process of sanctification also has a non-religious dimension. Kenneth Pargament describes the process of sanctification as thus. It is a process:

'Through which people view seemingly secular aspects of life as holding significance and character. Sanctification may be best understood as a different way of perceiving the world … when people sanctify, they look at life through a sacred lens… Through this lens, the visual field shifts and changes. What once appeared monochromatic, unidimensional, and ordinary becomes multicoloured, multilayered, mysterious, rich, unique, awesome, alive and powerful.' (Pargament, 2007, p35)

This process of sanctification can have a theistic or a non-theistic root. For some, the process of sanctification relates to seeing God's involvement in every aspect of daily life. Here people perceive aspects of life as manifestations of God and interpret their experiences with the presumption that God is somehow involved. However, *'people can also sanctify objects indirectly by attributing qualities to them that are associated with the divine'* (Pargament, 2007, p38). By listening to people's stories and reflecting carefully on the ways in which they sanctify the ordinary aspects of their day to day lives, it is possible through the methods of qualitative research to capture and assess the importance of spirituality in its wider forms. People may name 'the spiritual' differently depending on whether or not they are religious. Qualitative research allows us to hear and understand these differences and their potential for understanding and clinical practice.

An example qualitative study of 'the spiritual'

Qualitative research studies are an excellent way to gain a picture of the attitudes, values, perceptions and understanding that surround people's experiences within a particular area. A brief reflection on the user-led Somerset Spirituality Project (Mental Health Foundation, 2002b) will help illustrate this point. This project used qualitative methods in order to gain a deeper understanding of the spiritual experiences of people who are using mental health services. The Somerset Spirituality Project team comprised primarily of people with experience of using local mental health services. The service users decided on the research topics and were at the heart of the research process. The study consisted of interviews with 27 mental health service users – 17 women and 10 men. All interviewees had been in contact with mental health services in Somerset for at least six months, and most for over 10 years. The majority (22) were or had been Christians; seven described themselves as spiritual rather than religious, six were Pagan and one was a Buddhist (Mental Health Foundation, 2002b). Participants were encouraged to use their own definitions of spirituality and allow this to shape and form the researchers' understanding of the nature of spirituality.

The findings highlighted the support people received from services and community groups as they sought to explore their spirituality. For example, the final report highlights some of the difficulties of interpreting a spiritual experience such as psychosis: *'While the project recognised the considerable importance of links between 'psychotic' and 'spiritual' experience, this personal area was touched on only if raised by interviewees themselves. One person said that "the two are just different ways of … moving deeper into the paradox". Others had experienced strong links between personal and universal suffering, and reflected on the voice-hearing experiences of many mystics. One person described times of severe distress or breakdown as: "You experience both heaven and hell … in a sense the very worst depths of despair, but also moments of joy".'* (Mental Health Foundation 2002a)

The study highlighted the importance of support from fellow service users. Many interviewees spoke powerfully of the support received from fellow service users. Such peer support was particularly helpful in that other service users know and understand the experiences firsthand. Most people found this peer support especially helpful because other service users know the experience, which leads to a greater sense of acceptance and assurance: *'In the end one of the greatest helps is to have one or two people around who you feel completely safe with and you can talk to and yell at, cry with or whatever. It's as simple as that.'* (Mental Health Foundation, 2002a)

The report also highlighted the importance of the experience of the presence of God:

'Some interviewees talked movingly of the presence of God and what this meant to them. For one the voice of God had prevented him from taking his own life. For others their experiences of distress and the spirit, belief in the sanctity of life, or faith that brought them through gave them a sense of meaning and purpose in life.' (Mental Health Foundation, 2002a)

Importantly, the report draws on these deep, meaningful and important expressions of spiritual experience in order to make recommendations for improving spiritual assessment and the provision of appropriate spiritual care for staff, faith leaders and other service providers. Thus policy and practice emerge from careful listening to the stories of those who in other circumstances may well find themselves silenced.

Quantitative research

That is not to suggest that quantitative research is of no use in researching spirituality. Quantitative research relates to the gathering and analysing of measurable data. It has to do with statistics, numbers, quantities and that which can be generalised across populations. Quantitative research is focused on the number of people who feel or respond in the same way to a particular phenomenon, be that drugs, physical or relational interventions or spirituality and religion. The underlying assumption is that there are certain qualities and experiences that human beings share in common, which can be captured statistically and related to others via general criteria that is exchangeable across contexts. The data gathered through quantitative research is thus assumed to be generalisable (applies to all people with the same characteristics), replicable (anyone, in principle can replicate this piece of research), and disprovable (it should in principle be hypothetically possible to disprove the results of the study). So, for example, a statement like 'God is real' makes no sense quantitatively as it cannot ever be disproved.

An example quantitative study of 'the spiritual'

The questionnaire-based study carried out in Birmingham and Solihull Mental Health NHS Foundation Trust provides an example of how a quantitative research project into spirituality might work. Here, a quantitative approach was used to explore staff attitudes to spiritual care in clinical settings. The questionnaire was designed to collect both qualitative and quantitative responses. We will concentrate on the quantitative results. The statistical responses were put into graphic form, which highlighted the general attitudes to, and knowledge of, spiritual care that staff recorded in a 'tick box' style survey. The results demonstrated, for example, that 75% of respondents (144 of 194 people asked) agreed that 'spirituality' for some people can be expressed through religion, but this is not always the case. Similarly, other percentages collected from the survey results indicated the number of staff who thought spirituality was important to address during a service user's care. These quantitative results firmly demonstrated the nature of current opinions around spirituality and how people in that context perceived its role in mental health care provision. In turn, the data helped to shape and inform the design of a training package for all clinical staff as areas of concern and gaps in knowledge were identified from the research (see Parkes *et al*, 2010).

Service users in research

'Knowledge produced by users is likely to be the most authentic, because it reduces the distance between experience, interpretation and knowledge.' (Sweeney *et al*, 2009)

Much of the research done within health and social services is done by professionals in relation to either a funded research project or some form of educational project. Such projects may or may not include the people the researchers are looking at or talking with and when this is the case it is important to emphasise the importance of service user research. Service user research is a mode of participatory research that attempts to do research with, rather than on participants. We have already given an example in the Somerset project highlighted above. However, it will be helpful to offer a little more detail about this approach. A participatory approach to research seeks, as far as possible, to include people as co-researchers within the research process. Involving service users in all stages of research, right from the initial conception of the idea to the dissemination stage, is becoming increasingly valued. Service users often have important insights into the reality of experiencing mental and physical illness that may affect the question the research team asks or how they go about conducting the study. This may have an impact on how the findings of the research are used and whether or not they make a practical difference to the people that are impacted by the findings. The value of involving both service users and carers has been recognised, for example, by the Institute of Psychiatry which has one of the largest units in European universities dedicated to the Service User Research Enterprise (SURE) group. Within research funding providers, such as the National Institute for Health Research (NIHR), emphasis on the importance of stakeholder participation is increasing, particularly for the funding of the Biomedical Research Centre for Mental Health (BRC). It is noted that the aim of this involvement is to ensure that new research, specifically around preventing, diagnosing and treating mental illness '*are* [sic] *used to benefit service users and carers*' (Biomedical Research Centre for Mental Health website, 2010).

Additionally, for many service users, involvement in a research project can be therapeutic. The authors have found that users who have been involved in research have been able to transform their difficult experiences of mental illness into a positive contribution to a research field. Feeling 'part of the team' also enables service users to overcome some of the isolation felt as a result of having a mental illness, and feel a renewed sense of being valued by others because of the insights they are able to give the rest of the team. The value of user-led research is increasing, and more often user groups that have an interest in collaborating with researchers are emerging, such as the SURE Search (Service User Research Network) based at the University of Birmingham.

Some guidelines for beginning a research project

In concluding this chapter it will be helpful to offer some basic pointers with regard to beginning a research project. We would suggest that readers use our thoughts as a general guide that might be useful in structuring a research project and to follow through on the references in the bibliography which will give more formal detail and structure.

Find a research mentor

Research can be a confusing and often lonely enterprise. We would advise that anyone starting out for the first time should find themselves a research mentor; someone with experience and time to share that experience and who will guide and advise them as they put the project together and work through the complex issues that emerge as it develops.

Be realistic about time and resources

Research often takes longer than anticipated. Often there are certain procedures that need to be cleared before it can commence, and surprising amounts of both time and energy are often used to do something as simple as finding out what is already known about research in any particular field. To do this would involve much trawling of journals, scientific and academic databases, as well as chasing up leads and contacts which could take weeks. There is no 'one resource' to find out what is already known.

Work in a good team

Research can sometimes be a lonely job, so working with a team will encourage enthusiasm and motivation. Working in a team, preferably made up of different disciplines, will ensure a wide variety of opinions, participation in the generation of ideas, and will enhance the study's possibility for making positive practical and theoretical change. Service users should be involved where possible in all areas of the research.

Don't be put off by research 'elitism'

The world of clinical research can be very competitive, with strict protocols and rules, and often with a focus on statistically reliable and concretely measurable studies and results. To contribute to the scientific evidence base, these standards are needed, as only the highest quality research should be used to make decisions that will impact the lives of thousands of people. However, service improvements can still be made through smaller research projects and audit projects that will help teams to identify the best ways to deliver spiritual care.

Make sure you have a good tight idea that has clear benefits for patients

Any formal research project needs to have a question, as the aim of the research project is to answer that question definitively. For this reason, it is important that the question is precise. It is, for example, more effective to ask: Does the spiritual intervention of attending a religious service on the ward help people with bipolar disorder to feel less distressed?; rather than asking: Does spirituality help someone with a mental illness feel better? The first question is tight and specifically focused. This enables you to develop or find a research tool and approach that will help you to understand and capture the complexities of bipolar disorder. The second question is vague and open to multiple interpretations, both of the question and the outcomes. Questions should generally address one specific area of spirituality, one specific mental health issue, and one specific 'outcome' ('feeling less distressed' or 'reducing the length of time in hospital'). Such a tight focus will make for a better and more accurate research study.

Clarify your terms and concepts

We have already seen how conceptually complicated the field of spirituality and religion is. That being so, the research team needs to define clearly what it means by terms such as 'spirituality,' 'mental illness,' 'health' and 'well-being', and what it means to 'feel better' etc. The vast majority of research in the efficacy of religion has focused on psychological, social, or physical health criteria. However, it is important to note that the primary criterion for religious believers is spiritual. Well-being within religious traditions is not gauged by the absence of illness or distress, but by the presence of God in the relationship. If the model of health held by the researcher differs from the assumptions of those being researched, then there will be obvious difficulties.

Make sure the ethics of your project are clear and appropriate

Research ethics might be described as a set of practical philosophical tools that a researcher draws upon to help them reflect on and explore the possible implications of the research for participants and for the integrity of the research process. Research ethics within a healthcare context enable the researcher to ensure that participants are safe and that the researcher's work is rigorous and credible. All formal research projects require ethical approval. This involves sending an outline of the proposed research study to a local research ethics committee, which will check that the study will not cause harm or distress to participants. Once the study gains approval from the ethics board it can begin.

Research design

All stages of the research project need to be designed. This includes asking a question and/or posing a hypothesis based on current knowledge (gained from a literature review) and then describing the steps taken to answer the question or proving the hypothesis. The steps taken are usually called the methodology, which forms part of a larger document that describes the whole design of the project, often called a research protocol. Methodology should describe what information will be collected (eg. spiritual understanding of psychosis), how (eg. questionnaires, including example questions) and from whom (eg service users experiencing psychosis, aged between 18 and 65.) Often the methodology is very detailed, describing every experience a participant might go through as part of the study.

Data collection

This is the part of the research study where the information that will be needed to answer the question is gathered. This may be through questionnaires, recovery scales, interviews, focus groups, or other methods that gather information from participants.

Analysis

The penultimate stage of the research involves analysing all the data that has been collected. There are many different methods of analysis. Analysis of large quantities of data for quantitative studies might utilise data analysis software and require statistical calculations to be made. For qualitative studies there are lots of methods to interpret data, such as analysing themes that are emerging from the responses (thematic analysis) or the personal experiences of the participant (Interpretative Phenomenological Analysis). Each analysis method has its own philosophy and protocol. Which method you choose depends on how your data is collected and what you what to find out.

Dissemination

The final stage of the research is to distribute the findings as widely as possible. An excellent finding that could impact people's health and well-being should not be left on a bookshelf. Dissemination can include presentations at conferences, journal articles and telling the participants of the research's result. This final stage is important as it contributes the research to the established evidence base.

With these thoughts in mind we offer the reader a list of further resources at the end of the chapter that will help them to see precisely how these thoughts and principles fit in with the formal structuring of a research project.

Conclusion

Perhaps the most important aspect of the research project has to do with passion. Research changes things; it is a creative and constructive process that not only brings about new knowledge but also changes situations and people within situations. This is particularly so with action-oriented approaches (Swinton & Mowat, 2006) but it is really the case for all research. In order to do research well we think that the researcher needs to have a real passion for the issues that they are working with. Passion sustains them through the difficult times and drives them on to work creatively towards the dual, but deeply interconnected goals of knowledge formation and practical changes. It is true that passion can, if misapplied, lead to bias, skewed results and a tendency to see in the data what you might want to see. Passion requires reflexivity (Swinton & Mowat, 2006) ie. the ability to reflect on one's self and the reasons why one makes particular decisions and chooses and works with some approaches, theoretical frameworks and methods rather than others. Nonetheless, we believe that reflexive passion leads to good research that has the potential to make a difference in a world that clearly needs changing. We hope that our thoughts and suggestions laid out in this chapter will help people to step on the road towards reflexive, passionate research and that readers will pick up the challenge and move on to make a difference.

References

Basset T & Stickley T (2010) *Voices of Experience: Narratives of survival and mental health.* Oxford: Blackwell/Wiley.

Bauer-Wu S & Farran CJ (2005) Meaning in life and psycho-spiritual functioning: a comparison of breast cancer survivors and healthy women. *Journal of Holistic Nursing* **23** 172–190.

Biomedical Research Centre (2010) NIHR Biomedical Research Centre for Mental Health website [online]. Available at: http://www.slam.nhs.uk/about-us/biomedical-research-centre/about-the-brc/translational-research.aspx (accessed November 2010).

Brady MJ, Cella DF, Mo F, Bonomi AE, Tulsky DS, Lloyd SR, Deasy S, Cobleigh M & Shiomoto G (1999) Reliability and validity of the Functional Assessment of Cancer Therapy-Breast quality-of-life instrument. *Journal of Clinical Oncology* **15** (3) 974–986.

Brady MJ, Peterman Ah, Fitchett G, Mo M & Cella D (1999) A case for including spirituality in quality of life measurement in oncology. *Psychooncology* **8** (5) 417–428.

Coward DD & Kahn DL (2005) Resolution of spiritual disequilibrium by women newly diagnosed with breast cancer. *Oncology Nursing Forum* **31** (2) 24–31.

Hill PC & Pargament KI (2003) Advances in the conceptualisation and measurement of spirituality. *American Psychologist* **58** 64–74.

Koenig HG, McCullough ME & Larson DB (2001) *Handbook of Religion and Health.* Oxford: Oxford University Press.

Leshner G, Cheng I-H, Song HJ, Choi Y & Frisby C (2006) The role of spiritual health locus of control in breast cancer information processing between African-American and Caucasian women. *Integrative Medicine Insights* **2** 35–44.

Meisenhelder JB & Chandler EN (2000) Prayer and health outcomes in church members. *Alternative Therapies in Health and Medicine* **6** (4) 56–60.

Mental Health Foundation (2002a) *Spirituality and Mental Health Updates* **4** (6). London: Mental Health Foundation.

Mental Health Foundation (2002b) *Taken Seriously: The Somerset Spirituality Project.* London: MHF.

Merriam-Webster (1998) *Merriam-Webster Collegiate Dictionary* (10th edition) Springfield, MA: Merriam-Webster.

Pargament KI (1997) *The Psychology of Religion and Coping: Theory, research, practice.* New York: Guilford.

Pargament KI (2007) *Spiritually Integrated Psychotherapy: Understanding and addressing the sacred.* New York: Guildford.

Parkes M, Milner K & Gilbert P (2010) Vocation, vocation, vocation. *The International Journal of Leadership in Public Services* **6** (3).

Reyes-Ortiz C, Berges MI, Raji, Mukaila A, Koenig, Harold G, Kuo, Markides & Kyriakos S (2007) Church attendance mediates the association between depressive symptoms and cognitive functioning among older Mexican Americans. *The Journals of Gerontology* **63** (5) 480–486.

Sloan R (2008) *Blind Faith: The unholy alliance of religion and medicine.* London: MacMillan.

Sure Search (2010) Official website. Available at: http://www.suresearch.org.uk/ (accessed November 2010).

Sweeney A, Beresford P, Faulkner A, Nettle M & Rose D (2009) *This Is Survivor Research.* Ross on Wye: PCCS Books.

Swinton J & Mowat H (2006) *Practical Theology and Qualitative Research Methods.* London: SCM Press.

Further reading

Barnes C (1992) Qualitative research: valuable or irrelevant? *Disability, Handicap and Society* **7** (2) 115–24.

Bowling A (2002) *Research Methods in Health.* Maidenhead: Open University Press.

Colin R (2006) *Real World Research: A resource for social scientists and practitioner-researchers.* London: Blackwell.

Cornwall A & Jewkes, R (1995) What is participatory research? *Social Science and Medicine* **41.**

Greenhalgh T (1997) How to read a paper: assessing the methodological quality of published papers. *British Medical Journal* **315** 305–8.

McLeod J (2001) *Qualitative Research in Counselling and Psychotherapy.* London: Sage.

Mowat H (2008) *The Potential for Efficacy of Healthcare Chaplaincy and Spiritual Care Provisions in the NHS: A scoping review of recent research.* Aberdeen: Mowat Research Limited.

Swinton J (2001) *Spirituality and Mental Health Care: Rediscovering a 'forgotten' dimension.* London: Jessica Kingsley Publishers.

Van Manen M (1990) *Researching Lived Experience: Human science for an action sensitive pedagogy.* New York: State University of New York Press.

Ward L & Flynn M (1994) What matters most: disability, research and empowerment. In: MH Rioux & M Bach (Eds) *Disability is not Measles: New research paradigms in disability.* Ontario: L'Institut Roeher.

Zarb G (1992) On the road to Damascus: first steps towards changing the relations of disability research production. *Disability, Handicap and Society* **7** (2) 125–38.

Chapter 3

Spirituality and mental health services

Peter Gilbert and Peter Richmond

Introduction

This chapter sets out a brief history of mental health services, and how spirituality has always been an important element in the delivery of a humane and effective service. It considers the drivers towards a spiritual approach in the 21st century and goes on to look at the specific policy and practice issues around the delivery of spiritual care.

Asylum or 'the asylum'?

We have a habit of using and abusing words in this country. A word denoting a positive concept, such as community, stemming from ideas of people grouping together and working with each other, can be overused, such as in the case of Care in the Community policies, which are then denigrated. When Frank Dobson MP, as the then Secretary of State for Health, stated that Care in the Community had not worked, many informed commentators suggested that it had never been tried! In a similar vein, the concept of asylum has come to mean a number of different things to different people. The word itself comes from the Greek *asulon* meaning refuge, and also a denial of the right of seizure. We still talk about individuals and groups seeking 'political asylum' as a positive sense of refuge from oppression, but in mental health the word 'asylum' conjures up the now forbidding Victorian building on a hill. This image is perhaps best summed up by Enoch Powell, when as Secretary of State for Health in 1961, he spoke of closing down the old institutions (then representing 75,000 hospital places) and replacing them with community facilities.

As he said at the time: *'This is a colossal undertaking, not so much in the physical provision which it involves as in the sheer inertia of mind and matter which it requires to be overcome. There they stand, isolated, majestic, imperious, brooded over by the gigantic water-tower and chimney combined, rising unmistakeable and daunting out of the countryside – the asylums which are our forefathers built with such immense solidity. Do not for a moment underestimate their power of resistance to our assault'* (Jones, 1972).

But, of course, as Jones and others (see Gilbert *et al*, 2010) point out, the Victorian asylums were built with the good intention of providing a public place (as opposed to a much abused private system) with state of the art facilities and appropriate professional oversight. The 19th century county asylums were often modelled on the most revered buildings of the previous centuries, such as the Palace of Versailles. The medical superintendents who worked in such places often had high hopes for the care and treatment they would be able to provide, and a good fictional description of this is presented in the well-researched novel *Human Traces* by Sebastian Faulks (Faulks, 2005). The superintendent at St Francis Hospital, Sussex, wrote in his official journal of his hopes for such a new institution.

In Sussex, although an act of 1808 had empowered counties to build asylums for 'pauper lunatics', it was not until the Lunatics Act of 1845, which brought about the creation of a permanent Commission (the forerunner of the regulatory system we have today) led by the charismatic Lord Ashley, who himself experienced profound episodes of mental distress, that the Sussex worthies stirred themselves. In the end, after many arguments between east and west Sussex and Brighton, with the counties accusing the metropolitan area of Brighton of having far more 'lunatics' than the counties and therefore needing to pay more, the county asylum was built near Hayward's Heath between 1857 and 1859. It was placed on a hill, which was seen as having health benefits, and away from the picturesque villages of Lindfield and Cuckfield. The superintendent's report for Christmas Day 1859 speaks of 303 patients. One lyrical passage in his report speaks much for the hopefulness engendered in that period. *'The beauty also of the site of the asylum, looking out on the free downs, which are ever changing their distance and their shape, as the lights and cloud-*

shadow sail on them and over the graceful forms of those endless varieties of slopes, the eye wanders ... within an entrancing feeling of fullness and a restful satisfaction of the pure sense of form.' (East Sussex County Records in Gilbert *et al*, 2010, p26)

The report speaks also of order and discipline reducing into *'harmony and good conduct some of the most violent and unpromising cases of insanity which the mental superintendent had ever met with in practice'* (East Sussex County Records Office in Gilbert *et al*, 2010, p26). The superintendent is hopeful of the *'curative employment, the weekly dance and weekly visiting'* (East Sussex County Records Office in Gilbert *et al*, 2010, p26).

Unfortunately, as we know, despite the huge investment that the Victorians put into the asylums, and their many good intentions, the rapid increase in numbers, as workhouses and the prison system saw an opportunity to move large numbers of people into the county asylums; the physical separation of so many inmates from their communities; and the absence of effective treatment, meant that increasingly people became institutionalised.

Common themes in social policy

Lord Ashley's reformers realised that, for inspection to be effective, some visits had to be unannounced so that inspectors could actually see what was really happening, rather than what was being prepared for them to see. It is interesting, if somewhat depressing, that this obvious factor seems to have been forgotten in current times and only rediscovered in the scandals surrounding acute hospitals, such as Mid Staffordshire and Basildon and Thurrock in 2008–2009.

It is worth thinking about a number of common themes in social policy which keep reoccurring (see Midwinter, 1994; Gilbert *et al*, 2010).

▶ **The public/private balance.** In the last couple of decades, the private sector in healthcare in the UK has come back into the equation as a way of sharpening up the NHS. The public/private sector balance has also been a major factor in President Obama's healthcare reforms in the USA in 2009/10.

A monolithic state healthcare system can become sclerotic and resistant to change. But it is also worth remembering that the 19th century mental health reforms in England were brought about by abuses of the private system.

▶ **The central/local balance.** Currently, there are major debates around the deadening effect of central government targets, but also concern from citizens that there shouldn't be a 'postcode lottery'. In mental health, the National Institute for Mental Health in England (see Gilbert & Clark, 2010) was an ethical and imaginative attempt to bring together central policy, regional direction, and local concerns and innovations.

▶ **The domestic/institutional balance.** The recent debates in the UK about the care of older people and its funding have had underlying ethical and financial themes around the best type of care for individuals and couples, and the cost of care at home, or care in a residential or nursing situation. Since the National Service Framework for Mental Health in 1999 (see Gilbert & Clark, 2010) specialist teams have been set up across England to try and keep people out of institutional settings. Sometimes, however, while a lengthy stay in a care unit can cause institutionalisation, people need a period of respite and this isn't always forthcoming, so the care pathways always need careful attention. The focus on personalisation (see Carr, 2010; Bogg, 2010) will hopefully continue to push towards a more domestic and community orientation. The stress needs to be on 'interdependence' as well as 'independence', and it is vital that the coalition government's focus on the 'Big Society' isn't an abandonment of those areas of health and social care which have less popular support.

▶ **Cash/kind balance.** Again, a theme which is coming back into prominence with issues around personalisation and self-directed budgets.

▶ **Liberty versus safety.** The whole history of mental health legislation could actually be summed up as a struggle for a balance between the liberty of the individual and the safety of that individual, plus the safety of the general public.

(see also 'The journey out of the institutions' in *Leadership for Personalisation and Social Inclusion in Mental Health* by Allen *et al*, 2009, p25)

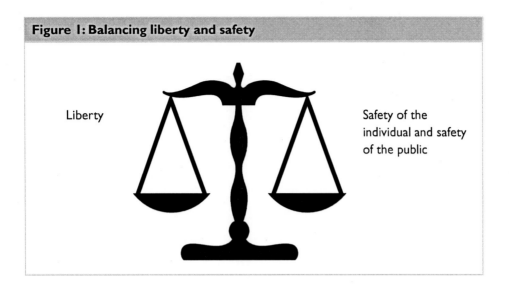

Figure 1: Balancing liberty and safety

Liberty

Safety of the individual and safety of the public

Early and mid 19th century legislation was primarily about protecting the individual from false imprisonment, and building public provision. This occurred following a number of scandals where people were taken to private 'madhouses' by their doctors at the request of relatives who wanted to get hold of their finances, or by people who wanted to get rid of an inconvenient partner.

In contrast, the 1890 Lunacy Act was a lawyer's dream, and Kathleen Jones' comments about it are striking. *'Nothing was left to chance, and very little to future development'* and *'The result from the legal point of view, was very nearly perfect. From the medical and social viewpoint, it was to hamper the progress of the mental health movement for nearly 70 years.'* (Jones, 1972)

When we get to the 20th century, the 1959 Mental Health Act was farsighted, but it lacked the community resources to enable it to be effective. The 1983 Mental Health Act had a greater accent on the liberty of the individual, and the pendulum then swung back in the 1990s following the celebrated cases of Christopher Clunis and Michael Stone. There was, in effect, a battle between a powerful Home Office and a less influential Department of Health, which then saw enacted the 2007 amending legislation to the 1983 primary legislation (see Slay, 2010). It was the subject of 10 years' debate, and has resulted in considerable confusion as to what the underlying values of the legislation actually are. In 2011 the whole of adult legislation requires an urgent overhaul and rationalisation.

Spiritual care

There is a long tradition in philosophy and religion for seeing 'madness' as something to be celebrated rather than feared. The ancient Greek philosopher Plato quotes Socrates as preaching that *'the greatest blessings come by way of madness, indeed of madness that is heaven-sent'* (Phaedrus). Aristotle also felt that melancholy was a necessary element in artistic creativity. Jewish society accorded some respect, even reverence, to those thought to be uttering what might be prophecies. Mosaic law recognised the appointment of guardians for those who are not in possession of their faculties. Mediaeval Christianity, through its monasteries, offered sanctuary for people with mental and learning disabilities. In fact, the word cretin is derived from the French word *chretien*, meaning Christian, as these deprived Christians gathered around the monastic sanctuary. King Edward II's Law *De Praerogativa Regis* afforded the protection of property for 'lunatics' and also 'idiots' or 'natural fools'. Writers such as the Swiss physician, Paracelsus in the early 16th century referred back to the Christian New Testament and the concept of the irrational perhaps being closer to God than the rational: *'The wisdom that is also in fools, like light in a fog, can shine through more clearly'* (Gilbert & Scragg, 1992).

But, of course, sometimes care deteriorated into fear, supervision and infantalisation, and some of these concepts and responses are set out in tabular form in Gilbert and Scragg (1992, p29). Exorcism was sometimes used inappropriately, and is still sometimes used by faith groups today, as in the tragic case of Victoria Climbié.

During the Reformation, and the dissolution (or privatisation) of the monasteries, the first welfare state in this country effectively broke down. Midwinter comments: *'The part of charity in religious life weakened with the advent of the Protestant creeds, with their emphasis on individual self-help and salvation'* (Midwinter, 1994).

Of course, charitable impulses resurfaced, in the setting up of alms houses, many of which have been reinvented as sheltered housing for older people today. But these were much more tied to individual benefactors and specific issues of care – mainly for 'the deserving poor'. The move from a predominantly feudal economy, to the primarily capitalist and monetary economy of present time, linked to a rise of capitalist endeavour and the enclosure of common lands; followed by the industrial revolution, meant that many who before had coped reasonably well, and were, at least partly accepted in communities, began to be much more identified and less tolerated than before. Professor Andrew Scull contends that: *'Many of the transformations underlying the move towards institutionalisation can be more plausibly tied to the growth of the capitalist market system and to its impact on economic and social relationships'* (Scull, 1984). This is, of course, increasingly evident in western society today (see Mental Health Foundation, 2010) and in the faster growing developing countries (Brannigan, 2010).

Bartlett and Wright (1999) caution that the interaction between the community and the institutions, which began to gather momentum in the 19th century, was much more fluid than it is often described. It is clear that an increasing number of people were seen as 'outsiders' or 'deviants'. Perhaps this was exacerbated during the years of the English revolution in the 17th century (see Hill, 1972; Jones, 1993). Workhouses and prison institutions began to be built to constrain and restrain people who could no longer be catered for in their local communities. It is an irony now that so many of the Victorian hospitals have been turned into genteel housing developments and often 'gated communities'. The French philosopher, Michel Foucault speaks about 'the great confinement' and makes the point that: *'By a strange act of force, the Classical Age was to reduce to silence the madness whose voices the Renaissance had just liberated, but whose violence it had already tamed'* (Foucault, 1961/2001).

Again, novels are often a helpful insight into contemporary thinking, though it is worth remembering that there is often a time-lag between what is depicted in a novel and policy progress, especially in the 19th century. Charlotte Bronte's *Jane Eyre*, first published in 1847, appears to sympathise entirely with Mr Rochester and Jane, where Rochester's first wife remains as a 'maniac' locked in an attic with an untrained attendant. By contrast, Wilkie Collins' 1869 novel *The Woman in White* depicts Anne Catherick, who has learning disabilities, as 'an object of pity' (see Jones, 1972; Wise, 2010).

It's all about values

Societies have always had to work out how to deal with people who don't immediately fit in. Human beings need to form a view about behaviour, and whether it has a value to individuals, families and society as a whole.

As Dr Paul Keedwell from Maudsley Hospital, London, has recently suggested: *'depression is such a common theme in humanity, that it must play some positive role in evolutionary progress'* (Keedwell, 2008).

How we define mental health and mental illness; how we relate to individuals; what care we provide and in what form; how we define and legislate for liberty and safety are issues that all societies face. What answers we come up with are dependent on our values. While a purely religious and spiritual perspective on mental illness had its disadvantages, the Enlightenment, with its accent on rationality, also had its pros and cons. Pietro Leopoldo, Grand Duke of Tuscany, came to rule Florence in 1865 (Keys, 2010) and modernised his new realm by banning capital punishment; reforming the economy; outlawing torture; introducing civil rights; producing protection for people who were mentally ill; instituting smallpox vaccination; and rehabilitating juvenile delinquents. But an overemphasis on rationality also led to the growing band of professionals in mental health ignoring the stories told by those with the lived experience. Psychiatrists Patrick Bracken and Philip Thomas describe this as 'reductionism' – an attempt to explain aspects of our meaningful reality in terms of non-meaningful entities, such as genes and neurotransmitters, with a focus on:

▶ the importance of experts – those who hold privileged accounts of what is happening

▶ technological framing of problems – focus on establishing cause or processes that can be scientifically manipulated

▶ methodological individualism – focus on decontextualised aspects of a persons behaviour, eg. symptoms.

(Bracken & Thomas, 2005)

From the late 1990s, mental health has been seen as an issue of increasing importance, not least because economists such as professor Richard Layard have stressed the importance of mental health in a knowledge economy (Layard, 2005).

At the same time the government made mental health the first of its National Service Frameworks (NSF) (Department of Health, 1999). The NSF had seven standards, including ones on mental health promotion, primary care and access to services, effective services for people with severe mental illness, carers' needs, and preventing suicide.

The NSF, and its resulting specialist teams, concentrating on early intervention and effective treatment and care in the community, set a basic foundation for New Horizons (Department of Health, 2009b), where the promotion of a healthy society is seen as paramount: *'Mental health is everyone's business. In 2020 mental health will be seen as an important asset for our society, one in which we all have an investment and to which we all – individuals, employers, the further statutory sectors, local authorities, the health service and all government departments – have an important contribution to make.'* (Department of Health, 2009b)

Sociologist Erving Goffman's classic text on institutionalisation and the characteristics of the total institution (Goffman, 1961/1991) is a warning that all systems of care can turn into the system, and all models, however progressive, can turn into the model. This underlines the importance of recovery approaches, which are based on lived experience and service user empowerment, and described in a recent publication as: *'Common themes in recovery include the pursuit of health and wellness; a shift of emphasis from pathology and morbidity to health and strength; hope and belief in positive change; meaning and spiritual purpose of distress; service supports reconceived as mentoring not supervisory; identity explored as a cultural issue; social inclusion (housing, work, education, leisure); empowerment through information, role-change, self-care; awareness of positive language – use in framing the experience of illness; personal wisdom encouraged in professional practice; and creative risk-taking replacing overcautious risk assessment* (CSIP, RCP & SCIE, 2007)

But there is always a danger of professional hegemony and invasiveness. One of the most important spiritual approaches is to ensure that we do listen to the narratives that people relate to us – the individual's story (see Hornstein, 2009).

Empathic ignorance

While it is important that those caring for us have a degree of knowledge, absolute certainty in health and social care professionals, in religious leaders, in the new atheists like Richard Dawkins and Christopher Hitchens, can actually be very disempowering. It can undermine our own story, which we need to tell.

While it is easy for a reductionist approach to undermine someone's spiritual and/or religious beliefs, it is by no means true that all science is dismissive of the spiritual dimension. Physicist and cosmologist Paul Davies in his book *The Goldilocks Enigma* (Davies, 2006) argues that the existence of the conditions which make the universe habitable are quite incredible, like Goldilocks' porridge. The neuroscientist David Eagleman whose recent novel explores belief about the afterlife states that: *'Every time you go into a book store, you find a lot of books written with certainty – you find the atheists and you find the religious and everybody is acting like they know the answer. I think what life in science really teaches you is the vastness of our ignorance. We don't really understand most of what's happening in the cosmos. Is there any afterlife? Who knows. We don't have any evidence for it. We don't have any evidence against it. The thing that has always surprised me is that people are always acting as though they know the answer... There's a meta-message and that meta-message is that we don't know'* (Eagleman, 2010).

As religious belief increases in most countries in the world outside Western Europe, and religious adherence and an emphasis on spirituality is also increasing in the UK in many areas, there are a number of drivers towards spiritual care.

▶ Personalisation, through government white papers and commissioning frameworks

▶ The need to create greater social cohesion and community well-being

▶ The equalities legislative and policy agenda

▶ The accent on promoting a healthier social and economic community

▶ The need to meet the aspirations recorded by service users and carers in surveys and through inspection reports

▶ The Patient's Charter, and its accent on respect for privacy and dignity, and sensitivity and respect towards religious, spiritual and cultural needs

▶ The evidence base on the contribution of spirituality and faith to physical and mental health (see chapter 2)

▶ The importance of ethnicity and a faith in individual and group identity

▶ The increased cost benefit analysis achieved through working with the motivations of individual service users, carers and community groups

► The social inclusion agenda in which spirituality has an important role to play

► The need for health and social care to be sensitive to user, carer and staff belief systems (eg. Department of Health, 2009a)

► Government policy accent on prevention and early intervention

► Research showing that social inequality and rampant consumerism can have an adverse effect on people's mental health

Equality and diversity, healthcare in community and the patient experience

Three overarching issues concern the management of risk, quality and value for money in the NHS. To give them their current full names they are: equality, diversity and human rights; patient and public community involvement; patient experience governance. When it comes to delivery and management of what is often called spiritual care, these three are particular markers for governance and justification for its expense. Call our topic – spirituality – by as many names as suit, just a few will suffice to make the point that there is a diversity of understanding in the population and within the professional ranks of health and social care. The most commonly used are: religion and belief; faith; culturally competent care; human flourishing and holistic care. The content of these abstract terms includes things people hold dear and provides measures by which the humanity of the services expected by patients, carers and the public may be judged. Whether they measure up therapeutically is a separate question from whether they may justly be expected to be provided.

It is accepted that people have the right to be treated as individuals and their chosen or particular way of life must be treated with respect. Whether a person sees their attitude or habits of life as religion, culture or otherwise is not the point, the values they choose to live by is the agenda the service must respond to. The NHS is not a place to argue over the merits of the various world religions and their offshoots and detractors, as healthcare workers we take people as they are, and with contexts with which they come. It is a person's right to exercise their beliefs and to express their choices as long as they are deemed ethically legitimate. Not responding to a person as having human rights regarding race, gender, sexuality, religion and belief, disability, age and the right to liberty and treatment will land any trust in trouble. Presently, the Care Quality Commission (CQC) will take particular interest in them all, although race, disability and age are probably the more politically sensitive.

One aspect of the Care in the Community philosophy and the recovery approach reminds us that people do not 'belong' to the health service as patient subjects. The increase in the use of the terms 'customer' and 'citizen' is a mark of that attitude. Staff probably should have a sense of identity with their place of work or among a team, but healthcare professional bodies set their service and capability standards on the basis that the patient belongs first and foremost in the community. The terms 'autonomy' and 'empowerment' are marks of that underlying presupposition. The person as patient may have become very much a part of the life of a hospital or unit, but that is not where they are to be encouraged to make their home for long.

Making and maintaining all sorts of connections between services and community enables the individual in the transition from inpatient setting to their domicile outside. The so-called patient journey is about intake from a place in the community (or lack of it), access to the services offered, and then moving back to a life mostly focused on living and belonging in the wider community. Having a good patient, community and public involvement strategy is essential to the main method of mental health care – the Care Programme Approach (CPA). Whatever judgement you want to make about the practice of organised religion and the living of personal lifestyle choices, most of the social capital available for recovery and support is in community settings, and not part of the NHS budget and organisation. Whether the source of support is religious or secular should make no difference to the community practice nurse or psychiatrist, as long as it has benefits for the individual and they want to go there – that should be all that matters. Key performance indicators (KPIs) are the main governance measure used by trusts, and spiritual care outcomes that contribute to the efficiency by which 'customers' move through the system again justify the place of spiritual care staff and spiritual care in the professional curriculum (see Harlow, 2010; Raffay, 2010; and chapters 15 and 16).

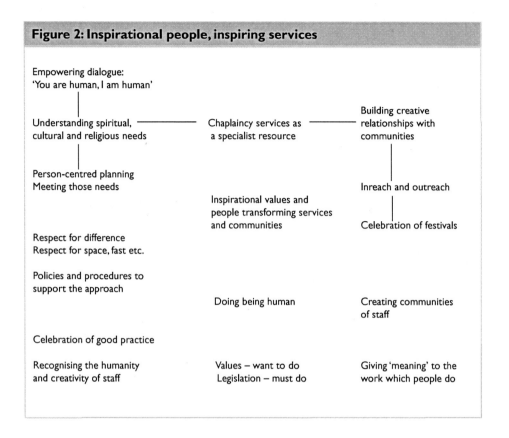

Figure 2: Inspirational people, inspiring services

Empowering dialogue:
'You are human, I am human'

Understanding spiritual, cultural and religious needs — Chaplaincy services as a specialist resource — Building creative relationships with communities

Person-centred planning Meeting those needs

Inspirational values and people transforming services and communities

Inreach and outreach

Celebration of festivals

Respect for difference Respect for space, fast etc.

Policies and procedures to support the approach

Doing being human

Creating communities of staff

Celebration of good practice

Recognising the humanity and creativity of staff

Values – want to do
Legislation – must do

Giving 'meaning' to the work which people do

(Taken from Aris & Gilbert in: Coyte *et al* (2007) *Spirituality, Values and Mental Health: Jewels for the journey*, p240 and reproduced with permission from Jessica Kingsley)

Anecdotal evidence from chaplains and clinical staff would indicate that recovery may be enhanced as a result of mental health interventions that include a spiritual care element. The word 'may' accepts that there are plenty of cases where this would not be the case. However, no patient should have to complain about what happened to them in the course of their treatment. Whether or not the patient's experience turns out to be therapeutically successful is a matter that accompanies the question as to whether the patient felt they were treated with dignity and respect, had access to all the services available and information was clearly presented. There is ongoing research regarding the place of spirituality within the variables affecting coping and recovery. The findings of such research may mean that we can assuredly add a fourth reason why the NHS must include spirituality in its service standards. However, the clinical effectiveness of spiritual care as a part of person-centred care remains research in progress. Nevertheless, patient experience governance has to measure how people feel about the way they were treated. Clinical governance will, we would hope, consider the effectiveness of the range of treatments, and whether or not they were able to access spiritual care as part of their treatment. From the point of view of patient experience, there is a much stronger case, and a simpler one, for meeting pastoral, spiritual and religious needs on the basis that we all do better (or feel that we do) when we are treated as whole people and enabled to maintain those things which we ourselves find helpful in coping with adversity. The spiritual and pastoral care team can then support and assist frontline staff in their endeavours (see figure 2 and chapter 21).

Reflection exercise

Does your organisation have a spiritual care strategy? (see Harlow, 2010)

Is there a spiritual care education programme involving all staff?

Are there opportunities for staff to discuss spiritual care as a vital element in the service? (see Parkes et al, 2010).

How strong and clear are the links between your particular service, the spiritual and pastoral care team, and local spiritual and faith communities/groups?

Who takes and shares the responsibility is an issue undergoing a period of change. Spiritual care can be taken as the responsibility of everyone to some extent. The traditional role of the nurse includes that of being a person who comes alongside, empathically, as well as being a trained professional with a range of clinical capabilities and competencies. It is from that model that spiritual care is taken as a shared duty. A nurse who is of an intrinsic religious disposition will know that faith itself is something that is set in a social context, connects to the fragility of the environment, affects the way we see ourselves and approaches questions about the divine with humility and an awareness of our own subjectivity. Such a person will bring with them a capability to listen and foster the spirituality of the patient, whether or not the patient they are working with shares their religious tradition. Anyone who recognises the importance of who we are to ourselves, who we belong to and how they respond to us, what kind of a world we inhabit and, how we make our way from birth to death, can be a spiritual care giver. The key concepts are the intrinsic values of the caregiver, so that what arises out of their own spirituality connects to the well-being of the patient as understood by the patient, and second, the mature way in which the caregiver reflects on his or her own subjectivity, is aware of its limitations but still has the confidence to use it as a guide to safe, ethical and effective practice. On the basis that we all have a spirituality of well-being connected to those common domains, we can legitimately ask every clinician to take cognisance of the spiritual needs of their patients.

Conclusion

As we saw in Chapter 1, Jean Davison was admitted to one of the original county asylums (re-designated post 1948, as a psychiatric hospital) after seeing a psychiatrist who she hoped would be '...*able to understand my difficulties in coming to terms with the loss of my religious beliefs, about life seeming empty and meaningless, and those hard to explain "what am I?" feelings*' (Davison, 2009).

Davison ended up having ECT and antipsychotic medication, and had a hard-won struggle to find herself and her life again. At the end of the book she remarks: '*How quickly, how easily, and on what flimsy 'evidence' diagnostic labels may be affixed and lives torn apart. Yet the serious flaws in the diagnostic process are still seemingly unacknowledged by those with unswerving belief in its scientific validity.*' (Davison, 2009)

The recent publication by the Royal College of Psychiatrists (Cook *et al*, 2009) gives a cogent support for an holistic and spiritual approach, and the policy direction seems firmly set towards personalised and community approaches.

But, as Clare Allen, author and survivor, wrote recently: '*A great deal has changed, but the past is still present in the minds of those who were there*'. Both our social policy and historical perspective are short-sighted and we are not on our guard to ascertain whether our natural inclination towards making a system into 'the System' (see Gilbert *et al*, 2010) is pushing us into building metaphorical walls around those we serve.

References

Allen R, Gilbert P & Onyett S (2009) *Leadership for Personalisation and Social Inclusion in Mental Health.* Adult Services Report No 27, November, 2009. London: SCIE.

Aris S & Gilbert P (2007) Organizational health: engaging the heart of the organization. In: ME Coyte, P Gilbert & V Nicholls (Eds) (2007) *Spirituality, Values and Mental Health: Jewels for the journey.* London: Jessica Kingsley.

Bartlett P & Wright D (1999) *Outside the Walls of the Asylum: The history of care in the community* 1750–2000. London: The Athlone Press.

Bogg D (2010) *Mental Health and Personalisation.* Brighton: Pavilion Publishing.

Bracken P & Thomas P (2005) *Post-psychiatry: Mental health in a postmodern world.* Oxford: Oxford University Press.

Brannigan T (2010) Held in a mental hospital, the Chinese woman who challenged bureaucrats. *The Guardian,* 1 September 2010, p25.

Carr S (2010) *Personalisation: A rough guide* (2nd edition). London: SCIE.

Cook C, Powell A & Sims A (Eds) (2009) *Spirituality and Psychiatry.* London: RCPsych.

CSIP, RCP & SCIE (2007) *A Common Purpose: Recovery in Future Mental Health Services.* Joint Position Paper 8, May, 2007. London: SCIE.

Davies P (2006) *The Goldilocks Enigma: Why is the universe just right for life?* London: Allen Lane.

Davison J (2009) *The Dark Threads.* Glamorgan: Accent Press.

Department of Health (1999) *Modern Standards and Service Models: National service framework for mental health.* London: HMSO.

Department of Health (2009a) *Religion or Belief: A practical guide for the NHS.* London: DH.

Department of Health (2009b) *New Horizons: Towards a shared vision for mental health.* London: DH.

Eagleman D (2010) My brighter idea: We won't die, we'll live forever as a download. *The Observer, The New Review,* 4 April 2010, p26.

Faulks S (2005) *Human Traces.* London: Vintage.

Foucault M (1961/2001) *Madness and Civilization: A history of insanity in the age of reason.* London: Routledge Classics.

Gilbert P with Bates P, Carr S, Clark M, Gould N & Slay G (2010) *Social Work and Mental Health: The value of everything* (2nd edition). Lyme Regis: Russell House Publishing.

Gilbert P & Clark M (2010) Waking the sleeping giant: reflections on leadership and the National Institute for Mental Health in England 2002–2009. *The International Journal of Leadership in Public Services* **6** (2).

Gilbert P & Scragg T (1992) *Managing to Care: Issues in services for people with learning disabilities.* Sutton: Reed Business Publishing.

Goffman E (1961/1991) *Asylums: Essays on the social situation of mental patients and other inmates.* London: Penguin.

Harlow R (2010) Developing a spirituality strategy – why, how and so what? *Mental Health, Religion and Culture* **13** (6).

Hill C (1972) *The World Turned Upside Down: Radical ideas during the English Revolution.* London: Maurice Temple Smith.

Hornstein GA (2009) *Agnes's Jacket: A psychologists search for the meaning of madness.* New York: Rodale.

Jones K (1972) *A History of the Mental Health Services.* London: Routledge and Keegan Paul.

Jones K (1993) *Asylums and After: A revised history of the mental health services from the early 18th century to the 1900s.* London: Athlone Press.

Keedwell P (2008) *How Sadness Survived: The evolutionary basis of depression.* Oxford: Radcliffe Publishing.

Keys D (2010) Tuscan masterpieces return home after two centuries in exile. *BBC History Magazine*, April 2010.

Layard R (2005) *Happiness: Lessons from a new science.* London: Allen Lane.

Mental Health Foundation (2010) *The Lonely Society?* London: MHF.

Midwinter E (1994) *The Development of Social Welfare in Britain.* Buckingham: Open University Press.

Parkes M, Milner K & Gilbert P (2010) Vocation, vocation, vocation. *The International Journal of Leadership in Public Services* **6** (2).

Phaedrus by Plato. In: Boardman J, Griffin J & Murray O (Eds) (1986) *The Oxford History of the Classical World.* Oxford: Oxford University Press.

Raffay J (2010) Training the workforce in spiritual healthcare. *Mental Health, Religion and Culture* **13** (6).

Scull A (1984) *Decarceration: Community treatment and the deviant. A radical view* (2nd edition). Cambridge: Polity Press.

Slay G (2010) The vital equilibrium – social work and the law. In: Gilbert P with Bates P, Carr S, Clark M, Gould N & Slay G (2010) *Social Work and Mental Health: The value of everything* (2nd edition).

Wise S (2010) A novel for hysterical times. *History Today* August 2010, p46–52.

Chapter 4

The service user view

Peter Gilbert, with Joanna Barber and Madeleine Parkes

Starting with the person

'Anna Skolimovska' came to work in England a few years ago. She had no relatives here, but worked hard in the retail industry and struck up what seemed to be a positive relationship with a man who had grown up in the city where she was working. When the relationship became abusive and 'Anna' had to use a woman's refuge; she began to experience persecutory voices, which complicated and intensified her already tangible experience of persecution; and she was admitted to an acute ward at her local psychiatric hospital.

The care on the ward was helpful and supportive, and the staff quickly discovered, in a non intrusive way, both her ethnicity and her religion, which was Roman Catholic. The ward staff were not surprised when Anna said she would like to see a priest and would welcome communion. The staff had a helpful handbook on different religious faiths, which had been written by the spiritual and pastoral care team. One of the nursing staff was surprised, however, when Anna said urgently to her that she would need to confess. The staff member said gently: *'I'm sure you have nothing to confess, it was you who was badly treated, Anna.'* But this reasonable response made Anna very agitated. The staff knew about confession, but were surprised at the urgency of Anna's request. Sensibly, they spoke to one of the chaplains who explained that for many Eastern European Catholics, they would feel it imperative to go to confession prior to receiving communion, an injunction which might not be so strictly adhered to by Western European Catholics. Anna was helped by the chaplaincy and the ward staff, and connections were made, with her permission, with her parish priest. Anna has since made a full recovery.

This instance highlights the complexity regarding faith and cultural issues. While written guidance is useful it can only skim the surface, and the fact that somebody says that they are a Muslim, Christian, Hindu, Jain, Sikh or Jew etc. doesn't give the whole story by any means. A service user in London who had come to the UK from Africa made the point that many African Muslims are sympathetic to the Sufi mystical tradition, which was once more widely prevalent in Islam (Armstrong, 2009) and this will have quite a considerable impact on their attitudes and faith practices.

And, of course, a large number of people will subscribe to having a spiritual dimension, which is not connected to a religious faith. As a service user puts it in a trust's strategy document: *'Spirituality is not confined to the followers of a particular religion, or of all religions. It can be described as breath, the essence of human beings, or what brings them to life and provides hopefulness, energy, direction and motivation in their lives. The identification of spirituality is, therefore part of the process of seeing and understanding people holistically, and plays an essential role in the individual's recovery.'* (Cambridgeshire and Peterborough NHS Foundation Trust, 2010)

Reflection exercise

How equipped do staff members feel in responding to a service user or carer's spiritual gifts and needs?

Does your organisation have a spiritual and pastoral care/chaplaincy team?

Is there a spirituality strategy for the organisation?

Is there some written guidance of what faith communities believe and what their important rites, rituals and festivals are?

Does your organisation have a training programme in spiritual care?

Has your organisation got a shared booklet on spirituality for service users, carers and staff like the one produced by Joanna Barber for Birmingham and Solihull Foundation Trust called *Handbook of Spiritual Care in Mental Illness* (Barber, 2010)?

The author, William Styron, speaks of the suddenness and totality of the depression which engulfed him: '... *and my brain had become to endure its familiar siege: panic and dislocation, and a sense that my thought processes were being engulfed by a toxic and unnameable tide that obliterated any enjoyable response to the living world.'* (Styron, 1990/2004)

And, in fact, he terms his experience '*darkness visible*' (Styron, 1990/2004), and quotes the Book of Job:

'*For the thing which
I greatly feared is come upon me,
and that which I was afraid of
is come unto me.
I was not in safety, neither
had I rest, neither was I quiet; yet trouble came.*'

At the end of his journey, Styron says movingly and graphically: '*And so we came forth, and once again beheld the stars.*' (Styron, 1990/2004)

K Redfield Jamison, a qualified psychiatrist working in academia who has a lifetime experience of bipolar disorder, speaks in her beautiful memoir, *An Unquiet Mind*, of '*moods and madness*' and about whether she would have chosen to '*have manic depressive illness*' (Jamison, 1996). She suggests that if she hadn't had good care, medication that worked for her, and love from her fellow significant others, she wouldn't have chosen to go down that life path. But with this support, she continues to muse: '*Strangely enough I think I would choose to have it. It's complicated. Depression is awful beyond words or sounds or images; I would not go through an extended one again. It bleeds relationships through suspicion, lack of confidence and self-respect, the inability to enjoy life...*' (Jamison, 1996)

She continues:

'*I honestly believe that as a result of it* [the illness as a whole], *I have felt more things, more deeply; had more experiences, more intensely; loved more, and been more loved; laughed more often for having cried more often; appreciated more the springs, for all the winters, warn death "as close as dungarees", appreciated it – and life more; seen the finest and most terrible in people and slowly learned the values of caring, loyalty and seeing things through. I have seen the breadth and depth and width of my mind and heart and seen how frail they both are, and how ultimately unknowable they both are.*' (Jamison, 1996)

At one point Jamison speaks of *'the crushing movements of a mental sea'* and love being an *'extraordinary part of the breakwater wall.'* (Jamison, 1996)

As somebody who has experienced a crippling depressive illness, thankfully for a relatively short space of time, and as someone who is perhaps latently manic depressive, with high levels of activity and the occasional plunge into the chasm, I attempted to capture this and the human manifestation of love and community, including that from the Benedictine community of Worth Abbey, in a poem in 2007.

'Years later...
when the tomb door was shut on me
so sand silted up my ears,
my eyes, my brain, and heart.
The crypt sealed with a metal trapped door – tight!
Bolted down.
Then it was human hands
reached down to me
and pulled me up.

Because I couldn't hear,
couldn't bear,
the music,
I sought the comfort
of my faith family
and listened to the rhythm
and measure of the psalms
the rhyme and rhythm bore me up,
like the waves ... beating, carrying.
The listeners delved,
and dug out the silted, cloying sand,
with their ears and hands,
listening with ear of the heart.
They digested the grit for me.
So, another conversion
in conversation,
communion
in communication

flow and ebb, blue on blue
the restless sea,
the restless heart,
for there is a me, and there is a you.

(Extract from Peter Gilbert's poem 'Restless sea' in Coyte *et al* (2007) *Spirituality, Values and Mental Health*, p275–276; see also Bassett & Stickley, 2010.)

So for all of us experiencing mental distress, we are thrown back on:

▶ our sense of identity – who we are

▶ what makes us tick – our inner spirit

▶ what helps us in a time of crisis

▶ what is the meaning and purpose of our lives in life as a whole and in the roles we play.

As Jamison's memoir makes clear, suffering is terrible, but as Viktor Frankl, Nazi concentration camp victim and psychotherapist, points out, it is the lack of meaning in suffering which is the most soul destroying thing about it (Frankl, 1946/1984).

For most of us our experience will be set out against the parameters of secular society and the particularity of our family, ethnicity, values, faith and community, as set out in figure 1.

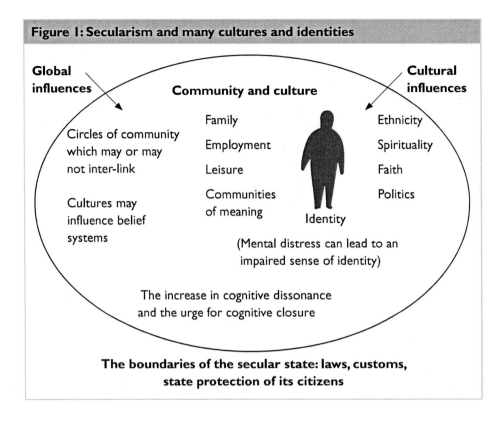

Figure 1: Secularism and many cultures and identities

Global influences

Cultural influences

Community and culture

Circles of community which may or may not inter-link

Cultures may influence belief systems

Family

Employment

Leisure

Communities of meaning

Ethnicity

Spirituality

Faith

Politics

Identity

(Mental distress can lead to an impaired sense of identity)

The increase in cognitive dissonance and the urge for cognitive closure

The boundaries of the secular state: laws, customs, state protection of its citizens

(First published in Gilbert with Bates *et al* (2010) *Social Work and Mental Health: The value of everything* (2nd edition), p11, and reproduced with permission from Russell House Publishing)

There is a range of aspects which will affect people's experience. The word 'compassion' means to 'suffer with', so:

▶ part of our resilience will be how compassionate we feel towards ourselves; can we suffer with our own spirit, or do we stay distant and disapproving from our own self?

▶ what our support networks are and whether people suffer with us or do unto us

▶ the strengths and weaknesses of faith communities are set out in chapter 1

▶ our ethnic and cultural backgrounds may well be a factor (see Sewell, 2009)

▶ faith and culture may be a complex mix (Bhui *et al*, 2007)

▶ age and cultural experience will also be a factor (see MacKinley, 2010).

Many people will identify with the portrait of physical and intellectual decline in old age written in Barb Noon's poem *Burning Bright* (2004), using spiritual language:

'Sometimes I picture myself
like a candle.

I used to be a candle about eight feet tall
burning bright.
Now everyday I lose
a little bit of me.

Some days the candle will be
very small
but the flame will be
just as bright.'

First published in the *Journal of Dementia Care's* creativity calendar 2004.

This is mirrored beautifully by Barbara Pointon's description of her relationship with her late husband, Malcolm, who suffered from pre-senile dementia.

'I have come to realise that despite all Malcolm's obvious mental and physical attrition, his spirit still shines through. Several of his carers have remarked upon Malcolm's still "being there"; we all lack the vocabulary to talk quasi-scientifically, or even anecdotally, about it, but it is strongly felt… To stand stripped of everything the world values and to see each other as we really are is a very precious and humbling experience, and one which I would never have encountered were it not for the ravages of dementia. Paradoxically, Malcolm's "losses" have turned into "gains".' (Pointon, 2007)

In 2010 the Roman Catholic Church, concerned about the possible lack of a spiritual dimension in dementia care, brought out a DVD entitled 'It's Still ME, Lord…' (CSAN, 2009), which gives a very clear message about the relationship of the individual with a creator – despite our 'losses', our essential self is still here.

The spiritual crisis

For many service users their crisis is not so much a mental crisis, as a spiritual crisis – a sudden lurch in identity and meaning.

It is fascinating that people will often use philosophical or religious language to describe an event, which the dominant medical discourse will put in much more scientific terms. It is because of this that it is most important that we consider the approach of psychiatrists like Pat Bracken and Phil Thomas (Bracken & Thomas, 2005) who stress the importance of the lived experience and the service user narrative.

Many people from a scientific background such as K Redfield Jamison, Dr Lewis Wolpert and Dr Liz Miller, all use language which is instantly recognisable to us. Dr Miller was working in the highly competitive field of neurosurgery when she suffered a breakdown. Being a doctor didn't help at all she recalls: *'The thing is, in medicine we live on this myth that illness is for other people. Doctors don't get ill. Illness is for patients. And so I swallowed it – the whole medical thing.'* (O'Hara, 2008)

Miller recalls that coming from a high-achieving family with a great many doctors in it and giving up neurosurgery was a real assault on her whole identity: *'In the past, I prided myself on my brain. I could get by on my wits. And suddenly your mind goes, and it actually goes to the core of who you are. It says something about you as a person. You ask yourself, "why me?"'*

As we have seen in chapter 1, embryologist Dr Lewis Wolpert describes himself as *'a hardline materialist'*, but uses the idea of 'soul loss' to describe depression.

Phil Barker and Poppy Buchanan-Barker quote the New Zealand poet and mental health advocate, Gary Platz, who was given a diagnosis of psychosis, and felt that psychiatric treatment invalidated all of his experiences, not just his spiritual side. He wrote about the stigma of mental illness as: *'this stigma acid eats my soul'* (Barker & Buchanan-Barker, 2008, p65). Barker and Buchanan-Barker talk about Platz's struggle to reclaim his voice and human identity as being central to his recovery: *'For me (Gary) spirituality wasn't a factor in recovery from madness towards some form of sanity. Rather, madness was central in the recovery process from a spiritual crisis.'* (Barker & Buchanan-Barker, 2008, p65)

Gail Hornstein's work, *Agnes's Jacket* (Hornstein, 2009), demonstrates the difficulties that people designated as mental health patients have always had in telling their story. The title of the book refers to the story of Agnes Richter, who, skilled with a needle, sewed her story into her jacket, having been placed in a German asylum in the 19th century.

One of the most illustrative narratives of the journey of faith and medicine is told by Premila Trivedi who describes her path in poetry. In the poem 'Aum Shanti, Shanti', Trivedi talks about:

'Growing up, I constantly saw it in front of me,
my Hindu faith
holding us in, controlling us
dictating every aspect of our lives.'
(See Coyte *et al*, 2007, p67)

Peter Gilbert sometimes describes religious traditions as a *'climbing frame'* or a *'straightjacket'* (See Chantler *et al*, 2002). A number of people have found *'their faith repressed and controlled them'* and have spoken about *'how they had to free themselves in order to define their own spirituality, either separately or within the tradition in which they grew up'* (see Chantler *et al*, 2002). Many return to their faith of origin, but with a stronger sense of identity in which to use the framework and reject the straightjacket. *'Mental health crises can ironically be times of such freeing and rediscovering, if time, space and attention are given to this process.'* (See Salem & Foskett, 2009)

As Premila Trivedi grew up, she moved away from her faith but didn't realise how *'embedded it remained in her soul'*. Her breakdown, followed by psychiatric treatment, did not offer any degree of freedom, rather the reverse:

'Valium, psychiatrists, falling more into the abyss
of white man's medicine
hospital, enforced activity, constant cajouling
to fit their characterisation of me,
all the time denying me, my pain, my heart, my confusion
and in the end I saw it their way, the guilt was mine.
So I have the privilege of existing in their world –
of experiencing their values, their beliefs
their prejudices, their power.
What does it matter that I died in the process.'
(Reproduced with permission © Trivedi, 1992)

In Trivedi's 2007 poem she speaks of her sister's death, and how she, perhaps to her surprise, found the family mourning within a faith tradition to be helpful:

'And we came together in our grief
to say prayers and sing bhajanas,
to help her on her journey into the next life
and then, gathered together once more,
our hearts ached and our tears flowed freely
as the pandit lit a holy fire to purify the air
and said some final prayers
completing my sister's ceremony
enabling her to move on.'
(Reproduced with permission © Trivedi, 2010)

Trivedi found a Christian chaplain helpful in her journey. Listening to another's story, from whichever tradition we are from and they are from, is perhaps the most powerful way of being and doing human.

What do service users want from services and professionals

'I'm tired of being talked about, treated as a statistic pushed to the margins of human conversation. I want someone who will have time for me, someone who will listen to me, someone who has not already judged who I am or what I have to offer. I'm waiting to be taken seriously.'
(Mental Health Foundation, 2002)

All inspection reports on services state clearly that people want to have the best technologically advanced and effective treatment possible, but they also want to be treated as human beings, with respect for their individual dignity, culture, beliefs, orientation, identity, relationships and role in society. For too many people, however, they find that the Victorian taboo on sex has been replaced by a new one: religion. The poet and survivor, Sue Holt, in her poem, 'Year 2000 on a Section 3', puts it thus:

'I was excited; today was the Lord's birthday
and I was going home for dinner.
I masked my emotions,
otherwise they would keep me.
I had to behave myself today,
no talking of God'
(Reproduced with permission © Holt, 2003)

Service users tell us that what they want from services and staff is:

▶ to be seen as a whole person, within their whole environment

▶ for staff to 'start where I am! Not where you think I am!'

▶ for staff to be empathetic and listen

▶ time – we all know that time is short, but quality time is essential

▶ attendance to both emotional and practical needs

▶ for staff who work with, not do to, to find solutions to issues

▶ to be seen as having strengths as well as needs.

(See also chapter 6)

What service users might want to ask from services, in terms of their spiritual resources and needs

Be reassured that spirituality and religion are increasingly being recognised as an important part of your holistic care and recovery.

Please tell staff about your spiritual and/or religious beliefs, and what you need to explore and express these – perhaps a quiet space or a religious/belief text.

If you have no particular religious faith, talking about what gives you hope for the future, what gives you meaning in life and what motivates your recovery and discovery can be very important areas of your life that should be addressed in your care.

Do find out what your options are for exploring your spirituality or religion further. For example, there may be spiritual and pastoral care (chaplaincy) services that will listen to your concerns and thoughts, and can provide you with spiritual or religious booklets, further guidance and helpful community links.

(Gilbert, Kaur & Parkes, 2010)

The Somerset Spirituality Project is a good source of information about what people want when they experience a crisis. People want to talk about what is most important to them.

'When I was suicidal I would have liked somebody just to support me. I feel very guilty about it; it's not Christian... After a while when things calm down you forget, and it's only when you ask me the questions I think I should have done something about it. I do need to talk to somebody about this.' (Cracknell et al, 2002)

Retaining connections with people's faith family or community is also important.

'Church is like a family … it's like going back to meet old friends … everyone there shaking my hands. "Oh, I hear you've been ill … but we'll get through this together" … it's very much one big family really.' (Cracknell et al, 2002) Several respondents said how helpful various professionals had been; one spoke about her GP, and the fact that the GP, the spiritual side of her life and the medication, all seemed to coalesce together. Another mentioned that her community practice nurse had been most helpful, despite the fact that he had no religious affiliation, but had realised its importance to her.

Case study

Mrs A is a black African-Caribbean woman in her late 30s; she has two young children (five and nine years old) and a supportive partner. She and her family are evangelical Christians. She has been under the care of the mental health services for some years following the birth of her children, when her mental health began to deteriorate. She had been supported by her community practice nurse for some years who provided monitoring and antipsychotic medication.

Mrs A was referred initially on 27/8/2008 to me, as an approved social worker in the home treatment team for an assessment under the Mental Health Act (1983), with a view to an urgent hospital admission. It was felt by the mental health professionals at this time that this was the only option. I had been told that her partner had moved out of the family home with the children as he could no longer cope with her bizarre and demanding behaviour. There were concerns regarding her continued refusal to accept medication, and consequently Home Treatment could not be used.

During the assessment it was clear that she was mentally unwell but she stated that she was refusing medication because she believed her faith would cure her. It was evident that her mother and wider family also felt this strongly. Both the GP and the psychiatrist present felt that she should be admitted under the Act for treatment, but she did not want to go to hospital. I agreed to delay admission (losing the bed) given that she had agreed to stay at her mother's house with her sisters, a place where she felt safe, and where she would be visited daily by Home Treatment. The risk of harm to others or herself was limited and minimised by this.

I visited daily and discussed the matter further with her family and herself, who all felt very adamant that her faith would heal her and that medication was a bad thing. Her partner, however, felt that medication would improve things, as it had in the past. He accepted that going to hospital would be destructive for her, but if it was the only way of getting the family back together then it would be necessary. Home Treatment struggled with visiting her daily and attempting to engage her and her family. I had made attempts to contact the family pastor, which I felt could be helpful in enabling the family to see that medication could have a role to play in improving Mrs A's mental state. However, I did manage to speak at length to the mother's family pastor who clearly felt that medication could not be of any help.

Eventually, out of frustration, I discussed the case with a senior social work colleague who understood the importance of faith and recommended that I contact the pastor attached to my mental health trust. The trust's pastor was able to work with the family's pastor, who in turn was able to work with the family – attending reviews and meetings. Over some weeks this resulted in Mrs A accepting medication. I felt strongly that if we did not include the wider family and the active part that their faith plays in her life, we ran the risk of alienating the woman and her family and this ultimately would be detrimental not just to her well-being, but to the community as a whole.

With the support of the trust pastor and building a genuine rapport with Mrs A and her family, mother and husband, it was possible to avoid hospital admission. Her care has now been returned to her community practice nurse and the community team, and she continues to accept medication and lives with her husband and children once more. Mrs A's faith continues to be a vital aspect of her life.

Catherine Myers

(Gilbert with Bates *et al*, 2010, p112–113)

It is vital for staff to consider the whole person in the light of their whole situation, and part of that will be working with their faith or spirituality and faith or spiritual community. The case study in this chapter is a very good example of this. In the end, we are all on this journey together, struggling for a sense of meaning and purpose. As Jean Davison puts it: *'And would the psychiatrist be able to understand my difficulties in coming to terms with the loss of my religious beliefs, about life seeming empty and meaningless, and those hard to explain "what am I?" feelings?'* (Davison, 2009).

Leading to recovery

The causes of mental illness are wide and varying from person to person, and recovery from mental illness is just as varied. Every survivor will have their own story to tell about what helped them most – and least – during their recovery journey. 'Recovery' is a term that gets used a lot, and has a broad range of meanings. However, it does encompass a holistic approach. Recovery from mental illness is most effective when a holistic approach is considered – including psychological, emotional, spiritual, physical and social needs (NIMHE, 2005), or as the joint position paper by CSIP, the Royal College of Psychiatrists and SCIE (2007) puts it: *'adopting recovery as a guiding purpose for mental health services favours hope and creativity over disillusionment and defeat'* (see also SPN, 2007) .

Recovery is a journey that goes beyond discharge from hospital or a reduction in medical symptoms. For those with serious or enduring mental illness, a large part of recovery involves learning to cope when we get home and the doctors have stopped visiting. For some, the isolation and loneliness that has arisen out of illness means that a large part of recovery is facing getting up alone everyday and seeking to build new relationships. For others, coping with the spiritual or existential experience of illness can form a major part of recovery. Finding answers to 'who am I?' and 'what do I do with my life now?' are questions that are often difficult to answer. So recovery is not just about achieving an absence of symptoms. It's about coping with some of the wider challenges mental illness can bring, and about learning to live with some of the residual symptoms that may be present in the form of low self-esteem, anxiety and fear of relapse.

Psycho-social and spiritual recovery may take a long time. Losing friends and relationships, possibly a home, losing self-esteem, and wondering what people will think of you, are all very difficult and quite important aspects of the recovery journey that service users are increasingly concerned about. Noticeably, more and more user voices are coming into literature on recovery, and they are highlighting the importance of all these aspects. The Recovery Model and the WRAP (Wellness Recovery Action Plan) utilise this user-defined view of recovery, and attempt to address the journey of recovery as an holistic one.

Some key aspects of recovery:

▶ having hope for the future

▶ managing symptoms

▶ improving resilience against relapse

▶ building meaningful relationships

▶ recognising recovery as a journey, with its ups and downs

▶ being seen as a person, not an illness

▶ learning new skills and having new experiences

▶ finding meaningful work and activities

▶ achieving goals I've set myself

▶ personal growth

▶ learning to both give and receive.

The role of spirituality in recovery

The Ten Essential Shared Capabilities (Department of Health, 2004) document acknowledges that hope can be an important part of the recovery process. Hope, meaning, purpose, identity and connectedness are often considered to be spiritual and/or existential areas of life, and staff are encouraged to address these with service users and carers.

So where can spirituality fit into the recovery journey? A person's spirituality may change throughout their illness and recovery. This is important to recognise as some people will depend on their sense of spirituality in different ways, at different stages. A recent piece of research conducted with service users around spirituality and recovery in Birmingham and Solihull analysed the comments and stories of those who had something to say about how spirituality related to their mental illness and health (Parkes, forthcoming/2011). For many, spirituality was 'the bottom line' – the final foundation that could be held onto as illness set in when all other aspects of life were lost. People described their only source of connectedness and hope as God, or the stilling of the mind that came from meditation, or seeing the beauty of nature that tempted them not to give up because they wanted to see more of it. Sally Clay has written about her experiences and echoes the idea of 'the bottom line', choosing to refer to it thus:

'We who have experienced mental illness have all learned the same thing... We know that we have reached the bare bones of spirit and of what it means to be human... There is something to be learned here about the mystery of living itself, something important both to those who have suffered and those who seek to help us.' (Clay, 1999)

Importantly, spirituality was recognised as a sense of connectedness in many expressions – through God, nature, community, family, music, art and personal 'soul searching'. This theme of connectedness was echoed by all in the room and, significantly, it was identified that when this is absent – when the spiritual side of them no longer holds significance – this is the point when service users know their illness has taken over their lives in a serious way.

Strangers in a strange land – our pilgrim journey

One of the major problems with human approaches to individual and social issues is that, in fact, an approach which starts with a positive vision and hope can so easily turn into something that is institutionalised – a system turns into 'the system'. Some people have raised issues about the possible 'colonisation' of a recovery approach by professionals. Premila Trivedi, in *Voices of Experience: Narratives of mental health survivors* (Bassett & Stickley, 2010), considers how *'concepts may become distorted when taken on board by mainstream mental health services'* (Trivedi, 2010; see also

Weinstein, 2010). Trivedi describes herself as '*a black service user who has tried for many years to work with "the system"*', but found that institutional racism was often only paid lip service to within the service system, and that 'liberation' might be a more relevant term than 'recovery' for some individuals and groups.

Peter Chadwick speaks about the need for considering experiences realistically but also as positively as possible: '*There was no doubt that seeing our psychoses as relating to positive things in us – such as high sensitivity, imaginativeness, empathy, creativity and capacities for depth and intensity of feeling – was helpful and uplifting and strengthened our self-esteem. Seeing ourselves as "diseased" and riddled with deficit and dysfunction, however, was weakening and demoralising. It also did not inform us of what strengths and capacities we had to cultivate and build on so we did not really help people to move forward.*' (Chadwick, 2010a; see also Chadwick, 2010b)

As with some of the connections and differences between spirituality and religion, there is a need for us to listen to each other's individual stories, but also there is strength in solidarity and looking for common threads and meeting places as we move forward on our pilgrimage (see Weinstein, 2010).

As we saw in chapter 1, there is always a tendency for rationalistic approaches to overcomplicate matters and there may be a need to remind ourselves that human beings are always on a journey, sometimes alone and sometimes in the company of others. That journey is both inward and outward. Whether consciously or not, we are always battling with the fundamental questions of where did we come from? Why are we here? What is the meaning in our lives and work? Where do we go to when we die? Recent anthropological work on the differences between human beings and Neanderthals, who for many decades lived alongside each other, seems to indicate that human beings have a greater ability to make connections between concepts, in practical activities like the making of tools, and in transcendent imagination. Human beings also have an innate instinct to look for a transcendent being, as well as looking outwards to other human beings (see Bering, 2010; Williams, 2010).

As Karl Rahner puts it: '*And even if this term (God) were ever to be forgotten, even then, in the decisive moment of our lives, we should still be constantly encompassed by this nameless mystery of our existence… Even supposing that those realities which we call religion … were totally to disappear… The transcendentality inherent in human life is such that we would still reach out towards that mystery that lies outside our control.'* (Hay, 2006, p122)

In a handbook where we are considering issues around spirituality, it is perhaps sensible to use the word 'pilgrimage' instead of 'journey'. The word pilgrim is derived from the Latin *peregrinus*, meaning a foreigner, and it is our modern predicament to find ourselves strangers in a strange land (see Gilbert *et al*, 2008). While many users of mental health services describe themselves as being in exile or a form of asylum seeker, all of us have an experience of exile in our lives at some stage; we all experience heartache, disappointment, loss and despair at some point, because this is the human condition. The prophet Moses reminded his people the great lesson of empathy: *'you should not oppress the stranger,* (some translations use the word 'alien') *because you yourselves were once strangers in the land of Egypt.'* (Exodus, 23:9)

In a recent newspaper column, survivor, Clare Allan remarked that: *'It's a sudden awareness of how much sand has slipped through the timer unnoticed. And it urgently requires to know what I intend to do with the rest of it. I think about death a lot these days but it isn't death that worries me; it's the bit between now and then. As author Victor Hugo put it: "to die is nothing, but it is terrible not to live."'* (Allan, 2010)

It is interesting that many of the designated 'holy people' in the world's religions have experienced visions, moments of great joy and also despair – it was St John of the Cross who experienced 'the dark night of the soul'.

In chapter 18, Sarah Carr mentions the experience of a number of gay people who speak of a connection with God, despite being placed in exile by some proponents of organised religion.

The great challenge for people who run mental health services, and indeed faith communities, is that every human being is individual and unique, but services often have to provide for a range of needs, with an increasing accent on personalisation. Sometimes, when journeying together, we have to accede to group norms to make life bearable for everyone travelling the same road. On the other hand, do manifestations of exuberance or eccentricity have to be treated as abnormal? The following testimony from Katherine Taylor illustrates this.

Spirituality is intensely personal

Spirituality to me cannot be defined or communicated easily, it is intensely personal (while including shared experiences) and mysterious. My ideas are just that – ideas, and they differ from everybody else's, and this made me reluctant to write about them. But perhaps that is the key; everybody's ideas of spirituality differ. In the context of mental health and healthcare services, this is an insight that can be often overlooked. I have experienced a tendency to consider beliefs symptomatic and behaviours pathological, when in another individual without a diagnosis they may be easily explained as 'spiritual'.

In March 2010 I had the pleasure of going on an away day with my colleagues. We climbed Loughrigg Fell in the Lake District, to the incredible view at the top. The descent was quick, the day balmy, and we had been walking for a few hours. Rydal Water could be seen, and its cool, tranquil waters were completely enticing to me. I loved the thought of a refreshing, wild dip in this beautiful lake and the stillness I would feel when I swam out to the middle.

The awesome power and beauty in nature are my 'gods', my spirituality, and the opportunity to bathe so naturally felt lucky and instinctive. Luckily, my supervisor, a senior clinical psychologist, was just as keen as I was. Yes, it was cold, freezing cold, of course we got wet, but I felt amazing. Other colleagues said we were mad; we thought they were.

Later that week I had made a precautionary appointment with a psychiatrist. I am due to face a potential stressor; beginning a Doctorate in clinical psychology. I know goal attainment is linked to manic episodes and I wanted to talk about a plan for if I became over-excited or stressed by the demands of the course. I spoke to a social worker beforehand and described the away day. She scrunched up her face and said apologetically: 'I wouldn't tell the psychiatrist that if I were you.' I turned to her, incredulous, and asked: 'Why not?' All she said was: 'Well, you know...' I am afraid I do, as I have found that behaviour deemed spontaneous, wild, or indeed natural, can be 'misconstrued' as symptoms. Of course, I understand that spontaneity and recklessness, for example, should be monitored, and am beginning to appreciate the complexities in trying to navigate such experiences sensitively in the context of mental health. But this incident was not unusual for me; I was accompanied by a senior colleague and it felt like a calming experience more than anything else. I felt a sense of sadness that something I particularly enjoyed and did not cause any harm, could be used as part of an argument for me being ill. I was advised that because I have a diagnosis of bipolar disorder (a diagnosis I fully agree with), I ought to be taking medication. The psychiatrist tried to persuade me to take antipsychotics, and asked me why I thought I did not need them. I believe that a successful, episode-free three years without medication indicates exactly that; I do not need them, and questioned what would be the benefit of me taking antipsychotics given their undesirable side effects. As I was leaving, she gently suggested that perhaps I could come back when I had a more open mind, but my mind is open to life and experience; I may need medication again sometime, but it has to be in the context of living life!

Katherine Taylor is a researcher at the Spectrum Centre, Lancaster University

When Peter Gilbert was asked to set up the NIMHE project on spirituality (see Cox *et al*, 2007), he had no training in this kind of work, and describes himself going around the country in a state of 'empathic ignorance' (Cox *et al*, 2007). What was immediately evident was that huge numbers of service users and carers, and also staff, wished to discuss this subject and see the spiritual dimension of their lives recognised and attended to. Working in Birmingham and Solihull, where a high percentage of the population in the wards of the city have a clear spiritual and/or religious affiliation, faith and belief are a vital element in health (Parkes & Gilbert, 2010).

For a significant number of people the idea that a transcendent being – transcendent, but in some traditions immanent – and connected to us in love, gives an abiding sense of hope. As the poet, Sue Holt describes, God is *'wrapping sacred arms around'* human beings in trouble (Holt, 2009). We may not be in 'recovery', but we are always on a voyage of 'discovery', and it should be service users, carers and staff on a shared pilgrimage.

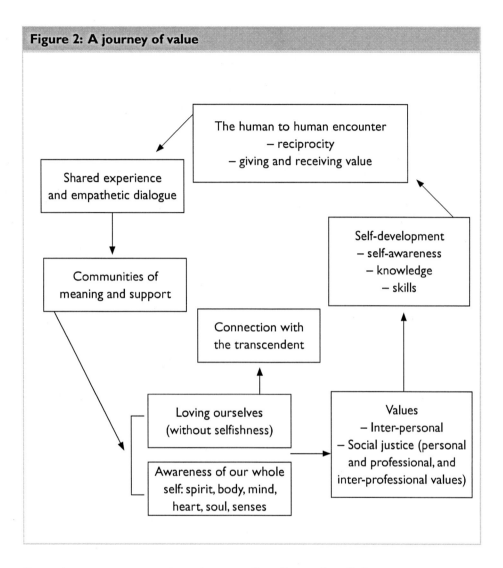

Figure 2: A journey of value

So we journey on, sometimes in a small, solitary, fragile boat, sometimes in convoy, at other times in a larger, more crowded ship. As the novelist Jeanette Winterson puts it, we are in many ways still like the early Celtic pilgrims who navigated across wide uncharted oceans and overwhelming seas and tides: *'The earliest pilgrims shared a cathedral for a heart ... love, it was that drove them forth. Love that brought them home again. Love hardened their hands against the oar and heated their sinews against the rain. The journeys they made were beyond common sense; who leaves the hearth for the open sea? Especially without a compass, especially in winter, especially alone. What you risk reveals what you value. In the presence of love, hearth and quest become one.'* (Winterson, 2001)

References

Allan C (2010) What worries me is what to do between now and death. *Society Guardian* 6 October 2010, p2.

Armstrong K (2009) *The Case for God.* London: The Bodley Head.

Barber J (2010) *Handbook of Spiritual Care in Mental Illness.* Birmingham: BSMHFT.

Barker P & Buchanan-Barker P (2008) Spirituality. In: R Tummey and T Turner (Eds) *Critical Issues in Mental Health.* Basingstoke: Palgrave Macmillan.

Basset T & Stickley T (Eds) (2010) *Voices of Experience: Narratives of mental health survivors.* Chichester: Wiley/Blackwell.

Bering J (2010) *The God Instinct: The psychology of souls, destiny and the meaning of life.* London: Nicholas Brealey.

Bhui K, King M, Dein S & O'Connor W (2007) Ethnicity and religious coping with mental distress. *Journal of Mental Health* **17** (2) 141–151.

Bracken P & Thomas P (2005) *Post-psychiatry: Mental health in a postmodern world.* Oxford: Oxford University Press.

Cambridgeshire and Peterborough NHS Foundation Trust (2010) *Spirituality and Recovery Strategy 2009–2014: Embracing and nurturing the human spirit.* Cambridge and Peterborough: CPNHSFT:

Caritas Social Action Network (Bano B) (2009) *It's Still ME, Lord: A film exploring spirituality and dementia.* London: CSAN.

Chadwick P (2010a) Recovery from psychosis: strategies and reflections from hostel living. *British Journal of Wellbeing* **1** (6) 24–25.

Chadwick P (2010b) The antidote to madness: crystallising out the real self. In: T Basset & T Stickley (Eds) *Voices of Experience: Narratives of mental health survivors.* London: Wiley.

Chantler K, Burman E, Batsleer J & Bashir C (2002) Inside you're almost dead. *Mental Health Today* October 2002, p21–24.

Clay S (1999) Madness and reality. In: Barker P, Campbell P & Davidson B (Eds) *From the Ashes of Experience: Reflections on madness, survival and growth.* London: Whurr Publications.

Cox J, Campell AV & Fulford KWM (Eds) (2007) *Medicine of the Person: Faith, science and values in healthcare provision.* London: Jessica Kingsley.

Coyte ME, Gilbert P & Nicholls V (Eds) (2007) *Spirituality, Values and Mental Health: Jewels for the journey.* London: Jessica Kingsley.

Cracknell P, Foskett J, Matthews R, Macmin L, Nicholls V & Roberts A (2002) It would have been good to talk: The Somerset Spirituality Project. *Mental Health Today* October 2002 p18–20.

CSIP, Royal College of Psychiatrists & SCIE (2007) *A Common Purpose: Recovery in future mental health services.* Joint position paper, No. 8. London: SCIE.

Davison J (2009) *The Dark Threads.* Glamorgan: Accent Press.

Department of Health (2004) *The Ten Essential Shared Capabilities: A framework for the whole of the mental health workforce.* London: DH.

Frankl VE (1946/1984) *Man's Search for Meaning.* New York: Simon and Schuster.

Gilbert P, Bodhoo J & Carr S (2008) Pilgrimage. *Openmind* **151** May/June 2008.

Gilbert P with Bates P, Carr S, Clark M, Gould N & Slay G (2010) *Social Work and Mental Health: The value of everything* (2nd edition). Lyme Regis: Russell House Publishing.

Gilbert P, Kaur N & Parkes M (2010) Let's get spiritual: belief systems and mental health. *Mental Health Today* October 2010.

Hay D (2006) *Something There: The biology of the human spirit.* London: Darton, Longman and Todd.

Holt S (2003) *Poems of Survival.* Brentwood: Chipmunka.

Holt S (2009) *Psychotic Interlude.* Brentwood: Chipmunka.

Hornstein GA (2009) *Agnes's Jacket: A psychologist's search for the meanings of madness.* New York: Rodale.

Jamison KR (1996) *An Unquiet Mind: A memoir of moods and madness.* London: Picador.

MacKinley E (2010) *Ageing and Spirituality Across Faiths and Cultures.* London: Jessica Kingsley.

Mental Health Foundation (2002) *Taken Seriously: The Somerset Spirituality Project.* London: Mental Health Foundation.

NIMHE (2005) *The National Institute for Mental Health in England's Guiding Statement on Recovery.* Leeds: NIMHE.

Noon B (2004) In: S Benson & J Killick (Eds) *Journal of Dementia Care: creativity calendar.*

O'Hara M (2008) Doctors Orders: Interview with Dr Liz Miller. *Society Guardian* 11 June 2008.

Parkes M & Gilbert P (2010) Gods and Gurdwaras: The spiritual care programme at the Birmingham and Solihull Mental Health NHS Foundation Trust. *Mental Health, Religion and Culture* **13** (6) 569–583.

Parkes M (2011 forthcoming) *What Spirituality Means to Me: Mental health service users and survivors speak.*

Pointon B (2007) Who am I? The search for spirituality in dementia. A family carer's perspective. In: M Coyte, P Gilbert & V Nicolls (Eds) *Spirituality, Values and Mental Health: Jewels for the journey.* London: Jessica Kingsley.

Salem MO & Foskett J (2009) Religion and religious experiences. In: C Cook, A Powell & A Sims (Eds) *Spirituality and Psychiatry.* London: RCP.

Sewell H (2009) *Working with Ethnicity, Race and Culture in Mental Health: A handbook for practitioners.* London: Jessica Kingsley.

Social Perspectives Network (2007) *Whose Recovery is it Anyway?* SPN Paper 11. London: SPN.

Styron W (1990/2004) *Darkness Visible.* London: Vintage.

Trivedi P (1992) *Survivors Poetry: From dark to light.* London: Survivors Press.

Trivedi P (2010) A Recovery Approach in Mental Health Services: Transformation, tokenism or tyranny? In: T Basset & T Stickley (Eds) *Voices of Experience: Narratives of mental health survivors.* London: Wiley.

Weinstein J (Ed) (2010) *Mental Health, Service User Involvement and Recovery.* London: Jessica Kingsley.

Williams M (2010) *Pre-historic Belief: Shamans, trance and the afterlife.* London: The History Press.

Winterson J (2001) *Written on the Body.* London: Vintage.

Chapter 5

The only verity is my soul – the carer's view

Barbara Pointon and Jacqui Miller

Introduction

My husband, Malcolm, was diagnosed with Alzheimer's disease at the age of 51. I cared for him at home for 16 years, with the exception of two years in the middle of the journey which he spent in a nursing home. During that bumpy journey, and indeed afterwards, I needed not only practical advice and help, but emotional and spiritual support to help me on the way. It's a two-way system. If a carer's emotional and spiritual needs are nurtured, they in turn are enabled to offer emotional and spiritual support to nurture the person they care for.

The key points of the journey where I needed such support (but did not always receive it) were:

▶ around diagnosis

▶ adapting to a new approach to life

▶ dealing with perplexing behaviours and aggression

▶ receiving poor quality services; battles with officialdom

▶ palliative care, death and bereavement.

Running throughout the story is a red thread: the importance of good relationships. Not just between us and our family and friends, but also with the many health and social care professionals involved in Malcolm's journey. Love, compassion and empathy are at the heart of spirituality; they are also at the heart of offering quality care and support.

During our journey, I became all too aware that Alzheimer's was gradually taking away the most important thing in my life – my husband and soul mate – so no wonder my sense of 'soul-loss' became keener as time went on. Caring for someone with dementia can produce enormous challenges and sometimes, looking back, I wonder what kept me going. It must have been something deeply innate, felt but not named, something to do with our core values and the love which sustains and protects the giver as well as the recipient.

Around diagnosis

▶ Why early diagnosis is important to the relationship

▶ Barriers to diagnosis

▶ Impact of the diagnosis on the carer and the need for support

Malcolm was treated for endogenous depression for two years before he received the right diagnosis. I look back on that time and am ashamed how impatient and tetchy I had become with him when he refused to do something he'd always done – such as top up the oil in the car. I thought he was being deliberately awkward, but the real reason was that he could no longer remember which bit of the engine it had to go in. Bills, which were usually promptly settled, went unpaid or were paid twice, and unbeknown to me, two years of tax returns languished in his desk. Not realising at the time that his sense of number must have been slipping, I cringe when I remember how I rebuked him.

My elderly mother who lived with us had become a bit cantankerous in her last years and Malcolm, usually so patient and gentle, began to treat her with uncharacteristic brusqueness, creating a difficult emotional atmosphere in the house. If only Malcolm had been diagnosed earlier, we could have made allowances and protected our family relationships. I know of couples who have separated, even divorced, because of a breakdown in the relationship created by undiagnosed early dementia or Huntington's disease. A special, loving, trusting relationship is part of our sense of who we are; protecting it is a compelling reason why early diagnosis and information are vital.

One serious barrier to obtaining a diagnosis is 'patient confidentiality'. Patients can hold their own in a short GP consultation and believe nothing is wrong, or have forgotten. I know of carers who, worried sick about things happening at home, have been refused a separate GP consultation to discuss their concerns. The Carers Strategy (HM Government, 2008) and the Nuffield Council on Bioethics (Nuffield Council, 2009) both recommend that carers should be openly involved with diagnosis and be able to exchange information with professionals on 'a need to know' basis, and from then onwards whenever it impacts upon the giving of care. The new Triangle of Care guide (NMHDU/Princess Royal Trust for Carers, 2010) makes this partnership very clear (see also Ramsay *et al*, 2001).

Diagnosis is the gateway to information and support for the person with dementia and their carer. At the moment in England only about 40% of people displaying symptoms of dementia receive a diagnosis (including the type of dementia) – so there must be something like half a million hidden carers of people with dementia struggling alone.

Reflection exercise

Frances is 81 and her husband John who is 76 has been displaying tell-tale signs of dementia for some time. Frances won't confide in their GP because she doesn't wish to be disloyal to John. Not in good health herself and showing signs of real strain and downright impatience with him, their loving relationship is coming under threat. What might be done to support them?

When Malcolm was diagnosed, I went into shock and denial, compounded by the fact that Malcolm wasn't told for another six months (in order for tests to be repeated). The knowledge weighed heavily on me because we had never withheld secrets from each other. I raged against it, prowling the house at night; 'Why us? It can't be true'. But it was, and Malcolm had to give up his job; worries tumbled in from all sides and for the next three years, until we came to need services, I had to root out information and advice on my own and without any moral support except from family and friends, who were as shocked and out of their depth as I was. I am hoping that the new dementia care adviser role, when properly developed, will provide that essential holistic support from the point of diagnosis – including to self-funders, who are often dropped into thin air.

At diagnosis, in common with many others, I didn't think of myself as a 'carer'. I was just Malcolm's wife, doing what families do in times of crisis. We had a long family history of caring for elderly relatives, but caring for Malcolm was another ballgame – quite different from frail elderly people who still retain their cognition. Before long, Malcolm required someone to be present at all times and I too had to give up a job I loved, together with several hobbies and interests. I don't think you can give wholehearted support and care for someone with dementia unless you really love them and are willing to make some adjustments to your personal life. If it is done simply out of duty, before long resentment will set in and spoil the relationship. This was my first glimpse of the role that spirituality plays in care and support.

Box 1: Recent legislation on carers
Carers (Recognition and Services) Act (1995)
Carers and Disabled Children Act (2000)
Carers (Equal Opportunities) Act (2004)

Adapting to a new approach in life

▶ Uncharted territory

▶ Learning to let go of the usual social norms

▶ A fundamental shift in the relationship

On the surface, much seemed the same, but deep down changes were happening to Malcolm which subtly altered many of the things we took for granted in the family. For example, Malcolm, a brilliant and inventive pianist and composer, had built from scratch lots of electronic music equipment for composing and performing in his studio at home. On his enforced retirement, students and colleagues had given him a splendid new keyboard, but for the first time Malcolm was totally baffled. Our son offered to help him. None of us realised that in dementia the most recent knowledge and learning is the first to disappear and new information is simply not retained. Real frustration and exasperation on all sides erupted. Unwittingly, we had put Malcolm into a humiliating situation, seriously dented his confidence and jeopardised our usual easy-going relationships.

His diary entries at this time speak volumes about his mental and psychological state: *'Head full of cotton wool ... thoughts and actions slipping from my grasp – a mental fog ... didn't feel secure in the shops today – stayed close to Barbara ... as for the keyboard, I still haven't a clue'*. For all of us, this was uncharted territory.

When offering Malcolm reassurance and support, too often I found that through my lack of understanding of what it feels like to have a dementia, we ended up at cross-purposes. Like so many other carers, I wore myself to a frazzle trying to make things 'normal' and would correct, contradict or argue, when I should have simply kept quiet and acknowledged that things would never be the same again. At one point Malcolm was insisting on going to bed with his trousers on. This resulted in a fractious 'bedroom scene' each night until I got in touch with the Alzheimer's Society's support worker (see www.alzheimers.org.uk). Her kind advice transformed my life: *'But there's no law against going to bed with your trousers on. Whose problem is it? Yours or Malcolm's? If it's a problem for you, just let it go'*. From that point on, engraved on my heart was *'Go with the flow, however bizarre it seems'* and suddenly caring became a lot easier and our relationship less fraught. Every carer should have easy access to expert dementia care advice because otherwise even loving relationships can suffer. For people from ethnic minorities there may well be additional complexities and networks.

As for helping with personal care and other tasks, it took me a long time to realise that it's not what you do, it's the way that you do it that counts. Bossiness is just not on. Doing with people, not for them, allowing them to do things in their own way and in their own time, helps to preserve independence and dignity. Rushing the person only provokes resistance. When talking with Malcolm I had to remember to pause, give him time to work out the question and find the words to reply, and not break the awkward silence with more explanations, thus confusing him even further. At mealtimes, did it matter if he ate his mashed potato with his fingers, if that meant he was still trying to feed himself? Slowly, I realised that insisting on the usual norms for social behaviour is a recipe for disaster.

Where is spirituality in all this? For a start, there was a substantial shift in our relationship. It used to be equitable – meeting halfway. I now had to meet him more than halfway while still protecting his feelings: looking beneath the surface of the physical task to understand how it might be for him in order to preserve his sense of autonomy, dignity and selfhood. Empathy matters.

> **Reflection exercise**
>
> A new care worker from an agency is on a 20-minute call to help someone living alone with their personal care and to prepare breakfast. The client has dementia, is wet and soiled, but refuses to get washed and dressed and pushes the care worker away. It goes down in the care book as: 'Client resistant to care. Abusive, and prefers to be dirty. Left her eating cornflakes out of the packet.'
>
> What issues does this raise for the client, care worker, agency, local authority commissioner and the client's daughter who lives 30 miles away?

Dealing with perplexing behaviours and aggression

▶ Was Malcolm being deliberately aggressive or difficult?

▶ Seeking reasons behind the behaviours

▶ Trying to maintain a life of my own

▶ Solidarity from the community

Whenever I re-read the journal I kept during this stage of the illness, I still can't believe what I went through. A typical entry: *'For nearly three weeks I have been a battered wife. Not only have I the bruises to show for it, but I feel emotionally drained. I've had a karate chop in my neck, a thump in my ribs, a swipe across my mouth, a cuff on the ear, crushed fingers and my thumbs bent back ... the hatred in his eyes is genuinely frightening ... if I burst into tears, he sneers with "little girl!" or "Here we go again" ... I feel intimidated, angry and humiliated ... but there's no battered wives' refuge for me – I can't abandon him in his helplessness'.* And this was from the kindest, most gentle man you could wish to meet, who had never laid a finger on me or our two sons. Was Malcolm being aggressive in order to deliberately hurt me?

Maybe some of it was because, in my ignorance, I was being too bossy. But with 20/20 hindsight there was something else afoot. As well as taking it out on me, Malcolm used to shout, shake his fist and swear at his own reflection in the mirror. The only explanation doctors and nurses gave me was that he was getting angry with himself because he could no longer do the things he used to do, like read, dress himself or safely go for a walk unaccompanied.

However, it's only now that I understand what was really going on. Malcolm's memories were being erased in the reverse order they were laid down and he was time-travelling backwards. In his head he was young again and didn't recognise the older man in the mirror as himself. In addition, a high proportion of people with Alzheimer's have visuo-spatial perceptual problems – they can see, but the brain doesn't accurately process what they see, so they misunderstand their environments or other people's actions. This is at the root of many perplexing behaviours. So Malcolm must have thought that his reflection was a real person waving his fists at him (in the same way that he believed people on TV were actually in the room). He would then wonder: 'Who's this strange man in my house? Is Barbara being unfaithful?' No wonder he held me by my wrists against a wall with a look that could kill. The only answer from clinicians was to increase his antipsychotic medication (haloperidol) which caused him to stoop, shuffle and lose control of his bowels. It is now known that antipsychotic drugs should only be used in the last resort and in the short term. Poor Malcolm – he was on them for quite some time. When all I should have done was take the mirrors down. Another important source of explanation for perplexing behaviours is to be found in a person's past history. (For real-life, eye-opening, detective-type case studies, see Stokes, 2008).

My journal continued: *'The violent episodes have severely altered my relationship with Malcolm and I confess I'm looking after him more out of duty than out of love'*. Because I didn't know what Alzheimer's was doing to him, I thought the aggressive actions were deliberate assaults on me. Our soul mate relationship and that deep spiritual link between us nearly foundered because of a lack of expert dementia advice. I became very distressed and sought help from a counsellor. Just unloading some of the corrosive feelings, and having a neutral person to offer emotional support, proved invaluable.

The professional reaction was to provide Malcolm with day care and respite care so that I could have a break. He often came back from respite care in a worse physical condition than when he went away (over-medicated as well, if the break had been in a mental hospital ward) and psychologically, he would blank me out for several days afterwards. Would you send your five-year-old child to strangers for a week? It used to take me even more time and energy to get things back on track. Several times I received a phone call after a couple of days asking me to fetch him back because they couldn't cope. If the professional care is not good enough, then carers simply will not take the breaks, thus increasing their chances of exhaustion, sense of failure and health problems of their own. On the other hand, quality care benefits the person, gives peace of mind to the carer and allows them to carry on caring for longer. Our mutual quality of life depends on it.

A break is not just about having a physical rest – it's also an important time when carers can rediscover themselves and recharge their emotional and spiritual batteries. I still remember driving to the sea, sitting on the beach, drinking in the pleasures of freedom, the space, colours and sea-sounds, reading a paperback from cover to cover non-stop and sleeping that night without interruption. I came back the next day wholly refreshed.

Many carers do not know that they are entitled to an assessment of their own needs, including regular breaks from caring. At the moment carers have to take the initiative and request an assessment from social services, usually through the carers' support lead. Carers' organisations believe it would be fairer if all those involved in giving substantial care were identified and offered an assessment as a matter of course. And the Care Quality Commission needs to have a role in ensuring that local authorities do not merely carry out assessments, but that appropriate action follows.

The Carers Strategy emphasises the value of breaks, and in 2009 £150 million was made available to GPs (through PCTs) for this purpose, but it was not earmarked, so much of it disappeared into general budgets. Carers' personal budgets are now being introduced so that carers can, if they wish, buy in whatever kind of help suits them best, including help with housework or gardening. The Carers' Strategy also calls for regular health checks of the carer (because they are often so busy that they put their own health needs on the back burner) and a more realistic carer's allowance. The Standing Commission on Carers (of which I'm a member) continues to influence the implementation and development of the strategy and is still working hard to improve the quality of life for all carers, whatever their age or cultural background, including the important and sensitive issues raised in Jacqui Miller's BME perspective in the following box on race, religion and belief.

Box 2: Race, religion and belief – involving BME carers in helping the service user journey of recovery and wholeness

This is written from the perspective of a carer, mental health professional and lay minister.

I personally have supported a member of my family with mental illness for over 20 years. I have also supported friends in the BME community (including faith community) who have had loved ones suffering with mental ill health.

On a professional note I have worked as an approved social worker and have had to both protect and advocate on behalf of service users with mental ill health.

Beginning with the end in mind, it is first of all essential to see the patient as a whole – body, mind and spirit. This is equally important for the carer, who contributes to caring, recognising all realms of recovery eg. practical, emotional, and spiritual.

A question that I have had to grapple with from some mental health professionals is: who and where are the BME carers? They seem hard to reach? Or as one person suggested, they are easy to ignore?

National carers research suggests that BME carers:
▶ could not identify with the word 'carer'
▶ carers with no experience of knowledge of services were unable to imagine how services could help them
▶ carers want services, for the persons they support, to be culturally appropriate carers valued services that help them take part in cultural activities (see also chapter 7).

My experience shows that within BME communities there may be a more natural sense of duty to care for loved ones. However, this should not be linked with the myth of different communities 'looking after their own'. It is more a sense of what else is there in terms of services for BME service users?

The Delivering Race Equality Programme in Mental Health often referred to '*fear of services, or a lack of culturally appropriate services for BME communities*' (Department of Health, 2003).

The BME carer, therefore, is often creative in supporting their loved one in various ways, including practical, emotional and spiritual care; making sense of an oppressed world; interpreting culture and language; and often making sense of the world addressing different generational issues.

In my experience, I had to adopt all of the above roles and more, and thus felt a destiny to care for my loved one. This destiny often has no limits or boundaries, no financial or other reward or recognition, no job description and sometimes, can seem like there is no end in sight.

So where is the hope for BME carers? What we must not overlook is that the person most appreciative of the carer is the cared for.

The cared for are helped in the following ways via the BME carer:

▶ addressing barriers in generational issues – origins, dress, food, religious practice, attitudes to illness
▶ expressing BME user and carer concerns
▶ beliefs about illness causation – supernatural and natural, spiritual healing
▶ addressing common myths about BME communities
▶ understanding cultural heritage
▶ helping professionals 'make sense' of the presentation of BME patients
▶ empowering BME carers in a cultural context
▶ supporting access and information pathways
▶ involvement in service delivery
▶ widening choice – including spiritual health care interventions
▶ protecting the rights of BME users and carers.

Although I worked in the mental health system, it was still hard to find answers to the simple questions in the mental health world:

▶ clear information on diagnosis, symptoms, signs, side effects
▶ clarity of roles of staff involved in caring for a loved one
▶ being 'sectioned' – what is the impact on families
▶ medication – lots of drug therapy; less opportunities for psychological therapy
▶ does doctor really know best?
▶ sedation – side effects
▶ general information for family members – similar to that given when someone is suffering from physical ill health.

A model offered to involve BME carers must involve the following:

▶ consultation – what are the options to involve/support BME carers?
▶ choice – who would be best placed to offer this support and involvement? (inclusive of faith communities – see case study in Gilbert with Bates et al, 2010, pp 114–115)
▶ confidence – what comprehensive information is available of all relevant organisations to support BME carers (statutory and non-statutory)?

Finding the right help at the right time is achievable, as long as you have the right signposts – it's often only a telephone call away.

And what worked for me as a carer?

The carer cries out to so many, but who really listens?

Crying out:
For their own distress and comfort amidst the complexities of their caring role, a cry out from the spirit – for a miracle of healing, wisdom and understanding, a cry out from the spirit for help to live through the suffering.

Race, religion and belief – often a neglected area for all sections of society.
What are the benefits of spiritual health care – this is what I found:
▶ new experiences of hope
▶ relief from suffering, healing and wholeness
▶ a sense of belonging
▶ in faith a great extended family
▶ words of comfort and promise
▶ a vision of a desired future
▶ strength (day by day).

God grant me the serenity to accept the things I cannot change, the courage to change the things I can, and the wisdom to know the difference.

The community can also offer support to a carer. Many people with dementia love walking about – sometimes it is called 'wandering', but a more plausible description is that they walk with a purpose, but have forgotten what it is. Malcolm used to slip out of the house when my back was turned (often as it was getting dark or starting to rain) and our son and I spent hours in the car sweeping the countryside for him in the dark. With the M11 only a mile away, our anxiety was palpable. It was no use locking doors because Malcolm would try to kick them down. This is where solidarity in the community played its part. Neighbours would phone me if they saw Malcolm walking past alone, or helped to search for him. Then the dog-walkers and habitual strollers formed a rota to take Malcolm for a long walk almost every day. It was bliss to have a little uninterrupted time at home to get on with an important job or just have a nap. And new friendships were formed, which still persist.

As Malcolm needed 24/7 vigilance, I gave up several hobbies and interests. I was a governor of the local primary school and, reluctantly, handed in my resignation. But both the head teacher and chair said that they wanted me to stay, and please bring Malcolm along to the meetings as well. However unorthodox, it enabled me to carry on with a life of my own and was another marvellous example of community empathy. This too touches on spirituality – individual or group altruism, reaching out to us to offer their support with understanding and compassion.

Reflection exercise

The client has started to confuse day and night and the carer is becoming exhausted through lack of sleep. Previous respite care experience has resulted in reluctance to go down that route again. What would you advise to meet their needs? If there is a conflict of interests, how might it be resolved?

Quality of care: relationships with professionals in the later stages

▶ Domiciliary agency care

▶ Care in a care home

▶ Health and social care professionals at home

▶ Personal qualities at the heart of quality care

As the disease progressed, we changed from having morning domiciliary care plus some day care, to live-in carers. Unfortunately, the agency sent us 14 different people in eight months, none of whom was dementia-trained. Reasonably well-equipped for the basic tasks of physical care, they were unable to fully understand Malcolm's wider needs. Too many just wanted to watch TV with Malcolm (who wasn't in the least interested), or spent ages on their mobile phone rather than trying to engage with him. The procession of new faces bewildered Malcolm, who eventually took to taking the sitting room apart, throwing furniture around to express his anger at being ignored. To cap it all, he took his anger elsewhere and three lots of day care collapsed because staff couldn't understand or cope with his extraordinary behaviour either. I became totally exhausted, and put Malcolm into a nursing home. I felt I had failed him. It was for my sake, not his, and I still feel guilty about that.

What could have prevented my crisis? Undoubtedly, greater continuity of staff, and dementia training; less obvious, but equally important, an understanding that family carers who share the physical load 50/50 are also trying to cope with the emotional anguish of caring for a deteriorating loved one. I would have welcomed some psychological and emotional support. As for head-on criticism (for example, about the home-cooked food we shared with them as our guests), I needed that like a hole in the head.

The nursing home warmly welcomed us and Malcolm settled in. But I returned home to a house usually full of hustle and bustle, where the silence descended on me like a pall. Then the doorbell rang. It was the vicar's wife with flowers in her hand, saying that she'd heard I was having a tough time. A kindly act, a conversation full of understanding, a hug, and my tears flowed. It was just what I needed. A week later, I wrote: *'Last week was black. I found myself in tears on several occasions. My hands feel empty. It's like being bereaved, but with no body, no ceremony, no proper reason to mourn, no line drawn under it. His chair and bed are empty. For the first time in my life, I am alone'.* I felt an immense loss mixed with a dash of self-pity.

A friend who was a bereavement counsellor helped me through. The early mornings were the worst and she encouraged me to pull the sheets over my head and weep until I could weep no more. It was totally exhausting, but afterwards there came a wonderful sense of cleanliness and refreshment. Someone once told me that strong emotions – loss, grief, anger, frustration, resentment or whatever – produce chemical reactions in the body and tears are the only way we can expel those toxins. If we bottle it up, it can produce physical illness. How strange that modern society considers tears as a sign of weakness, to be avoided, when maybe they are beneficial.

Care in the nursing home was generally good, the atmosphere tranquil and Malcolm's aggression thankfully ebbed away. But there arose a period of serious over-medication with sodium valproate (Epilim) against the consultant's advice. Done simply for the benefit of the staff, it left Malcolm rigid and bed-bound. Carers' dilemma: do we make a fuss or keep silent in case there are repercussions on the relationships between Malcolm, the staff and me? I chose to make a fuss, ably supported by our social worker, the dose was reduced and within a week Malcolm was walking about again, somewhat gingerly, but with a smile on his face. This touches on how the staff see their relationship with carers: are we an 'interfering relative' or, as the Carers Strategy insists, more properly, a 'partner in care'?

Malcolm became gaunt and was fretting; he was given six months to live, so I decided to bring him home again. He went on to live for a further seven years; he always was a nonconformist. This time round I fought for and eventually obtained direct payments so that we could employ our own live-in carers. Malcolm had also become too afraid to venture out of his familiar environment, so any breaks for me were via a consistent replacement carer at home, which worked brilliantly. During this time we were also supported by several kinds of nursing professionals. It was a complex web of care at home (see figure 1) and it isn't often realised how time-consuming it is for the carer to co-ordinate.

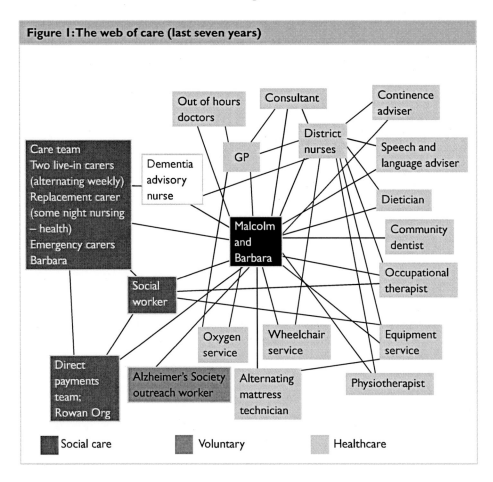

Figure 1: The web of care (last seven years)

Sometimes their advice was contradictory; very few health professionals knew enough about how the overlay of severe dementia affects normal medical treatment and nursing procedures. I spent a lot of time and emotional energy I could ill afford in battles with officialdom (notably for

NHS continuing care) and the one thing which would have helped, and would have made our pathway simpler and smarter, would have been one dementia advisory community nurse (eg. an admiral nurse) as our main source of advice and continuous assessment. The Alzheimer's Society support worker remained a tower of strength, visiting to offer advice and a shoulder to cry on, but she couldn't trigger services or funding.

What makes for quality care, wherever it is offered? My background is in teacher education, and however academic and aware of classroom techniques my students were, if, when they went into a classroom to teach, they had difficulty in making relationships with pupils, it would all go pear-shaped. Similarly with social and health care professionals, competencies alone tend to produce mechanistic, task-driven care. The most successful staff and the ones who derived most personal satisfaction from the job were those who could make a really good relationship with Malcolm, and incidentally with me. It was a triangular flow of trust, taking cues from each other and putting Malcolm's needs first. In recruiting staff I began to rely more heavily on a candidate's personal qualities, their core values, ability to empathise and to walk in our shoes, and their interest in care beyond the physical. Skills can be taught, but deep-down personal attitudes are hard to change. I greatly valued those who brought to the job not just hands and head, but heart as well. Love, compassion and empathy form the core of both spirituality and emotionally enlightened care.

Reflection exercise

Today's formal assessments of the quality of care require hard evidence of measurable standards. What aspects do you believe make for quality care? How far is there a danger of measuring only that which is easily measurable and missing out on essentials?

Box 3: Carers Strategy identified priorities

▶ Access to specialist services
▶ Personalisation – eg. flexibility over personal budgets
▶ A lead professional
▶ Review of benefits
▶ Increase in respite care
▶ Extended NHS services, including training for GPs on carers' needs
▶ Protection for young carers
▶ Better information
▶ The annual carers grant

Palliative care, death and bereavement

▶ Care beyond the physical and its effect on the carer

▶ Letting go

▶ When the caring stops

Five years before he died, Malcolm had become doubly incontinent, mute, immobile, unable to understand what was said to him, could do nothing for himself, had tonic-colonic seizures and was losing control of swallowing and temperature. He was as helpless as a baby. But he was not 'a vegetable'. Many visitors fell away because they were uncertain about how to handle it, perhaps seeing the ravages of the disease rather than the real Malcolm still in there. I was grateful for visits from our local vicar, for he gave me moral and spiritual support and laid his hands in blessing on both of us. Care staff sometimes queried this, saying Malcolm 'wouldn't understand'. But I believe Malcolm still recognised the rhythm of the familiar words and the soothing hand as a deep-rooted, special and meaningful gesture – a rite in itself.

All the superficial things the world values were wiped away: his knowledge, basic and finer skills, abstract thinking, rationality and social awareness – followed by almost all of his basic functions (eg. talking, walking) being shot to pieces. But there still remained his deeper sensory, psychological and spiritual self. We tried to meet his sensory needs – sight, smell, taste, and especially hearing (we talk to babies who can't talk back, don't we?) and touch (stroking a hand or his face, giving a hug), and also his psychological and spiritual needs (ensuring that he felt safe, loved and cherished). And in sharing those experiences with him, my own inner self was nurtured; I felt that I was still communicating with my soul mate at a very deep level. In return, a luminous trust flowed from him – you could glimpse it in his eyes – the very self he was born with. Call it his spirituality, essence, or what you will, it is something that was a truly precious experience.

> **Reflection exercise**
>
> If you should suddenly become seriously mentally and physically disabled, what sensory, psychological and spiritual experiences would be important to you? Make a list and give a copy to the person who knows you best.

I admit that the very late stages were sometimes grim and hard work;
I did 142 hours a week on duty or on call. In the last two years, with
Malcolm's rationality gone, an almost primitive sense of survival took over
and he went to the brink of death several times only to step back, creating
a psychological rollercoaster for me and the family. But in his last chest
infection, with swallowing completely gone, it was clear that he was ready
to let go. I declined admitting him to hospital for intravenous antibiotic
and maybe other aggressive interventions, because Malcolm had written
in his diary years before: 'When the end comes, I hope it won't be too messy'.
I also knew that for people with dementia, being in an unfamiliar, noisy
environment and among strangers can cause severe shock and rapid onset
of death. But making that decision on behalf of another human being was
one of the hardest things I've ever done, and I would have welcomed some
moral support. We were told that the local palliative team was only for
cancer; I'm delighted that hospices are now extending their outreach to
people dying at home from conditions other than cancer and to their carers.

Malcolm died peacefully, physically supported by the close family and
encircled with love. His spirit, shackled for those long years by his
Alzheimer's, could at last fly free like a bird from an opened cage. His death
was but the last loss of many, so my main emotions after his death were of
relief and release. As a result I couldn't grieve properly. Having declined
bereavement counselling because I felt I didn't need it, 16 months later,
illness hit me like a sledgehammer, both mentally and physically. The GP
duly treated my physical illnesses, but only now do I realise that it was a
delayed bereavement shock. Counsellors reckon that for long-term carers it
is on average a delay of one month for every year of caring. For me, it was
16 years and 16 months, on the dot. Whose radar should former long-term
carers be on?

Several months after Malcolm died I was sorting through some of the
diaries and notebooks he kept in the early days of his dementia. Out
fluttered a scrap of paper on which he had written: 'The only verity is my
soul' (John Donne). In the topsy-turvy world of dementia, when sense of
selfhood can be rocked in so many ways, Malcolm clearly felt that the only
safe ground, the only constant truth, was his soul. And because of that bond
of love between us, the same could be said for me.

References

Department of Health (2003) *Delivering Race Equality: A framework for action*. London: DH.

Gilbert P with Bates P, Carr S, Clark M, Gould N & Slay G (2010) *Social Work and Mental Health: The value of everything*. Lyme Regis: Russell House Publishing.

HM Government (2008) *Carers at the Heart of 21st Century: Families and communities* (referred to as *The Carers Strategy*). London: DH.

National Mental Health Development Unit/The Princess Royal Trust for Carers (2010) *The Triangle of Care Best Practice Guide in Acute Mental Health Care*. London: NMHDU.

Nuffield Council on Bioethics (2009) *Dementia: Ethical issues*. London: Nuffield Council on Bioethics.

Ramsay R, Gerada C, Mars S & Szmukler G (2001) *Mental Illness: A handbook for carer*. London: Jessica Kingsley.

Stokes G (2008) *And Still the Music Plays*. London: Hawker Publications Ltd.

Chapter 6

Professional attitudes

Madeleine Parkes and Joanna Barber

'Know thyself' is a little piece of philosophy carved thousands of years ago into a stone ruin at the Oracle of Delphi in central Greece. When thinking about spirituality, in particular professional attitudes to it, 'know thyself' is an excellent place to start. By understanding your own sense of spirituality, it will become much easier to empathise with and address the spiritual and religious needs of the service users you work with, even if you don't share the same beliefs or values. Knowing where you come from helps you to value where they come from.

Spirituality is briefly defined as whatever gives your life meaning and purpose. It is a highly individual, subjective and sensitive issue. Maintaining appropriate boundaries while being empathetic, compassionate and attentive to a patient's spiritual needs can be a challenge for professionals. These qualities form the basis of spiritual care for patients, and it demands a spiritual attitude from all the professionals with whom they come into contact. More often than not, these qualities can be found within the professional's own spirituality (see also chapters 1 and 10).

This chapter addresses the importance of having a spiritual attitude to patients, and how this can impact on every aspect of patient care. It also stresses the importance of knowing your own spirituality, and using this knowledge to understand the spiritual viewpoints of others (see Parkes, Milner & Gilbert, 2010; Parkes & Gilbert, 2011, forthcoming). This in turn will aid the quality of care that you can provide.

Does my field recognise spirituality as part of my role?

The word 'spirituality' has recently gained attention in many mental health disciplines. The Canadian Model of Occupational Therapy (in McColl, 2003) has the spirituality of the patient as the fourth dimension, placed in the centre to highlight its importance (Hammell, 2004). In the field of psychiatric nursing, Peplau (1952) introduced the idea of the therapeutic relationship between staff and clients, which is based on a spiritual attitude from staff. The British Psychological Society has a transpersonal and holistic special interest group, based on the spirituality of clients (Clarke, 2001). Clarke, an associate fellow of the British Psychological Society, runs a spiritual crisis network for patients who wish to work through problems they might have with their spirituality. Spiritual matters are deeply involved in the recovery model from mental illness, which arose during the 1980s primarily from the service user movement in the USA. More recently, the Royal College of Psychiatrists has explored spiritual and religious care in practice, and has issued guidelines as to how this might be delivered (www.rcpsych.ac.uk/spirit). It has also set up a special interest group in spirituality to discuss this further (see Cook *et al*, 2009).

However, the whole issue of delivering spiritual care and helping people with their spiritual needs may invoke fear, trepidation and confusion – especially if you do not really know what is involved. Evidence shows that if a clinician does not have a personal interest in religion, they are considerably less likely to acknowledge the religious and spiritual needs of a patient. The consequent attitude of the clinician will threaten the formation of a therapeutic relationship with the patient, as well as make it much less likely that the patient's specific spiritual needs will be met. A negative, dismissive or fearful attitude on the part of the professional will actually have an anti-therapeutic effect on the patient. Professionals need to explore their own views of spirituality, and, regardless of what they are and how they are expressed, need to be able to view every patient as a whole person, with a crucial spiritual dimension, and a contribution to make. A negative, dismissive or fearful attitude will have a negative impact on the patient as this attitude could affect the care given, removing spirituality from its holistic component. (See chapters 15 and 16)

What does spirituality mean to me?

Spirituality can come into play during the difficult times of life, particularly in times of distress, illness and bereavement. It can be expressed through formal religious adherence and practices, such as prayer, reading religious scripture or attending services at a church, mosque, temple or other religious institution.

Some people experience and express their spirituality through nature, arts and creativity. Some people find yoga and meditation a spiritual act. For some people the most important thing to them is their family and relationships – they might not see this as spiritual but it gives their lives a sense of meaning. For others their spirituality is exemplified in the values and morals they hold and act upon. A spiritual way of life works from deeply held beliefs and values that generate positive and compassionate ways of engaging with the self, others and the world (see Coyte *et al*, 2007).

In summary, spirituality is something outside ourselves that inspires us in life or gives us meaning and purpose. It is a very individual thing and can change over time depending on what challenges we may face.

Reflection exercise
▶   Which aspects of spirituality described above do you identify with most?   ▶   Can you think of any other aspects of spirituality that are important to you?

How can a professional have a spiritual approach?

'Healers do not need to have had the same experiences as patients, but, to be compassionate, they do need to recognise how they have shared similar emotions.' (Johnston-Taylor, 2007, p13)

In mental illness, the whole of your personhood is threatened. It changes the way you feel about yourself, how you relate to others and your ability to work. Self-esteem, identity, meaning and purpose are often lost. No one is the same: mental illness is a different experience for every sufferer. Many people do not even realise they are unwell, and blame themselves for not being able to cope. One of the most distressing things is the isolation felt by many sufferers.

These feelings cannot be resolved by medication. They require a person to care compassionately, in the simplest sense of the word, about the person who is suffering. A spiritual approach to this care involves the caregiver showing humility, compassion, empathy and respect. Valuing the person as a person – not an illness to be cured, or a problem to be fixed – can be very empowering for the patient. These are basic but crucial prerequisites for a very human relationship. These are not empty gestures, but can have a real impact on the patient and can sometimes be forgotten by staff when they have long waiting lists and are under pressure to meet targets.

Reflection exercise

▶ What do the words 'humility', 'compassion', 'empathy' and 'respect' mean to you?
▶ Can you think of a time you have been genuinely valued by others?
▶ How did this make you feel?
▶ How do you feel when you are not shown these qualities?

Examples of how effective these qualities can be in a therapeutic relationship – and examples of how patients feel when these qualities are absent – are described and discussed below through the real life reflections of a patient's journey through services. Note how they impact how the person feels about themselves, and the great effect the professional's attitude to the person and their sense of spirituality can have.

How can it go wrong?

'I went to my GP. It seemed like the only thing to do. I couldn't say much to him, but I think he understood something of the desperation that I felt. He said he thought that I really should be in hospital, and certainly be on medication. He said he thought a psychiatrist might be able to help me, and made me an urgent appointment. I went to the outpatient clinic, petrified, wondering what this psychiatrist would be like. All I can remember is the psychiatrist telling me that he had the power to admit me to hospital compulsorily. When I refused, he said he would give me 24 hours to think about it, and I had to come back the following day.'

In mental health services the attitude of the professional towards the client is crucial. Most patients are frightened, by the very nature of their illness, and often reluctant to divulge sensitive information. The building up of trust is essential for diagnosis and treatment, and the therapeutic relationship is fundamental. The way the professional communicates with the client themselves is important in its own right, but is also an example to be followed by the rest of the team. Clinical staff have the potential to make a large and positive impact on the patient in all areas of their life and journey through recovery, and this can be achieved in part by addressing spiritual needs and by utilising spiritual skills such as compassion and empathy during conversation.

'When I returned the following day, the doctor came in with lots of other people. He asked what the trouble was. He seemed impatient. I didn't know what to say. Where could I start, and would he understand? I was so ashamed and guilty, completely despairing. I couldn't find the right words to describe how I was feeling. Meanwhile the voices continued unabated.'

The very nature of mental illness makes a person question their value and worth, and wonder whether they will be listened to properly by someone who wants to understand. In the real life example above, the patient has been alienated and their suffering increased. No trust has been established, no respect shown to the patient, and little time spent trying to listen and understand. The possibility of making a therapeutic relationship with this patient is severely in jeopardy.

'I remained on that ward for several years. During this time I never trusted any of the clinical staff. In fact, I hated them all. I couldn't confide in any of them. I had to take tablets which made me feel worse, and my complaints about terrible side effects were not even acknowledged. I was not allowed out and there was nothing at all to do. The voices were still pretty bad. I had resigned from my job, and lost any friends I did have. It seemed that life was over and had become one long nightmare.'

The damaging effect of the whole situation is obvious from this example. The patient has no faith in the system and cannot open up to staff. Distressing experiences go unheard. The result for the patient is further isolation and loss of all meaningful life – an issue at the centre of a person's spirituality. As no information from the patient is forthcoming (but do we blame him for not disclosing information?), it is impossible to monitor treatment and try to find the best medication for this patient. Psychological therapies become out of the question. The whole experience of the patient is anti-therapeutic. The whole situation has arisen from the attitude of the clinical team treating this person.

Simple but fundamental insights
▶ Deciding upon appropriate holistic treatments depends upon getting to know the patient as a whole person – with psychological, biological, social and spiritual needs.
▶ Delivering and monitoring the treatments depends on having a trusting therapeutic relationship between staff and patients.

How can it go right?

'When the clinical team came to see me, I braced myself to tell them everything was fine. The consultant introduced himself and the other members of the team. He seemed kindly and interested in my plight. As usual I couldn't say much, but the doctor said he would come back the next day to see how I was. When he returned, he was on his own and seemed to have lots of time for me. He was patient and encouraging, and I found myself telling him things that I thought I could never have told anyone. It was such a relief to find someone that listened and seemed to understand, someone who was not passing judgement on me, and was not going to give up on me. When he said he thought we could work together to find the right medication, and that he was sure I could get better, I had no difficulty agreeing to be admitted onto his ward.'

In this part of the journey, the experience of the patient is completely different.

▶ The lead doctor shows genuine interest and compassion.

▶ He realises that he needs to spend more time with the patient before any decisions are made.

▶ He listens respectfully and tries to aid the patient to make the right decision about admission in a way that is in the best interest of the patient's long-term recovery.

▶ He reassures the patient that they will work together to find some helpful treatment.

▶ He wants to involve patients in decisions about their own treatment and management.

▶ He sincerely wants to help his patients, thinking of them as people in their own right with a contribution to make.

This doctor shows a high degree of spirituality in his attitude to this patient. His spirituality has made this doctor able to look outside himself and empathise with this patient. This attitude towards patients depends on a degree of spiritual awareness. His own selfish desires or self-importance as leader are put to one side.

'On the ward, the usual routines were kept. However, the staff seemed friendly and caring. One in particular, my named nurse, spent time with me, and I started to trust her a little. She arranged for a priest to come and give me communion, something I had wanted for a long time but had been too frightened to go into a church.'

In this case, the patient wanted to attend something religious, but the challenge of going to a formal service at a church was recognised by the clinical team. Again this demonstrated empathy and sensitivity to both the importance of religion the person held, but also the difficult feelings they may have around entering a church full of strangers. The team was able to identify appropriate people to refer the patient to – in this case, a member of the on-site chaplaincy team. In many cases such as this that both authors have witnessed and experienced, the staff member involved didn't share the faith or belief of the patient, but recognised both the therapeutic importance and deeply personal significance of enabling the person to explore and express their spirituality. It is the legal responsibility of the clinical team to enable opportunities for religious expression. This needs to be done on a practical level, such as making a phone call to the appropriate chaplain and escorting the person to the multi-faith room for daily prayers. This also needs to be done on an emotional and spiritual level of acknowledging, respecting, and if appropriate, exploring the person's spiritual needs and beliefs, while maintaining a clear awareness of one's own beliefs.

Staff are not expected to know the answers to deeply spiritual questions or problems that the patient might have. Simply listening – properly listening, with attentiveness and encouragement – is therapeutic for the patient in itself, as perhaps for the first time, their spirituality is being recognised as a part of them, and important for their recovery in terms of providing hope and meaning.

How do I do it?: practical issues

Think about what you value and where your strengths lie. This can become what you can offer in a therapeutic relationship, and also with members of your team.

▶ Are you a good listener? How do you do this?

▶ Can you offer someone words of comfort and hope?

▶ Are you a 'do-er' – can you arrange practical things to happen to allow patients to explore spirituality and express their religion?

▶ Are you an inspiring motivator? Can you encourage your team to think about their attitude to spirituality and help them understand what is involved in spiritual care?

▶ Are you reflective? Can you understand where your own beliefs come from and how it feels to have them? Can you relate these feelings to patients?

Members of the professional team can provide spiritual care in a number of ways, by playing to their own strengths and spiritual values.

Practical changes to the patient's care plan can also be made.

▶ Conduct a simple spiritual assessment to establish whether the patient has any spiritual and/or religious needs. You may need to do this several times depending on what stage the person is at in their recovery, and how important spirituality becomes for them (see chapter 10).

▶ Integrate spiritual care activities into the care plan. Does the patient want to see a chaplain, or make a link with the local faith community for support? Can you run activity sessions with spiritual themes, such as hope, peace, meaning and purpose? Can the patient's spiritual journey be acknowledged during their psychology sessions?

▶ Contact the chaplaincy team in your organisation for further support. Referrals can often be made to them and they can give specialist advice. This may be particularly important if the patient is experiencing religious issues that might be part of their illness. Follow up a patient's request to access quiet space for reflection and resources for prayer. If you do not have a chaplaincy team, enquire about local faith groups who might be able to offer advice. Remember the patient may already be part of a faith group and may want contact to be made with them (see Gilbert with Bates *et al*, 2010).

Please don't forget...

Giving someone permission to talk about their spirituality and simply listening attentively to them can be therapeutic for the person in itself. It may only be a five-minute conversation, and you may not say very much at all, but it could make a huge difference to the patient as they journey through distress to recovery. If you don't want to engage with them around spirituality, ask yourself what is stopping you and how you can resolve it.

Boundaries

There is a difference between acknowledging your own spirituality that will in turn enable you to affect the patient positively as part of your role, and letting your own views affect the role you do.

You are not expected to agree with the patient's religious beliefs or spiritual viewpoints, just as you wouldn't expect to share the same hobbies and interests as the patients. However, this should not prevent you from learning about their hobbies and interests, asking them questions to find out more, and putting into practice ways to allow them to express these. The same principle applies with spiritual and religious beliefs. It is OK to be genuine with the patient – if you don't share their faith, that's OK, but recognise that you can help them regardless of your own beliefs and viewpoint. Focus on the similarities rather than being divided by difference. As mentioned previously, little things such as listening and responding compassionately in a five-minute conversation can have a truly great effect on a person who feels isolated and afraid.

There has been much confusion around the issue of 'praying with patients'. Be aware that often there are chaplains or spiritual care advisers who are employed specifically to offer religious interventions such as prayer. These are specific religious needs that need to be met by a qualified and authorised professional. Activities such as prayer and conducting a religious service do not fall into your job description and should not be done – regardless of how much practice you might have had at home! There are countless stories of patients whose therapeutic relationship has been damaged by a well-intentioned but misguided professional.

The best advice concerning boundaries is when in doubt: don't. Check your organisation's policies and consult with diversity/chaplaincy teams.

How does it affect me?: personal issues

The importance of professionals exploring, understanding and valuing their own spirituality is increasingly being recognised and welcomed.

▶ For some, spirituality may be a confusing word, or a challenging idea.

▶ Others may not have thought about their spirituality before, and are prompted to do so after encountering a patient who is expressing theirs.

▶ Others may consider themselves to be deeply spiritual – but they can still learn from other people's spirituality.

Your professional responsibility to the patient is around identifying and providing for their spiritual care needs. This may be in a very immediate way, such as having a deep conversation. However, your personal beliefs should not in any way become the centre of the discussion – the patient's spirituality is what is being discussed, not yours. This is why understanding your own views is a useful exercise, as when they are challenged by the conversation, or leave you questioning your own beliefs, this can be acknowledged, and put aside for later reflection when your duty of attention to the patient's need is over. You shouldn't ignore your own beliefs around spirituality (whatever they may be). What we are asking is quite the opposite. We are asking you to bring your spiritual self into the therapeutic relationship in a way that is constructive and positive for the patient.

You may use your spiritual skills of listening, compassion and empathy, while being aware of, but temporarily putting aside your own convictions and struggles. Similarly, addressing a patient's spiritual needs is not an opportunity to convert them to your ideas. The patient's own world view has been with them their whole life – it would be unprofessional, unethical and pointless to twist a five-minute conversation into a conversion attempt.

Thinking about your own spirituality

The HOPE assessment tool can be used to assess the spiritual and religious needs of patients and service users. (See chapter 10 for further information on assessing spiritual needs). This particular assessment tool addresses areas of Hope, Organised religion, Personal spirituality and Effects on medical care. Please use some of the questions from the tool listed below to reflect on your own sense of spirituality. Think about how your values, beliefs and personal qualities can be brought into the work you do and the role you have. (For a deeper exploration of spirituality and values, see chapters 16 and 21).

Sources of hope

▶ What do you hold onto during difficult times?

▶ What sustains you and keeps you going?

▶ What are your sources of hope, strength, comfort and peace?

Organised religion

▶ Are you part of a religious community?

▶ Does it help you? How?

▶ How important is this to you?

▶ What aspects of religion are not so helpful to you?

Personal spirituality

▶ Do you have personal spiritual beliefs that are independent of organised religion? What are they?

▶ What aspects of your spirituality or spiritual practices do you find most helpful to you? (eg. prayer, yoga, meditation, hiking, listening to music, communing with nature)

Conclusion

The attitude of the healthcare professional to the service user is perhaps more important in mental healthcare than in any other branch of medicine. All staff need to show humility, patience and compassion – all spiritual skills – as well as empathetically listening and providing practical support to meet spiritual and religious needs. Every patient must be respected as a fellow human being, and every effort made to try and understand how each one uniquely views their problems. This attitude can be inspired by professionals reflecting on their personal understanding of 'spirituality'.

References

Clarke I (2001) *Psychosis and Spirituality: Exploring the new frontier*. Chichester: Wiley.

Cook C, Powell A & Sims A (2009) *Spirituality and Psychiatry*. London: RCPsych.

Coyte ME, Gilbert P & Nicholls V (2007) *Spirituality, Values and Mental Health: Jewels for the journey*. London: Jessica Kingsley.

Gilbert P with Bates P, Carr S, Clark M, Gould N & Slay G (2010) *Social Work and Mental Health: The value of everything*. Lyme Regis: Russell House Publishing.

Hammell KW (2004) Dimensions of meaning in the occupations of every day life. Canadian *Journal of Occupational Therapy* **71** (5) 296–304.

Johnston-Taylor E (2007) *What Do I Say? Talking with patient's about spirituality*. Conshohocken: Templeton Press.

McColl MA (2003) *Spirituality and Occupational Therapy*. Ottowa: Canadian Association Occupational Therapists.

Parkes M, Milner K & Gilbert P (2010) Vocation, vocation, vocation. *The International Journal of Leadership in Public Services* **6** (3) 14–25.

Parkes M & Gilbert P (2011, forthcoming) Professionals calling. *Implicit Religion*, not yet published.

Peplau HE (1952) The psychiatric nurse's family group. *American Journal of Nursing* **52** (12) 1475–1477.

Further reading

Barber J (2009) *Handbook of Spiritual Care in Mental Illness.* Birmingham: BSMHFT.

White G (2006) *Talking about Spirituality in Healthcare Practice: A resource for the multiprofessional healthcare team.* London: Jessica Kingsley Publishers.

An easy quiz to help you think through your beliefs can be found at: http://www.beliefnet.com/Entertainment/Quizzes/BeliefOMatic.aspx

Chapter 7

Ethnicity and spirituality

Hári Sewell

This chapter will offer a definition of ethnicity and religion and spirituality will also be discussed. Particular attention is paid to religion in this chapter as difference and inequality relating to ethnicity is likely to be more apparent within this context.

What is ethnicity?

The term ethnicity has its roots in the Greek word for people or tribe (Senior & Bhopal, 1994). Ethnicity represents those aspects of a person that relate to their sense of belonging. It may be food, dress, cultural habits, music, place of family origin and religion. Ethnic group is self-defined and may be changeable.

Definitions of ethnicity usually include a reference to religion or belief. For many people the structure of religion or faith provides a context for the expression of their spirituality. Though discussions of ethnicity and spirituality need not be explored only within the context of religion it is appropriate to pay some attention to religious expression. As the Mental Health Foundation executive briefing on spirituality and mental health states: *'for an individual, culture and religion may be inter-changeable'* (Mental Health Foundation, 2008). Religious symbolism and dress often become integral aspects of group ethnic identity. The naming systems in many cultures represent affiliation to a particular religion, making it inseparable from identify, regardless of whether someone is devout.

Individual expression of spirituality out with formalised religion is also a legitimate aspect of someone's ethnicity and identity. Any robust assessment of someone using mental health services will explore identity more fully than the 'tick box' prompts required by ethnic monitoring. The category 'Asian' conveys little of the richness that comes from further exploration of a person's identity that will help create more meaningful relationships between service user and staff.

Identity and intersectionality

Individual identities are a complex mix of our innate traits, our family experience, our ethnic and cultural experiences and our interactions with the wider world. This unique blend of psychology and socialisation means that no two individuals have exactly the same identity. At the level of service planning and development it is appropriate to identify patterns that relate to target groups of people who share common identities and experiences of discrimination. It is important, however, to consider the unique ways in which aspects of an individual's identity and experiences of discrimination intersect with each other.

Crenshaw (1994) describes the concept of intersectionality as the ways in which racial identity and being a woman intersect. The concept was developed in response to the violence and abuse women and girls suffered, and can be applied to all multiple identities (Kilomba, 2008). Intersectionality in relation to ethnicity, religion and gender was seen in the case of the hotel bosses in Cheshire who shouted and insulted a 60-year-old female guest who was wearing a hijab. During the abuse they accused her of being a bomber (*The Sun*, 2009). It is reasonable to assume that the hotel owners were more confident about verbally abusing a woman than they might have been a man. It may even be the case that the fact that the woman was older played a part in the lack of restraint shown.

Racism, religion and mutating discrimination

There has been a rise in Islamophobia and religious hatred, particularly since the September 11 attacks in New York in 2001. Martin Baker (1981) described the emergence of a new euphemism for racism. He cited examples

of how critical language less frequently referred to race but instead 'culture' was used. A decade and a half later Beckford *et al* (2006) stated the following: *'Over the last 50 years, the discourse in Britain about "racialised minorities" has mutated from "colour" in the 1950s and 1960s … to "race" in the 1960s, 70s and 80s … to "ethnicity" in the 90s … and to "religion" in the present time'.*

UK legislature does provide some protection and routes for redress in relation to inequality and specifically refers to intersectionality and multiple discriminations.

Legislative context

The Equality Act (2010) was enacted in April 2010 and a two-year timetable for sections coming into force began in October 2010. The act brings together several pieces of legislation designed to remove inequality and discrimination.

The public sector duty is to:

(a) eliminate discrimination, harassment, victimisation and any other conduct that is prohibited by or under the act

(b) advance equality of opportunity between persons who share a relevant protected characteristic and persons who do not share it

(c) foster good relations between persons who share a relevant protected characteristic and persons who do not share it.

Specific 'protected characteristics' (previously referred to as equality strands) are covered by the legislation. These are:

▶ age

▶ disability

▶ gender reassignment

▶ marriage and civil partnership

▶ pregnancy and maternity

▶ race

▶ religion or belief

▶ sex

▶ sexual orientation.

Achieving fairness often requires that reasonable adjustments are made to services to remove barriers to equality and the law stipulates that this must be done for disabled persons. Schedules are published to support the Equality Act (2010). They aid decision-making on reasonable adjustments and implementation of the act. The Equality Act (2010) permits public bodies to show favourable treatment of the target groups as a means of achieving equality, providing that the action does not contravene any other section of the act.

The Equality Act (2010) categorises religion and belief together and covers spirituality. As stated previously, spirituality does not require the structures of religion but is still covered within the Equality Act (2010). It is worth noting also that section 14 of the Equality Act (2010) refers to combined discrimination arising from two characteristics, for example race, and religion or belief. The Equality Act (2010) incorporates ethnicity into the definition of race.

Figure 1 shows the issues that are consistent across all or the 'protected characteristics' under the Equality Act (2010).

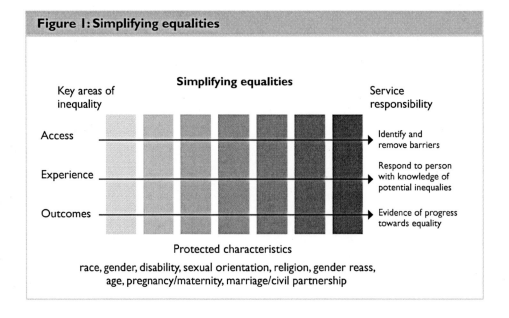

Figure 1: Simplifying equalities

Simplifying equalities

Key areas of inequality

Service responsibility

Access — Identify and remove barriers

Experience — Respond to person with knowledge of potential inequalies

Outcomes — Evidence of progress towards equality

Protected characteristics

race, gender, disability, sexual orientation, religion, gender reass, age, pregnancy/maternity, marriage/civil partnership

The key challenge for service providers is to understand the specific ways in which inequalities occur for each of the protected characteristics in terms of access, experience and outcomes. There will be common themes across all of the characteristics. There are, however, specific needs for each group. For example, ensuring sexual safety is particularly important for all women; avoiding offence or a sense of violation through any stranger male-to-female contact may be particularly important for some faith and cultural groups. Organisations and staff need to have understanding to take account of these needs.

Spirituality and recovery in mental health

Much of this book describes the potential for spiritual awareness to be helpful in recovery. People from BME backgrounds will experience some of the basic benefits of spirituality as anyone else. It is worth noting however that the annual census of psychiatric inpatients in England held in March 2009 and reported in January 2010 showed that compared with the white British, proportionately more people from the Asian and African and Irish groups said they had a religion (Care Quality Commission & NMHDU, 2010). People from BME backgrounds may find the expression of spirituality within the context of a religion or faith helpful for the reasons set out in box 1.

Box 1: The helpfulness of spirituality
Helpfulness of spirituality, particularly in the context of religious expression in people from BME backgrounds
It strengthens the sense of belonging and community.
Faith may be a protective factor in relation to preventing suicide.
It may provide people from BME backgrounds with a legitimised paradigm for understanding and interpreting their mental health problems. Cultural interpretation may be seen by mental health professionals as being less grounded than those related to an organised religion.
Spiritual expression can provide a context for reflective time to build resilience in someone who feels a compounded sense of isolation because of their particular mental health challenges, their ethnicity and perhaps other aspects of intersectionality.

Later in this chapter the potential challenges in relation to mental health problems, spirituality and religion faced by practitioners will be explored. First, it is important to focus on the strengths and potential benefits set out in box 1.

Spirituality and a strengthened sense of belonging and community

Newly settled ethnic groups often form communities in particular geographical areas. Over time (and generations) the sense of belonging to a community can become eroded. In the experience of many people from BME backgrounds, terms such as 'BME communities' or 'Asian communities' are misnomers. Belonging to a faith group and in particular to a specific place of worship creates more of a sense of community than simply ethnicity. Despite the existential reality of our aloneness, most descriptions of positive contributions to mental health include social connectedness (Friedli *et al* 2007; Marmot, 2010; National Institute for Mental Health England, 2005). This sense of connectedness may extend to a relationship with a higher being (Coyte *et al*, 2007). The greater sense of safety is important for people from BME backgrounds who may experience wider society as an unfriendly or discriminatory environment.

Faith may be a protective factor in relation to preventing suicide

Research (see chapter 2) has indicated that suicides are lower for people who belong to faith communities. Religiosity may therefore be a protective factor. Religious expression and faith is more popular in people from BME backgrounds and as such they are more likely to benefit from this protection (Sewell, 2004). As stated previously, faith and religion are defining features for many BME communities in the UK. The protective value of religion extends beyond devout followers. This is because of the extent to which culture and religion are sometimes bound together and the ways in which some cultures integrate conceptualisations of mind, body and spirit (Fernando, 2002; Mental Health Foundation, 2008).

Religion may provide a legitimised paradigm for understanding and interpreting mental health problems

Religion has for centuries provided a framework for understanding human distress and behaviours that are currently considered to be psychiatric illnesses (Read *et al*, 2004). People from BME backgrounds may locate their experiences within their cultural understanding but may choose to accentuate a religious dimension when they speak to mental health professionals. This is because world religions each have a recognisable belief system, traditions, rules of engagement and community (Hilton *et al*, 2002). Both the service user and staff may consider culture to be a less robust explanatory framework as it does not have the same voice of authority as is the case with religious leaders, nor the documented codes of behaviour as for religious texts.

The importance of this strategy should not be underestimated. Racism and discrimination in society have an impact, causing people from BME groups to feel that their culture and lifestyle is less valued and respected. This is in part because racism comes from a lack of tolerance of difference. Against this background BME people may feel that their religion has more credibility than their culture as an explanatory model.

Spiritual expression can provide a context for reflective time to build resilience

All people experience benefit to their mental health from replenishment through relaxation, good friendships and moments of stillness and reflection (Friedli *et al*, 2007; National Institute for Mental Health England, 2005). Toxic Interaction Theory (Sewell, 2009) describes the corrosive impact of dynamics in relationships between white people and those from BME backgrounds. The toxicity does not rely upon malevolent acts but is a damaging dynamic due to prior experiences of small unintended acts (such as a black man in a hotel lobby being assumed to be a bell boy) and which Chester Pierce refers to as micro-aggressions (Pierce *et al*, 1978).

Given the constant toxicity people from BME backgrounds face, compounded by stigma in relation to their mental health problems and perhaps other aspects of their identity, it may be particularly restorative to have time and space for spiritual expression. The previous sections in this chapter have explored the benefits of spirituality with particular reference to religion or faith. Here spirituality is being considered in its purest form – the essence of being that transcends the five senses that relate to the physical world (Department of Health, 2003).

One American study into homeless women found that African-American women had higher rates of spiritual well-being than the white comparator group (Douglas *et al*, 2008). Perhaps this reflects an aspect of culture that emerged from the focus on hope, which was essential in sustaining their ancestors through brutal regimes. Other BME groups will have their own historical influences on their religious cultures.

The exercise that follows in box 2 is designed to prompt thinking about the sort of gaps in the information practitioners have about service users.

Box 2: Exercise

Think of someone (preferably from a BME background) about whom you will be able to verify or augment information you already know about them, either through personal contact or reference to their records.

Step 1

Relying only on what you can recall, answer the following:

Does this person identify themselves as religious and if so to which religion do they belong?

Whether religious or not, does this person identify themself as expressing some form of spirituality?

How does this person think about good things and bad things that happen in their life – the causes and the potential help to get through the difficult things?

What helps to make this person feel calm and resilient?

What makes them feel positive about their ethnicity and identity more generally?

Step 2

Ask the person or check records you hold. Compare your recall or assumptions with new information gained.

Step 3

Think about the information you now hold in relation to what you previously knew. Think about how much more you probably do not know and how it might enhance your work if you knew. Set yourself a target to learn more about this person and use it to assist in your work.

Spirituality in mental health: the gift and the curse

In addition to the potential for a positive contribution to recovery, spirituality and religion may raise challenges to practice. These challenges may arise from the contribution made by either the service user and their family, the worker's own issues, or the particular service model.

Box 3: Challenges in relation to spirituality

Examples of challenges

These include the potential for:

▶ assumptions to be made about a person's religion based on their appearance

▶ negative or subdued reactions of staff because of their own issues with religion

▶ over-identification by staff, manifested in practice or collusion that is beyond the scope of a worker's role

▶ intolerance or prejudice within service user groups based on religious or faith views

▶ worker or service's lack of knowledge to enable them to interpret behaviour

▶ religious or spiritual beliefs that are tolerant of suicide

▶ gender and religion – patriarchy

▶ layers of service failures to meet needs in relation to ethnicity, language and faith, leading to profoundly poorer experiences and outcomes.

Each of the points in box 3 will be explored further.

Assumptions about a person's identity and religion

Despite the compound nature of identities there are points in time when one or more aspects of identity may feel more prominent or important to an individual (Kilomba, 2008). Services need to be mindful of this when making referrals and discussing options for the future. This is illustrated in the vignette in box 4.

> ### Box 4: Example of assumptions about identity
>
> Rakim is a 32-year-old Muslim of Bangladeshi heritage. He was studying to be an imam under the tutelage of his father. When Rakim Snr died suddenly, Rakim felt devastated at the loss of his father, mentor and tutor. Over time he became depressed and withdrawn and practised his faith with increasing fervour. During less guarded moments he expressed anger at Allah but quickly silenced himself.
>
> Rakim was admitted to a psychiatric ward as his regular fasting and weight loss was causing significant concern to his mother. During his admission he spoke very little to nursing staff. As part of his care plan he was referred to an Asian men's group. Staff were pleased to be referring him to a group that was attended by men of similar age and ethnic background. After several aborted attempts to attend, Rakim went to the group but felt isolated and concerned. Many of the young men who professed to be Muslim adopted lifestyles that he found to be alienating. They were more interested in hip hop music, particularly gangsta rap with its violent and sexually explicit lyrics. Rather than enabling social interaction, the setting caused Rakim to withdraw even more. This worsened the risk ascribed to him by services and he experienced the increased anxiety of staff as intrusion. Rakim's 28-day detention for assessment was followed by a six-month treatment admission under the Mental Health Act (1983).

Rakim's case shows the need to gather appropriate information through assessment and use of narrative approaches (narrative approaches are discussed in the concluding paragraphs of this chapter).

Assumptions are also sometimes made about a person's religion based on how they appear. Based on limited knowledge and exposure, staff may not consider the possibility of Asian Christians or Caribbean Muslims.

The extent of entrenched views is captured succinctly by Nesbitt in the opening paragraph of her article 'Invisible community? South Asian Christians in the UK'. She writes: *'Parents in a Catholic school in the north of England recently complained to the head about an influx of "Muslim" pupils into the school. The "Muslims" in question were in fact Catholics from South India.'* (Nesbitt, 2007)

Negative or subdued reactions of staff because of their own issues with religion

Mental health services often operate as if the workforce is comprised of a rare breed of people who have no hang-ups, no personal hurts that remain unresolved, or no prejudices. In reality, staff often experience strong feelings in relation to the histories and lives of service users. Professional training or short courses seldom resolve deeply held pain and prejudice (Bennett *et al*, 2007; Bhui 2002). Staff may feel hostile towards religion or faith because of early negative personal experiences or even abuse, and this is likely to have an impact on how they feel and respond (see Gilbert, 2008).

A challenge for the leaders in organisations is to enable the workforce to identify their own prejudices and manage the potential impacts within their relationships with service users. People from BME backgrounds may detect a worker's discomfort and, given prior negative experiences, this may be perceived as racism particularly where someone feels that their ethnic identity and religion are inextricably linked.

Over-identification by staff, manifested in practice or collusion that is beyond the scope of a worker's role

Staff from BME backgrounds often contribute valuable cultural awareness or acceptance from the perspective of BME service users. A shared culture creates many opportunities but also a risk of over-identification. Having a shared identity in belonging to a BME group and also spirituality or religion may complicate relationships between staff and service users. This can become manifested in a worker showing a lack of inquisitiveness about the motivations for a service user's behaviours and attitudes. For example, a service user's reference to 'hearing the voice of God' may be familiar to a member of staff whose response may then put them at odds with the clinical team. Staff and managers will need to mitigate these risks through reflection, supervision and professional development.

Intolerance or prejudice within service user groups arising from religious or faith views

Many religions consider homosexuality to be wrong (see chapter 17). Some of the teaching of world religions is considered to be sexist, though many within the faith communities would argue that drawing such conclusions is erroneous and comes from a lack of understanding of history, context and meaning, and the influence of male dominated cultural traditions (eg. Ahmed, 1992). The provision of specialist services for people from BME backgrounds has a strong potential for bringing together people who adhere to a religion or faith, or those who have been brought up within a culture that is still significantly influenced by it. This introduces the potential for a group of service users to openly express homophobic or sexist views for example, with little challenge from others in the group. This would usually be an infringement of the policies of a service provider and the handling of such a situation may be challenging for staff. This may be because they too are religious and find the conflict intolerable if they are required to challenge service users (when they do not disagree or because by challenging they will be publically upholding something which is against their religion). The interaction between aspects of identity potentially creates a dilemma for white workers who may feel that a challenge to discriminatory views in this way could be perceived as an attack on cultural values.

Worker or service lack of knowledge to interpret behaviour

The mix of an unfamiliar culture with an unfamiliar faith or religion can pose a major difficulty for staff in determining whether behaviours they consider to be unusual are actually normal within a culture or religion. This may also be compounded by language barriers or even the different use of idioms or cultural expressions used when speaking English. Workers are however required to gain intelligence from the service user and other sources (Bhugra & Bhui, 2001).

Staff who work with people from BME backgrounds and who are uncertain about interpreting behaviours may rely on family members to do so and this raises a risk that family views, as opposed to an authentic view from a faith leader, are utilised. Additionally, there may be a language barrier if other family members are relied upon to provide an explanation. Sometimes parents or extended families may not be as fluent in English as the service user and turning to them for help may create problems in communication. This may confound an attempt to obtain further clarity about the legitimacy of identifying behaviours as normal within a faith or culture.

Religious or spiritual beliefs that are tolerant of suicide

Some cultures which are influenced by religion may be tolerant of suicide because of a belief in reincarnation (Bhugra & Bhui 2001). This may affect the interaction between services and families, potentially leaving the worker feeling as though they are carrying all the anxiety about a risk of suicide and that the family are not as engaged as they should be.

Gender and religion – patriarchy

Much has been written about gender equality in world religions. Many people argue that the teachings about gender roles and the style of dress, for example in Islam and Christianity, are overtly sexist. Others, such as Leila Ahmed argue that such interpretations are erroneous and come from a lack of understanding of cultural context or, alternatively, that traditions rather than scriptures have introduced gender biases (Ahmed, 1992). Whatever the explanation or interpretation, many workers will at face value experience unfamiliar faiths and cultures as sexist and in conflict with their personal, professional and organisational values. Again, learning and development will be critical in resolving these tensions.

Exercise 1 is designed to use personal experience to promote consideration about the extent to which culture and faith may be internalised into identity.

Reflection exercise: the internalisation of culture and religion

Bring to mind an occasion when you were in a situation that made you feel uncomfortable because the people you were with did things that were far from what you were accustomed to. Recall the strength of your feeling in that situation. Try to separate how you felt from what you thought and how you rationalised the situation. Think again about how you felt when you returned home (whether to your home country or your actual home).

Ask yourself the following:
▶ What was different that made me feel uncomfortable?
▶ Why did it make me feel uncomfortable?
▶ Why do these things matter to me?
   (Think deeper than 'that was how I was brought up')

Choose one particular thing that made you uncomfortable and ask about the source. (eg. what role historically did religion, culture, family tradition play?)

Choose someone from a different background, religion or ethnic group with whom you have a good relationship. Use what you've learnt to explore their experience of difference. Think about this in relation to people from BME backgrounds in mental health services and note down what you could do to help improve their experience.

Meeting spiritual and ethnic needs in mental health

The primary objectives of workers should be to support and enable all the people who use services to make good progress on their continuous journeys of recovery. This is true even for those workers who fulfil statutory duties under the Mental Health Act (1983) (amended in 2007), such as applying sections of the act so that people may be detained, (see Slay, 2010).

It is clear from the challenges listed in box 3 that a worker will need to balance a number of perspectives which sometimes compete. This is represented in figure 2.

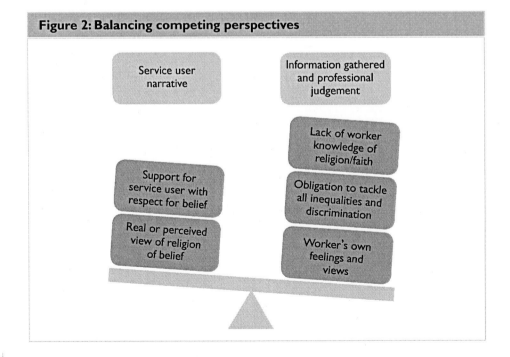

Figure 2: Balancing competing perspectives

Service user narrative

Information gathered and professional judgement

Lack of worker knowledge of religion/faith

Support for service user with respect for belief

Obligation to tackle all inequalities and discrimination

Real or perceived view of religion of belief

Worker's own feelings and views

The service user narrative and explanatory models will be central in enabling workers to gain an understanding of the mental health experience from that person's viewpoint. Narrative therapy was developed by Michael White and David Epston (1992). It is an approach designed to enable people to develop narratives about their lives and recall experiences that are not saturated with problems and negative descriptions. In narrative therapy the therapist listens to the person's stories about their life, culture, religion, relationships and other aspects of their lives to identify strengths and possibilities for strategies for coping and for further growth and recovery. The approach used in narrative therapy is utilised both in one-to-one work, group work and community work outside the formalised therapy context.

Explanatory models represent the concepts and frameworks utilised by people to describe the causes and course of their mental health problems and their recovery, irrespective of whether they view the problems as part of an illness. Chantler (2002) identified in her study of women from BME backgrounds in mental health services that many women had referred to faith and religion as part of their explanatory models. Allowing space for explanatory models requires that workers contain their desire to set people right. It potentially requires a suspension of belief in the orthodoxy of psychiatry and creating a space to appreciate the explanatory model of the other person by appreciating the personal experiences, context and culture that provide drivers for it. Listening to someone's explanatory models, no matter how unfamiliar, and apparently unusual, is not clinically unsound but potentially holds the key to working effectively with an individual (Bentall, 2009).

The knowledge and skill of a worker in utilising narrative approaches and explanatory models needs to be augmented by a set of attitudes, values and beliefs that stem from reflection and self-awareness. A worker will need to be conscious of their own attitudes and their epistemological standpoint and the influence these will have on their interpretation of what a service user does or says. Further, a worker must be equipped to ask questions about spirituality and belief systems, even if these are challenging. They must do so in a way that is respectful, genuinely inquisitive and driven from a desire to develop honest and balanced relationships.

Conclusion

Spirituality and religion have the potential to make a positive contribution to mental health but may also raise challenges for staff. Improvements are likely to come from approaches that give voice to the narrative of the service user rather than relying on assumptions. Staff need to be developed through supervision and other aids to learning so that their own concerns or lack of knowledge can be addressed.

References

Ahmed L (1992) *Women and Gender in Islam: Historical roots of a modern debate.* New Haven: Yale University Press.

Baker M (1981) *The New Racism.* London: Junction Books.

Beckford A, Gayle R, Owen D, Peach C & Weller P (The Mercia Group) (2006) *Review of the Evidence Base on Faith Communities – Report for the Office of the Deputy Prime Minister.* University of Warwick: OPDPM.

Bennett J, Kalathil J & Keating F (2007) *Race Equality Training in Mental Health Services in England: Does one size fit all?* London: Sainsbury Centre for Mental Health.

Bentall R (2009) *Doctoring the Mind: Why psychiatric treatments fail.* London: Allen Lane Publishing.

Bhugra D & Bhui K (2001) *Cross Cultural Psychiatry: A practical guide.* London: Arnold.

Bhui K (2002) *Racism and Mental Health: Prejudice and suffering.* London: Jessica Kingsley Publishers.

Care Quality Commission & National Mental Health Development Unit (2010) *Count Me in Census 2009. Results of the 2009 National Census Of Inpatients And Patients On Supervised Community Treatment in Mental Health And Learning Disability Services in England and Wales.* London: CQC. Available at: http://www.cqc.org.uk/_db/_documents/Count_me_in_2009_ (FINAL_tagged).pdf (accessed November 2010).

Chantler K (2002) The invisibility of black women in mental health services. *The Mental Health Review* **7** (1) 22–24.

Coyte M, Gilbert P & Nicholls V (2007) *Spirituality, Values and Mental Health: Jewels for the journey.* London: Jessica Kingsley Publishers.

Crenshaw K (1994) Mapping the margins: intersectionality, identity politics, and violence against women of color. In: M Fineman & R Mykitiuk (Eds) *The Public Nature of Private Violence.* New York: Routledge.

Department of Health (2003) *Inspiring Hope: Recognising the importance of spirituality in a whole person approach to mental health.* London: DH.

Douglas A, Jimenez S, Lin H & Frisman L (2008) Ethnic differences in the effects of spiritual well-being on long-term psychological and behavioral outcomes within a sample of homeless women. *Cultural Diversity and Ethnic Minority Psychology* **14** (4) 344–352.

Epston D & White M (1992) *Experience, Contradiction, Narrative and Imagination: Selected papers of David Epston and Michael White, 1989–1991*. Adelaide: Dulwich Centre Publications.

Fernando S (2002) *Mental Health, Race and Culture*. Hampshire: Palgrave.

Friedli L, Oliver C, Tidyman M & Ward G (2007) *Mental Health Improvement: Evidence-based messages to promote mental wellbeing*. Edinburgh: NHS Health Scotland.

Gilbert P (2008) *Guidelines on Spirituality for Staff in Acute Care Services*. Stafford: NIMHE/CSIP/Staffordshire University.

Hilton C, Ghaznavi F & Zuberi T (2002) Religious beliefs and practices in acute mental health patients. *Nursing Standard* **16** (38) 33–36.

Kilomba G (2008) *Plantation Memories: Episodes of everyday racism*. Munster: Unrast-Verlag.

Klienman A (1988) *Rethinking Psychiatry: From cultural category to personal experience*. New York: Free Press.

Marmot M (2010) *Fair Society, Healthy Lives*. London: The Marmot Review.

Mental Health Foundation (2008) *Spirituality and Mental Health*. London: MHF.

Nesbitt E (2007) *An Invisible Community? South Asian Christians in the UK* [online]. Available at: http://www.shapworkingparty.org.uk/journals/articles_0708/nesbitt.pdf (accessed November 2010).

National Institute for Mental Health England (2005) *Making it Possible: Improving mental health and well-being in England*. London: NIMHE.

Pierce C, Carew J, Pierce-Gonzalez D & Wills D (1978) An experiment in racism: TV commercials. In: C Pierce (Ed) *Television and Education* (pp62–88). Beverly Hills, CA: Sage.

Read J, Mosher LR & Bentall RP (2004) *Models of Madness: Psychological, social and biological approaches to schizophrenia*. Sussex: Brunner-Routledge.

Senior P & Bhopal R (1994) Ethnicity as a variable in epidemiological research. *British Medical Journal* **309** 327–330.

Sewell H (2004) Black and minority ethnic groups. In: D Duffy & T Ryan (Eds) *New Approaches to Preventing Suicide: A manual for practitioners*. London: Jessica Kingsley Publishers.

Sewell H (2009) *Working with Ethnicity Race and Culture in Mental Health: A handbook for practitioners*. London: Jessica Kingsley Publishers.

Slay G (2010) The vital equilibrium – social work and the law. In: P Gilbert (2010) *Social Work and Mental Health: The value of everything*. Lyme Regis: Russell House Publishing.

The Sun (2009) Hotel bosses' 'bomb rant', *The Sun*, 9 December 2009. Available at: http://www.thesun.co.uk/sol/homepage/news/2763674/Hotel-bosses-bomb-rant-at-Muslim-guest.html (accessed November 2010).

Chapter 8

Faith perspectives on mental health, and work with faith communities

Arthur Hawes and Qaisra Khan

Introduction

'Lord, let me know mine end, and the number of my days: that I may be certified how long I may live.' (Psalm 39)

Religion in general (rather than faith communities in particular) is under the spotlight at the moment. Yet whenever the Archbishop of Canterbury, the Chief Rabbi or the President of the Muslim Council speak, their words are reported, analysed and often criticised in the media. This is hardly surprising because, by definition, faith communities are 'counter cultural'. They apply values like human dignity to political statements and actions. They champion the marginalised (so often people with mental health needs) and pioneer new areas of human and social concerns. They look to the future on the basis of their shared ethics and value systems. In summary, they have an inherent knack of challenging and scrutinising the political system, which is burgeoning with 'sofa messiahs' (Redfern, 2009) and empty promises about raising standards of living.

All the religious faiths – there are nine usually recognised by public bodies in the UK, which are Baha'i, Buddist, Christian, Hindu, Jain, Jewish, Muslim, Sikh and Zoroastrian – promote spirituality and the spiritual life. At the same time each is encompassed by spirituality which has existed in human experience for 70,000 years – far longer than any world religion or faith community. Cave drawings indicate the importance of spirituality for early humans and witness to the primordial urge to search out the meaning of what it is to be human and to reflect upon human origins and destiny (Armstrong, 2009).

One working definition of spirituality is: *'Spirituality can be understood as that aspect of human existence which relates to structures of significance to give meaning to a person's life and helps them deal with the vicissitudes of existence. It is associated with the human quest for meaning, purpose, self-transcending knowledge, meaningful relationships, love and a sense of the Holy.'* (Swinton & Pattison, 2001)

Its value and place in mental health services, assessment, community care, palliative care, and chaplaincy is well argued and recorded in other chapters in this book. A further requirement is a summary of the contribution by the faith communities to people with mental health problems and the role of spirituality in diagnostics and recovery. There are eight main areas where faith communities contribute:

▶ building communities of faith

▶ social networks

▶ pastoral support

▶ healing

▶ the paranormal

▶ ecclesiogenics

▶ vocation

▶ the sacred. (Hawes, 2010b)

Faith communities

Each faith community or religion has its own theological framework. All welcome into their community the enquirer, the visitor, the foreigner (immigrant), the alienated, and the marginalised, and each person is afforded a dignity befitting their human nature. Underpinning such a welcome is the thought that *'you never know when you might be entertaining angels'* (The Bible).

Local faith communities are part of a worldwide network, a universal family with outlets on every continent and in every country. The Anglican Communion, for example, which is one small part of the Christian Church, numbers across the world 60 million people. A faith community is committed not only to welcoming people and respecting each person's individuality, but also to accepting them holistically. In theological terms to be human comprises body, mind, spirit, personality, origins, social milieu, and uniqueness. All of this and more contributes to being human. Being human involves not only living a life but undertaking a journey, searching the universe for meaning, recognising the possibility of the supernatural and aspiring to values which enhance and enrich human living.

In a faith community a person is offered privacy and, if appropriate, anonymity. The provision of anonymity is one role for the modern cathedral. Each person is named and sometimes chooses a new name (cf. religious orders) like a 'christian' name. Naming is reinforced theologically because it is part of the belief system that every person is known by name to God and cherished and precious in His sight. A theological framework offers an understanding of God, an appreciation of what it is to be human, insights into living a holy life in community, and a context for understanding need, sickness or any other adversity. For example, there is an understandable and growing concern for those who suffer from the organic mental illness dementia and the demands and pressures experienced by carers. This following extract from a recent paper seeks to reassure not only the sufferer but also the carer from a theological perspective.

Finally the context of the Christian faith is eternal. Here is real transformation as we are changed 'from glory to glory' – as it says in one Christian hymn. All that assailed us in our human experience is left behind. Here there is no place for mental illness, for dementia, for learning disabilities, and a whole range of other conditions. Here there is wholeness, mystery, glory, wrapped for eternity in the divine embrace of the God of love.' (Hawes, 2010a)

Social networks

It was Professor Anthony Sheehan (CEO Leicestershire NHS Mental Health Trust) who originally stated succinctly that anyone with a mental health problem needs: a roof, a job and a date at the weekend.

This now resonates with *New Horizons* (Department of Health, 2009) which states unequivocally that mental health services need to incorporate resources from housing, education and employment agencies.

A date at the weekend stresses the importance of social networks which are all too fragile in a society where both family life and community coherence are fragmenting (Lincolnshire Partnership NHS Foundation Trust, 2010). Nevertheless they are an essential factor in the recovery process, otherwise the loneliness, alienation and stigmatisation so often experienced by a person with a mental health problem, especially if it is severe and enduring, insidiously pervades and disrupts attempts to provide a recovery programme.

Community care, which replaced institutional care, has, after less than 20 years, been replaced by home care. It can be argued that this is laudable, appropriate and inexpensive. At the same time, it can also be isolating and de-socialising if not properly thought through. Where and how do the housebound meet other people? What opportunity do they have, to do what other people do naturally – chat, discuss and pass the time of day? How does being confined in a house fit into the choice agenda?

People with mental health problems and learning disabilities are confronted with a double measure of isolation because their very condition can have a separating effect. Some I have spoken with, caught in this trap, describe their house as a prison where they fear for their own safety, feel abandoned and lonely. The greatest care must be exercised to ensure that we do not develop a society in which everyone is an island. Faith communities are well placed to offer social networks across a rich variety of different socio-ethnic groups. Moreover, all the faith communities have their own buildings. In England alone, the Church of England has more than 16,000 buildings. These are rapidly being adapted for increased community use. In terms of mental health, they can provide 'drop-in' centres (Bishop of Leicester, 2010), café facilities, meeting rooms for a variety of group work and therapeutic/pastoral support, such as St Marylebone Healing and Counselling Centre.

Pastoral support

In addition to social networks, there is the ever present need of support especially in the early stages of recovery. A faith community not only provides the support of the local church/chapel/mosque/synagogue/temple/gurdwara but also a commitment to holism. This is translated practically in the life of the faith community by the provision of interpreters, advocates and pastoral teams. A pastoral team will have trained people available to visit in hospital, nursing homes and a person's own home. For example, if a person with a mental health problem has been detained on a section and is likely to spend some time in hospital, there may well be an anxiety about the security of the home. The pastoral team can ensure that the home is secure, pets cared for and the property aired and ventilated.

It is always an interesting question in any analysis of a faith community to ask what wider responsibilities members have in the local community. Frequently, there is ample evidence to indicate that the steward, administrator, secretary, churchwarden, ordinary member are also school governors, prison visitors, parish councillors, members of the WRVS, Samaritans; the list is both extensive and endless. What is inescapable is that the voluntary responsibilities in the wider community are initiated, stimulated and nourished by the person's commitment and allegiance to their faith.

This ministry of service in the locality is a measure and expression of the mission of the faith community. Ministry and mission go hand in hand, which is far better than the aggressive proselytising found in some extreme fundamental sects. Fundamentalism is, of course, not confined to groups within religions but is to be found in all walks of life. There is most definitely political fundamentalism and, where it exists, it stifles creativity and growth. This is because fundamentalists are unyielding in their doctrine, controlling in their actions and aggressive in their contacts with others.

Healing

As well as care and support, there is also spiritual healing. Germane to most faith communities is a ministry of healing which takes different forms depending on the particular faith. Prayer and meditation are cross cutting themes in all the major faiths. Meditation is a spiritual exercise which evokes in the believer an inner peace and tranquillity. Research indicates that 83% of patients view their spiritual beliefs as having a positive effect on their illness (Lindgren & Coursey, 1995). To be remembered in the prayers of a community not only offers the sufferer the efficacy of prayer but also reinforces a feeling of safety and security. Faith communities help people belong and safety and belonging are prerequisites in any recovery process for a person with a mental health problem.

Paradoxically the Victorian asylums, which are now mostly closed or used for alternative purposes, at their best, provided some measure of space and time. After 'feeling safe', these are the next two most important resources which contribute to mental healthiness. Sadly, both were sometimes absent in the first generation of modern psychiatric units, though a number of trusts have rebuilt the capacity for 'safe space' and nurturing in their progressive developments (see Harlow, 2010). If sufferers really are to confront their demons, and what it means for them to be a person, then they need time for reflection, conversation and someone to listen – listen to the music behind the words. Faith communities and their buildings are in a position to provide both space and time. Nearly all faith communities offer the faithful rituals and 'rites of passage' and help to provide a framework to cope with the changes these life events create. Some rituals are very simple, like blessings.

Case study

Let me introduce you to 'Jeremy'. The duty chaplain for the psychiatric hospital was called late one evening to the medical ward where patients were transferred when they had physical illnesses.

Earlier that evening a young man in his mid-20s had been admitted after being discovered in a very confused state. He had been sleeping in the open in the hedgerows, was badly scratched and in a poor physical condition. He was dehydrated and still displayed symptoms of confusion and deep anxiety. He refused to allow anything near him, would not eat or drink on the basis, he said, everything outside him was evil and that, if there was any contact with him by an external agent, it would destroy him. The ward manager decided to call the chaplain.

The chaplain was fully briefed by the ward manager and invited to meet the patient. The chaplain hoped that it would be possible to establish in Jeremy's (this was not the patient's original name) mind that goodness as well as evil existed in the world around him. He began by asking Jeremy whether there was anything he could think of that was good and he said that he thought human kindness was always good. The chaplain developed the conversation until he was able to ask Jeremy whether he would think that he (the chaplain) was also a sign of goodness and Jeremy thought that he was. It was becoming increasingly important to persuade Jeremy to drink some water because of his very poor physical condition. The chaplain asked Jeremy whether water was good and was told that it was not. At this point, he left to find a glass of water which he brought and placed in front of Jeremy. The chaplain then explained that he intended to bless the water by saying a prayer and making the sign of the Christian cross over the water. This, he assured Jeremy, would ensure that the water was safe to drink even if Jeremy believed that it was not good for him. The water was blessed and Jeremy was invited to drink it. He hesitated for a long time but did eventually sip the water and ultimately drank all of it. The chaplain then explained that it was not necessary for him to bless all the drink and food that Jeremy might care to have in the future because of the trust that Jeremy had already shown in the chaplain.

The next morning the chaplain returned to the ward only to be greeted by the ward manager whose face was wreathed in smiles. Jeremy had not only eaten a cheese sandwich but also agreed to have a bath! From that moment onwards he made steady progress and a full recovery.

In addition to rites and rituals, there are sacraments. The definition of a sacrament is *an outward and visible sign of an inward and spiritual grace*. In many faith communities a common sacrament is a sacred meal ie. the Jewish Passover, the Christian Holy Communion or the tea ceremony in some forms of Zen. Not only does the meal provide spiritual food for the journey and a focal point around which the community gathers, but also an opportunity for people (without distinction) to be incorporated into the life, history and culture of the faith.

The paranormal

One account of mental illness in some faith communities is of demon possession or the existence of jinns (jinns are not in Muslim theology a demon, but an alternative creation to humankind. Culturally though, mental illness may be thought of as possession). One remedy sometimes suggested is exorcism. A full exorcism with manual action and an intention to 'remove' an evil spirit by direct action is a procedure which fits the 'medical model'. The medical model of 'removal', when applied to exorcism, presupposes an independent evil force/spirit located, albeit invisibly, within a person's body. Locating evil in this way raises a problem for many faith communities, namely the question of dualism. For evil to exist independently means that it was created. Good and evil are then created from two separate sources – a god of good and a god of evil.

It is crucially important to distinguish spiritual torment from mental illness and never to carry out an exorcism on a person with a diagnosed mental illness. In the Christian tradition most dioceses in the UK have a trained team of practitioners, often including a psychiatrist. The team provides a 'deliverance' ministry (deliverance from evil). Not only do they minister to people in great distress (fighting their own demons) but also to people caught up in the paranormal. A good example is when a person has died in tragic circumstances and paranormal phenomena become apparent.

In such cases the team, together with the local vicar, offer prayers and sacraments for the person. Often the celebration of Holy Communion enables a person who has died to rest in peace. Frequently houses which are subject to paranormal activity are blessed and holy water sprinkled in each of the rooms. The Christian church's ministry of prayer and sacrament is usually sufficient and very few diocesan teams resort to prayers of exorcism and hardly ever to a full exorcism involving manual acts. (See Hawes & Jones, 2007)

Ecclesiogenics

Ecclesiogenics means illnesses which are caused or exacerbated by faith communities. Four examples follow.

1. Rather than valuing and encouraging the believer, there are some faith communities which increase feelings of guilt. At its best, participation in the life of the faithful has given new hope to those who have failed and built up the self-esteem of those who have lacked or lost it. However, it is also true that it has often functioned to reinforce guilt and shame as a result of harsh or insensitive theologies and failure to practise forgiveness and acceptance. The faith communities have sometimes been guilty of exploiting human vulnerability in order to create a sense of spiritual need which they could meet. This pattern of regressive dependence is contrary both to the human need for autonomy (self-direction) and the aspiration to mature faith (Gilbert & Kalaga, 2007).

2. Faith communities have the potential either to enhance or to diminish well-being. Through their traditions of worship and prayer they offer access to God as the supreme source of love, healing, guidance and inspiration. Through communal life they provide friendship, support, and a sense of

purpose to people experiencing stress and adversity. Through their support for families they seek to reinforce the elements of care and stability in people's lives. Through social and international connections they sustain a broader sense of human solidarity and obligation. They commend as pleasing to God many patterns of behaviour (such as abstention from abuse of alcohol and drugs) which strengthen mental health.

When this happy milieu is not present, religious sects can easily become so introspective and defensive people feel rejected and sometimes are literally excluded from membership. For a person with a mental health problem this only reinforces feelings of isolation, abandonment and rejection. It heaps stigma upon stigma.

3. All faiths have moral codes and standards of behaviour. Where they are rigidly and oppressively applied they demean (rather than enhance) human dignity and well-being. The spirit of the law is the dynamic which encourages, recreates and affirms the person, not the imposition of a cold, unqualified set of laws and regulations.

4. As well as making people feel guilty, there are occasions when anxiety is fuelled rather than dispelled. On the other hand, all these sources of 'nurturing heart and spirit' can fail, or worse, can operate perversely to threaten mental well-being. Faith communities have often displayed ignorance, indifference and hostility towards people with mental health problems. They have sometimes blamed those problems on personal sin, lack of faith or demonic possession. When they have tried to help, they have often been incompetent or destructive in resisting co-operation with mental health professionals. They need to examine their pastoral and spiritual care in the light both of the vision of restoration and healing and current good practice in mental health care.

Vocation

The following exemplifies the idea of vocation that so often accompanied a desire to serve other people, which happened to me.

'I well remember as a student spending time in a hospital for people with learning disabilities, what in those days was called a hospital for the mentally handicapped (very few such hospitals exist today). I was asked to

care for a boy of eight who had profound and multiple disabilities. In fact, the only senses he had were touch and smell. He could not see, hear, speak or walk. Tickle his feet and you were rewarded with an infectious smile which spoke of God. He died before he was nine. I struggled to make any sense of his life which had been so limited, so restricted, until his nurse explained that she needed him in order to be able to care and exercise her ministry. Of course, I then realised that the ministry was his to the nurse and to all the other carers.' (Hawes, 2010b)

Not only does this story illustrate what the sufferer can give to the carer, but it also highlights the way some feel called to the work they do. A core element in faith communities is the concept of a 'calling'. People feel called to a particular role, profession or ministry. Some feel called to the religious life, some to working with people on the fringes of society and others to devote their lives and skills to care for people with profound and enduring disabilities.

Today's postmodern world mitigates against the idea of vocation with its emphasis on regulations like the European Working Time Directive.

'The signs of this new age are beginning to emerge and naturally grow out of postmodernism. For example, on-duty replaces on-call; hours worked are strictly regulated with enhancement for unsocial hours and restricting health professionals' working hours jeopardises provision of choice – a very post-modern phenomenon dependent upon individuals having choice.

'The question is how, in future, are people who want to serve their neighbour, to be committed to caring for others and seek to value the individual, to identify and express their vocation? These are people who want to be 'on-call', comfort the dying and befriend the lonely. For the person who genuinely wants to care for their neighbour, it is becoming increasingly difficult to offer the milk of human kindness. Welcome to the post-vocational age where the calling is taken out of caring.' (Hawes, 2004)

The sacred

The sacred provides the last contribution by faith communities to the care of the mentally ill. Walk into any orthodox church (Russian or Greek) and the contrast between the plain exterior and rich interior is amazing. The interior is rich and colourful because it is part of the belief system that, by

crossing the threshold into the church, the person steps into heaven. Here the worshipper, the visitor, the enquirer can experience wonder, mystery, otherness, ultimacy, the numinous, transcendence, the very presence of god. Here is a place to be uplifted, to be taken beyond the physical and immediate to the spiritual and eternal. Here is a place to reflect, meditate, dream, envision, and pray. Here is the possibility of 'the awakening in each person of the other side of themselves'.

Working with faith communities from mental health services

Only connect! That was the whole of her sermon.
Only connect the prose and the passion, and both will be exalted,
And human love will be seen at its height.
Live in fragments no longer.
Only connect...

(EM Forster, (1910/1984) *Howards End*)

'Only connect' is a constant refrain in EM Forster's novels but in *A Passage to India* (Forster, 1924/1985) we see the limits of goodwill and intention in bringing about that connection that seems so vital to our own and societies' well-being. In the novel the two communities, in colonial India, stare at each other across a cultural divide, a history of imbalanced power relations and mutual suspicion. This could, at one level, describe the relationship between faith communities and mental health services.

A chaplaincy spiritual care service has been a part of the NHS since its inception but in a largely secular institution spiritual care has not developed significantly and 'spirituality' is often overlooked by the staff working in mental health services.

According to the Mental Health Foundation this '*may be because in the past, services have been heavily influenced by the "bio-medical model"*'. This sees mental health problems as caused by biological factors, leaving little room for spirituality and other important areas of people's lives. In addition, some staff interpret what service users say about their spirituality as a symptom of their mental illness. People with psychosis may hold unusual beliefs (delusions) describe hearing voices or have other experiences that seem out of touch with reality, but people who are mentally well may also describe this kind of experience. Some people have spiritual experiences that are like psychotic symptoms, for instance believing in angels or identifying themselves as a white witch or hearing the voice of God. When someone who has always held such beliefs becomes unwell, they continue to hold the beliefs and these experiences are not necessarily symptoms of their mental illness.

Taking someone's spiritual needs into account can support their path to recovery or help them live with their mental health problems in the best way for them as individuals. Encouraging service users to explore what is important to them spiritually can be a valuable self-help strategy. Encouraging people to talk about their experiences gives them an opportunity to be heard and understood, which demonstrates respect and may reduce any distress they feel (Mental Health Foundation, 2007).

Mental health services also need to reach out to faith communities because these groups are probably already supporting people who are living with mental distress and people in crisis approach faith leaders.

The faith community, however, may be distrustful of mental health services. First, because of the general lack of understanding within society of mental health and an impression that professionals do not respect or take seriously their contribution in the community. This may be of particular significance when the faith community is also a 'minority' community.

It is vital that these two communities do cross the divide but as the story in *A Passage to India* demonstrates, goodwill and intention are not enough on their own. Mutual respect, commitment, time, resources and patience are essential.

Oxleas NHS Foundation Trust is in southeast London and provides mental health and learning disability services in Bexley, Bromley and Greenwich boroughs and specialist services to Lewisham. The Spiritual and Cultural Care Service is a multi-faith service with an inter-faith approach. The trust and the service work with communities in a number of ways.

The Spiritual and Cultural Care Service is the focal point for links with faith communities because most of the people who work within it are a part

of a faith community. The team has made some very positive connections over the years. These have included chaplains visiting sites and making it easier for people to attend places of worship. This was best illustrated when one small group home requested some spiritual care. A relationship was brokered with the local vicar who visited the home and residents became regular members of the congregation. Residents also became valuable members of a community that could not fail to meet each other while doing daily chores such as going to the small local supermarket. One of the other chaplains had gone to the same school, was a member of the same congregation or was a neighbour to some of the people who had been admitted to the hospital.

There are similar stories to these across the NHS and spiritual care services. To enhance these links, however, we became a member of the South London Interfaith Group and Greenwich Multi-faith Forum. Membership of these two groups provided opportunities for meeting faith groups on a regular basis and participation in interfaith walks. Interfaith or multi-faith walks involve a group of people gathering together and visiting different places of worship. They are an excellent way of learning about another faith community and enabling people to visit a place of worship discreetly: that is in a large group it is possible to go unnoticed. It is hoped that the South London Interfaith Group can lead the Remembrance service at the Memorial Hospital. The Memorial Hospital was built as a memorial for the dead in the world wars, so the service and the place of the hospital in the community is significant. The contact with faith leaders also provides a valuable source of people who adhere to a particular faith and are often willing to share their knowledge and experience.

Developing Valued Lifestyles Partnership (Develop)

In Bromley, a network was developed to bring together faith communities and mental health practitioners. FaithNet came out of work undertaken by Developing Valued Lifestyles Partnership (http://www.developbromley.com/)

Develop began as a partnership of statutory and voluntary sector mental health organisations working across the Borough of Bromley with the aim of improving the opportunities and life chances of people. The partnership aimed to tackle issues around discrimination, stigma and social exclusion to help build a better Bromley for everyone.

Develop partners work in a person-centred way and look at people's life choices in a whole life or holistic approach. The opportunities and choices that we all face have been defined in eight key life domains.

▶ Home and neighbourhood

▶ Education

▶ Work

▶ Sports and leisure

▶ Arts and culture

▶ Volunteering

▶ Faith and spirituality

▶ Finance and advice

By working and respecting everyone's right to choose the direction and involvement they may wish to have within each life domain area, health professionals are able to tailor the level of support and service they provide.

Over the years the partnership has begun to reach out into the wider community to interact, form relationships and build bridges to mainstream organisations providing services within each of the life domains. This approach means that strong bonds and relationships are built at grassroots level, building social capital and ensuring that everyone works together to reduce social exclusion and offer local people welcoming and supportive access to ordinary opportunity. This has been achieved by sharing expertise, resources and network contacts.

FaithNet helps support the aims of both the spiritual and cultural care service and organisations interested in mental health. It would have been impossible, however, without the groundwork undertaken by the project manager who was employed to visit faith groups and talk about Develop and the realities of social inclusion.

The first FaithNet meeting took place in February 2007. The journey has not always been smooth but some key relationships were built and joint work undertaken.

Initially, time was taken up agreeing the terms of reference. This helped build relationships, but the debates were interesting because they highlighted some of the key concerns that people have in regard to mental health and religion. The main example being the use of the word 'supernatural' and inclusion of the following sentence in the ground rules: *'respect the experiences that people describe, be they spiritual or supernatural'*. I (Qaisra) was chairing the meeting at the time and was a bit taken aback by the suggestion that we include the word 'supernatural', that I had to consult a dictionary. Others also consulted their dictionaries and comment included: *'In my dictionary this is given three meanings, of which the third is "involving, or ascribed to occult beings"'*. This I find a problem, since I believe that the occult can sometimes be the cause of mental illness. Do we want witches or people who run 'psychic fairs' etc. represented in our group? I think we have to tread very carefully, since I suppose that even Satanists could claim to be a 'faith group'! But although 'supernatural' can mean divine events, to many people it does mean the occult. Another interesting debate was about recognising groups and organisations as 'mentally ill' and stopping them from blaming individuals for their own failings.

The terms of reference were agreed and the chair of FaithNet eventually passed to a local faith group which gave the group added dynamism. The agendas have included; information exchange and getting know the various groups that work in the borough, bereavement, the impact of exercise on mental well-being, impact of alcohol abuse, personality discharge and the discharge pack.

Spirituality: a spark to recovery

In September 2009 FaithNet held a successful workshop which brought together mental healthcare practitioners and people from various groups to think together about how:

▶ enabling people in mental distress to explore their own spirituality can be an aid to their recovery

▶ mental healthcare practitioners can best work within their own belief system to support the spiritual life of the people they work with

▶ people from faith groups can gain the understanding of mental health needs and services to enhance their support of people in mental distress.

The three topics discussed on the day were:

▶ vulnerability, safety and spirituality

▶ spiritual literacy and being open

▶ the role of spirituality in finding meaning and moving forward.

The workshop came about following a discussion where mental health practitioners discussed the difficulties they had with raising and discussing spirituality. It provided an invaluable opportunity to discuss the above issues and for the participants to understand each other.

People need to be able to search for meaning which can be a spark to recovery; it is important, however, when working with each other – particularly where there are professional boundaries or different communities – that we do this through a framework where we respect and try to understand the other.

Both of us have unashamedly written about faith communities and the world of mental health. This is because we believe that faith communities have a vital and important part to play in the delivery of spirituality. For some this may still appear to be contentious, especially in a society that has become increasingly materialistic. We hope that we have not only continued the debate but also offered new insights for others to reflect upon and use in their own local situations.

References

Armstrong K (2009) *The Case for God: What religion really means.* London: The Bodley Head.

Bishop of Leicester (2010) *Speech in the House of Lords.* Hansard, 23 February ref GC234.

Developing Valued Lifestyles Partnership (Develop). Available at: http://www.developbromley. com/.

Department of Health (2009) *New Horizons: A shared vision for mental health.* London: DH.

Forster EM (1910/1984) *Howards End*. London: Penguin Classics.

Forster EM (1924/1985) *A Passage to India*. London: Penguin Classics.

Gilbert P & Kalaga H (2007) *Nurturing Heart and Spirit: Papers for the multi-faith symposium held at Staffordshire University, 1st November, 2006*. Stafford Staffordshire University.

Harlow R (2010) Developing a spirituality strategy – why, how and so what? *Mental Health, Religion and Culture* **13** (6) 615–624.

Hawes A (2004) An old fashioned idea. *MedEconomics*. (contact author for access).

Hawes A (2010a) *Dementia and a Christian Perspective*. London: Church of England Mission and Public Affairs Council.

Hawes A (2010b) *Spirituality, Faith Communities and Mental Health*. Conference paper, Bolton. (contact author for access)

Hawes A & Jones C (2007) The christian perspective. In: P Gilbert & H Kalaga (2007) *Nurturing Heart and Spirit*. Papers for the multi-faith symposium, 1 November, Stafford: Staffordshire University.

The Holy Bible *The Epistle to the Hebrews*. Chapter 13, verse 2.

Lindgren KN & Coursey. RD (1995) Spirituality and mental illness: a two part study. *Psychosocial Rehabilitation Journal* **18** (3) 93–111.

Lincolnshire Partnership NHS Foundation Trust (2010) New Horizons – government initiative in the provision of mental health services – 2009. *In-Mind* **18** (3).

Mental Health Foundation (2007) *Making Space for Spirituality: How to support service users*. London: MHF.

NIMHE/MHF (Gilbert P & Nicholls V) (2003) *Inspiring Hope: Recognising the importance of spirituality in a whole person approach to mental health*. Leeds: NIMHE.

Redfern A (2009) *Public Space and Private Faith: A challenge to the churches*. Delhi: Indian Society for Promoting Christian Knowledge.

Swinton J & Pattison S (2001) Come all ye faithful. *Health Service Journal* **111** 24–25.

Chapter 9

Psychological approaches to spirituality

Sarajane Aris

'Western theories of counselling and psychotherapy have largely ignored the importance of the spirit, the soul, and the transcendent and altered states of consciousness.' (Cortright, 1997)

Introduction

The quote above very clearly reflects the state of psychological therapies before the 1980s. However, over the last 10 years in particular there has been a rapid development within the therapeutic and psychological field in looking for more holistic psychological approaches to both understanding and working with a person who is experiencing distress. Since the recent National NHS policy focus on health, happiness and well-being (see Layard, 2005; Department of Health, 2010), and the influence of the 9/11 tragedy, there has been a need for a broader and more holistic way of working psychologically and therapeutically with individuals, families, groups and society. The recent emphasis on developing, acknowledging and including a spiritual perspective in psychological approaches within mental health services, coupled with recent research which shows the positive impact of a range of meditative techniques on a person's well-being, has meant that psychological approaches can no longer ignore a spiritual dimension to therapeutic interventions.

Historical context

Prior to the 1980s, psychological approaches to spirituality had different terms within the field of psychology. An example is transpersonal psychology – a term coined in 1968 by a group of psychologists emerging from the humanistic field, such as Maslow, Sutich, James and Assagioli. Assagioli, a psychiatrist and psychoanalyst, developed the 'psychosynthesis' approach prior to transpersonal psychology. The approach included 'higher unconscious' in its model, from which altruistic and creative impulses arise relating to a holistic development, both of the person and humanity at large.

Transpersonal psychology included both this and eastern traditions and mystical experiences, taking into account the 'whole' person. Jung, himself, in the early 20th century, was working with what was termed at the time 'numinous experiences'. Transpersonal psychology first appeared in 1901 with William James following the Clifford Lectures on 'The varieties of religious experience'. It became a theoretical framework, viewing psychological interventions within a context of spiritual unfolding. The American Association of Transpersonal Psychology was set up in 1972, which had at its heart a wish to understand and research 'our impulse towards ultimate states' and an acknowledgement that realisation and understanding are dependant on direct practice related to a path of spiritual training and tradition. The UK followed America with the establishment of both the 'transpersonal section' and the 'consciousness section' within the British Psychological Society in 1997. Following the first British Transpersonal Conference in 2007, the Transpersonal Network for Clinical and Counselling psychologists was founded as a forum for therapists to meet and explore clinical issues, interventions, perspectives and developments associated with spirituality.

The work of Kabat Zinn and others in the 1980s and 1990s had a major impact on developing mindfulness within the psychological and therapeutic field. This will be discussed in more detail in the next section. Major research studies are now demonstrating the positive impact of mindfulness on a person's health and psychological well-being (eg. Teasdale, 2003). There is also a more generalised public interest in the area of meditation as its benefits are realised, particularly in our rather frenetic western society.

Current context

More recently, Gilbert (2010) demonstrates the major impact both compassionate mind training and meditation practices such as mindfulness have on a person's well-being. This is evidenced by major positive changes in a person's brain chemistry as they develop either a compassionate approach to themselves and others, and/or develop meditation and mindfulness practices. See chapter 19 for further information on mindfulness.

The cultural context of our world has developed; we have become more inter-connected over the last 10 years and psychological approaches and interventions are consequently reflecting this by becoming more culturally sensitive. They are encompassing a broader understanding of both spiritual and religious diversity, which is reflected in the developments of some of the current psychological approaches and interventions. Some of the major psychological approaches which incorporate a spiritual orientation or perspective and utilize tools associated with spiritual practices are described below in the next section.

Key psychological approaches encompassing or incorporating a spiritual perspective

'It is certainly tempting to identify therapy that incorporates a spiritual dimension through level of technique, for this is the most visible expression of therapy... But all techniques could be thrown away and the spiritual approach would still remain, ready to innovate with new techniques. For all techniques can be spiritual, given a spiritual framework. The larger perspective of therapies that incorporate a spiritual dimension or 'note', by not being limited to a specific approach, can be adapted to fit a number of technical variations. A spiritual dimension to therapy lies not in what the therapist says or does, but in the silent frame that operates behind the therapist's action, informing and giving meaning to the specific interventions. It is thus the wider container which can hold other therapeutic orientations within it.' (Adapted from Cortright, 1997)

This quote captures a crucial understanding of the importance of a spiritual framework or 'wider container' that underlies any therapeutic intervention. However, key psychological approaches have explicitly incorporated some of the 'skillful means' of many eastern spiritual traditions in both their theory and therapeutic interventions. Some of these approaches are shown in figure 1, as follows:

▶ dialectic behaviour therapy (DBT)

▶ cognitive analytical therapy (CAT)

▶ mindfulness

▶ acceptance and commitment therapy (ACT)

▶ transpersonal psychotherapies

▶ contextual modular therapy (CMT)

▶ emotional freedom therapy (EFT)

▶ spirituality in psychosis/spiritual emergency

▶ the recovery model and orientation

▶ positive psychology.

Case study

Robert experienced frequent bouts of depression and self-harm. He had lost his job. His children had left home and recently his wife had left him feeling unable to cope with his bouts of depression. He felt stuck, alienated from himself and the world, and with few friends he felt he could confide in. He had difficulty making sense of his life and felt suicidal. What could help him?

His therapist worked with him using a range of the above approaches such as mindfulness, meditative techniques and transpersonal psychotherapy, consciously utilising a spiritual frame or perspective. This helped him to explore the meaning of his experiences in his life and to evoke a sense of his higher potential. He was then able to connect with a deeper, wiser part of himself that he could trust. It moved him beyond his everyday experience of himself and helped him to see a wider perspective. He felt part of something greater than himself and felt uplifted. This in turn made him feel less alienated. He began to trust others more and started seeking friendships. The mindfulness and acceptance skills he began to learn also helped him to stay present in the moment rather than catastrophise about possible future problems. It also helped him to manage and transform his feelings of self-harm.

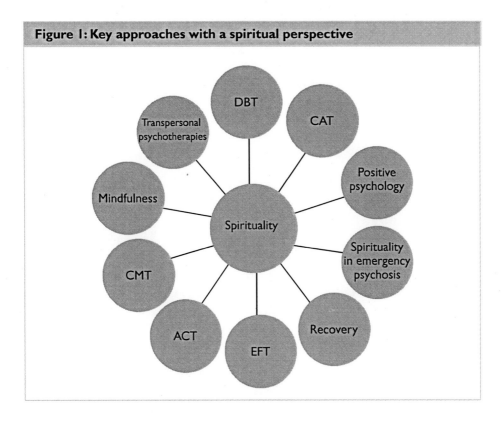

Figure 1: Key approaches with a spiritual perspective

The diagram shows the key psychological approaches or interventions that include a broadly spiritual perspective within their modality.

Approaches with spiritual orientations

Over the last 10–15 years a variety of psychological approaches have developed or incorporated a more spiritual orientation within their interventions and are utilising techniques associated with spiritual practices, such as mindfulness, meditation and present moment awareness. The case study on page 176 illustrates this briefly. This section will briefly give an overview of some of these key major interventions and approaches that incorporate a spiritual perspective. These include: dialectic behaviour therapy, cognitive analytic therapy, mindfulness, positive psychology, acceptance and commitment therapy, emotional freedom technique, recovery, spiritual emergency and transpersonal psychotherapy. Even cognitive therapy is now including some of the techniques, such as imaging, that are associated with a more spiritually oriented perspective. All of these are important developments and there will be brief overviews for some of the key psychological interventions and therapeutic approaches noted here. Compassionate mind training is covered in detail in chapter 19 so will not be covered in this chapter.

Dialectic behaviour therapy (DBT)

DBT was developed by Marcia Linehan in the 1990s initially to treat people with borderline personality disorder (BPD). DBT combines standard cognitive behaviour therapy for emotional regulation and reality testing, with concepts of mindful awareness, distress tolerance and acceptance, which were largely developed for Buddhist meditation practice.

DBT is the first therapy that has been found to be effective in the treatment of people with BPD. It includes four modules of skills training: mindfulness, distress tolerance, emotional regulation and interpersonal effectiveness. Mindfulness is one of the core concepts behind all elements of DBT. Mindfulness is the capacity to pay attention, non-judgementally, to the present moment. It is all about living in the moment, experiencing one's emotions and senses fully, yet with perspective. It is considered a foundation for the other skills taught in DBT because it helps individuals accept and tolerate the powerful emotions they may feel when challenging their habits or exposing themselves to upsetting situations. The concept of mindfulness and the meditative exercises used to teach it are derived from traditional Buddhist practice, though the version taught in DBT does not involve any religious or metaphysical concepts.

In brief, the skill of distress tolerance emphasises how to learn to bear pain skillfully, having to do with the ability to accept in a non-evaluative and non-judgmental fashion, both oneself and the current situation and becoming more focused on the present moment. The skill of emotional regulation utilises the mindfulness of current emotions and the body sensations associated with them. It teaches skills in 'letting go of emotional suffering'. The final module, interpersonal effectiveness, focuses on assertiveness and the development of interpersonal skills. This module also includes a combination of mindfulness and 'wise mind' skills, and focuses on developing self-respect.

Cognitive analytic therapy (CAT)

CAT was initially developed by Tony Ryle, a medical doctor and psychotherapist, in the early 1990s. It has been developed further to incorporate a broader range of skills and understandings based on spiritually oriented traditions by therapists such as Elizabeth Wilde McCormack and James Low. These include mindfulness and imaging techniques. Mark McMinn, former president of APA's Psychology of Religion Division and professor of psychology at George Fox University, Oregon, has written about cognitive analytic therapy in his book *Cognitive Therapy Techniques in Christian Counseling*. A growing body of evidence suggests CAT is an effective treatment for a range of problems, such as depression, personality disorders, eating disorders and forensic problems.

In brief, CAT is based on a 16 or 26-session framework of therapy. It works with an understanding of a person's familiar patterns of relating and behaving, which cause them to feel bad and experience pain. These are termed 'traps', 'dilemmas' and 'snags'. These are identified through the 'psychotherapy file' – a questionnaire that is given to a person at the beginning of their therapy to identify patterns and help formulate a person's 'problem procedures' that keep them repeating the same unhelpful ways of relating, and hence continuing to experience pain and suffering. On the basis of this a person is helped to target specific patterns and problems that may have prevented them from making changes in the past. The therapist will write a 're-formulation' letter which summarises their history and these patterns, and will work collaboratively with the client to create a personal map or diagram that the person can use to help them recognise or identify their patterns; what they do that keeps them 'stuck' in old ways of relating; and how they can 'exit' or change these patterns. The recognition and revision of patterns is a key part of CAT.

The client and therapist then work together over several sessions to revise these ways of relating and the behaviours. A 'goodbye' letter is exchanged at the end of therapy to summarise what has happened and to aid a person with the changes they have made. While this may sound very procedural, it is how the framework is used by a practitioner and what skillful means are utilised that will decide whether it is incorporating a spiritual approach, as the quote at the beginning of this section suggests.

Mindfulness

Mindfulness is an approach to life based on the understanding that *'the present is the only time that any of us have to be alive – to know anything – to perceive – to learn – to act – to change – to heal.'* (Kabat-Zinn, 1990)

Mindfulness-based cognitive therapy was originally developed to help people suffering from chronic pain and to help reduce relapse and recurrence of depression for individuals vulnerable to episodes of depression. This empowering way of working has gained significant empirical validation.

Mindfulness is the development of the ability to pay deliberate attention to experience from moment to moment, to what is going on in our mind, body and day-to-day life, and doing this without judgment. This accesses our own powerful inner resources for insight, transformation and healing.

Mindfulness-based learning involves finding ways into, and ways to dwell within, a new way of being with and seeing ourselves and our experience. It involves sustained, in-depth training in suspending our habitual ways of thinking and perceiving, and in redirecting our awareness to enable us to see freshly. Mindfulness-based approaches are intended to teach people practical skills that can help with daily and ongoing life challenges and physical and psychological health problems.

Mindfulness-based approaches are an integration of ancient understanding and the practice of mindfulness with current understanding and knowledge. The approaches are taught in a non-religious context and facilitate realisation and the accessing of our inner wisdom or understanding.

The two main approaches that have been developed at Bangor Centre for Mindfulness Research and Practice are mindfulness-based stress reduction (MBSR) and mindfulness-based cognitive therapy (MBCT).

MBSR is a group-based programme developed by Kabat-Zinn and colleagues in Massachusetts for populations with a wide range of physical and mental health problems. It has been extended into prisons, poor inner-city areas, to medical students and into corporate settings. It has been extensively studied since the early 1980s.

The ancient practice of mindfulness, adapted from its use as a spiritual practice, is therefore made into an accessible form for people suffering from a variety of difficulties. The programme involves intensive training in mindfulness meditation together with discussion on stress and life skills.

Evidence shows significant positive effects for participants with chronic pain, fibromyalgia, multiple sclerosis, generalised anxiety disorder and panic, psoriasis, cancer and health care provider self-care.

MBCT is an integration of MBSR with cognitive behaviour therapy (CBT) developed and initially researched through a three-site randomised control trial. It was developed to teach recovered, recurrently depressed participants skills to disengage from habitual 'automatic' unhelpful cognitive patterns. The core skill that MBCT is teaching is to intentionally 'shift mental gears'.

The focus of MBCT is on systematic training to be more aware, moment by moment, of physical sensations and of thoughts and feelings as mental events, as a way of teaching detachment from them. They are then seen as aspects of experience which move through our awareness rather than as a concrete reality in any given moment.

The evidence base shows that MBCT can halve the relapse rate in recovered individuals with three or more episodes of depression, and prevents relapse other than those provoked by highly stressful events. NICE guidelines recommend it as a treatment of choice for a variety of problems such as depression, eating disorders and personality disorder. Mindfulness approaches are covered in more detail in chapter 19.

Acceptance and commitment therapy (ACT)

ACT is a unique, empirically-based psychological intervention that uses acceptance and mindfulness strategies together with commitment and behavioural change strategies to increase psychological flexibility. Psychological flexibility means contacting the present moment fully and based on what the situation affords, changing or persisting in behaviour in the service of the chosen values. ACT helps a person to connect with a 'transcendent' sense of the self-known as 'self in context'– the 'you' that is always there, observing and experiencing – and yet is distinct from one's thoughts, feelings, sensations and memories.

ACT aims to help a person clarify their personal values and to take action on them, bringing more vitality and meaning to their life in the process, and increasing their flexibility.

ACT employs six core principles to help a person develop psychological flexibility.

1. Cognitive defusion: learning to perceive thoughts, images, emotions and memories as what they are, not what they appear to be.

2. Acceptance: allowing them to come and go without struggling with them.

3. Contact with the present moment: awareness of the here and now, experienced with openness, interest and receptiveness.

4. Observing the self: accessing a transcendent sense of self, a continuity of consciousness which is unchanging.

5. Values: discovering what is most important to one's true self.

6. Committed action: setting goals according to values and carrying them out responsibly.

Since 2006 ACT has been evaluated in over 30 randomised clinical trials for a variety of problems. It shows preliminary research evidence of effectiveness for problems including: chronic pain, addictions, smoking cessation, depression, anxiety, psychosis, workplace stress and diabetes management.

Recovery

Recovery is a model or approach to mental health rather than a psychological intervention. However, it is an approach that deserves inclusion in this chapter because of its focus on the 'whole person'. The main impetus for the model came from the survivor movement – a grassroots self-help and advocacy initiative, particularly active in the USA during the late 1980s and early 1990s. The professional literature, starting with the psychiatric rehabilitation movement in particular, began to incorporate the concept from the early 1990s in the USA, followed by New Zealand, and more recently across nearly all countries within the 'first world'. The cumulative impact of personal stories or testimony of recovery has also been a powerful force behind the development of recovery approaches and policies.

The recovery model emphasises and supports each individual's potential for recovery. Recovery is seen within the model as a personal journey – a journey of healing and transformation, enabling a person with a mental health problem to live a meaningful life in a community of his or her choice, while striving to achieve his or her potential. That may involve developing hope, a secure base and sense of self, supportive relationships, empowerment, social inclusion, coping skills, and meaning. The recovery model originates from the 12-step programme of Alcoholics Anonymous which has an implicitly spiritual orientation. It gained impetus due to a perceived failure by services or wider society to adequately support social inclusion, and by studies demonstrating that many can recover.

The recovery model has now been explicitly adopted as a guiding principle of many mental health systems worldwide. In many cases practical steps have been taken to base services on the recovery model, although there are a variety of concerns. A number of standardised measures have been developed to assess aspects of recovery, although there is some variation between professionalised models and those originating within the survivor movement.

The main elements to recovery are as follows: hope, a secure base, the development of 'self', supportive relationships, empowerment and inclusion, coping strategies, and meaning.

An approach to recovery, the tidal model, focuses on the continuous process of change inherent in all people, conveying the meaning of experiences through water metaphors. Crisis is seen as involving opportunity; creativity is valued and different domains are explored, such as an individual's sense of security, their personal narrative and their relationships.

Initially developed by mental health nurses, along with service users and based on research as well as values, the model emphasizes the importance of each person's own voice, resourcefulness and wisdom. The recovery approach will be discussed in more detail in chapter 22.

Spiritual emergency

A spiritual crisis can be described as a turbulent period of spiritual opening and transformation. Spiritual crisis is also referred to as 'spiritual emergency', where a process of spiritual emergence or awakening becomes chaotic and unmanageable for an individual. A person may experience psychological difficulties, hence the term 'psycho-spiritual crisis' is sometimes used. If understood and supported appropriately these experiences can be deeply transformative, offering the possibility of breakthrough rather than breakdown. This approach explores the interface between psychosis and spirituality.

Both David Lukof and Stanislav Grof have urged the new category in mental health of a clinical diagnosis of 'spiritual emergency'. In the early 1980s the Grofs founded the Spiritual Emergency Network at the Esalen Institute to assist individuals and make referrals to therapists for people experiencing psychological difficulties associated with spiritual practices and spontaneous spiritual experiences. Some types of spiritual crises at their peak include: past life experiences, near death experiences, possession states, communication with spirit guides and channeling.

Lukof has introduced the category of 'religious or spiritual problem' into the DSM-IV – the distressing experiences that involve a person's relationship with a transcendent being or force, but are not necessarily related to organised church or religious institution. This was an acknowledgement of distressing religious and spiritual experiences as non-pathological problems. The new diagnostic category came from transpersonal clinicians concerned with the misdiagnosis and mistreatment of persons in the midst of spiritual crises. The evidence base for this approach is developing and has been written about in some depth by Isabel Clarke.

Transpersonal psychotherapy

Carl Jung first coined the term 'transpersonal' which was built on the work of Maslow and humanistic therapy. It is *concerned with the study of humanity's highest potential and with the recognition, understanding and realization of unitive, spiritual and transcendent states of consciousness'* (Lajoie & Shapiro, 1992).

Transpersonal psychotherapy has been developed in the USA by Frances Vaughan, Roger Walsh and Ken Wilber, and has been pioneered and developed in the UK by therapists such as John Rowan, Barbara Somers, Ian Gordon Brown and Elizabeth Wilde McCormack. It describes any form of psychotherapy which places emphasis on the transpersonal, the transcendent or spiritual aspects of human experience. The focus of the therapy is on enabling spiritual connectedness and on the understanding of spiritual experiences. The goal of therapy is not merely the alleviation of suffering, but the integration and transformation of the physical, mental, emotional and spiritual aspects of a person's well-being. It is concerned with psychological processes related to developing the state of realisation and of making real states such as 'illumination' or 'transcendence'. It uses a variety of approaches, in particular imaging, to facilitate spiritual connectedness or connection to the 'self' – the wise aspect of ourselves.

As with spiritual emergency, the evidence base is developing through utilising qualitative measures rather than randomised control measures.

Positive psychology

This is a recent branch of psychology developed by Martin Seligman and Mihaly Csikszentmihalyi in 2000 which seeks *to find and nurture genius and talent and to make normal life more fulfilling, not simply to treat mental illness'*. It focuses on helping individuals to develop their strengths and 'virtues'. He delineates six of these, which are:

▶ wisdom and knowledge

▶ courage

▶ humanity

▶ justice

▶ temperance

▶ transcendence.

He defines three 'positive experiences' ie. mindfulness, flow and spirituality, and the key place that hope plays.

Positive psychology helps individuals and organisations to identify their strengths and to use them to increase and sustain their respective levels of well-being. All these strengths, virtues and positive experiences are associated with following and practising a spiritual tradition such as Buddhism.

Emotional freedom therapy

Emotional freedom therapy (EFT) utilises Craig's emotional freedom technique – often simply referred to as EFT or tapping. EFT provides a simple and effective way of managing stress, illness, pain, depression, trauma and other issues that arise in our life.

EFT is based on the discovery that imbalances in the body's subtle energy system have profound effects on one's personal psychology and physiology. Correcting these imbalances, which is done by tapping on certain body points or 'meridians', often leads to rapid change.

Tapping gently on specific meridian or acupuncture points while thinking about a certain issue can remarkably reduce the charge and effect of an issue or problem, restore peace and calm, and create lasting healing.

When EFT is properly applied over 80% of clients achieve either noticeable improvement or complete cessation of the problem, such as with trauma, abuse, stress anxiety, fears, phobias, depression, grief, addictive cravings, children's issues and many physical symptoms including headaches, body pains and breathing difficulties.

While this approach isn't specifically 'spiritual' in orientation, it is included because it utilises ancient eastern principles and methodologies of healing ie. meridian points which work with unseen energies.

Skills and interventions associated with psychological approaches incorporating a spiritual perspective

When looking at the various psychological therapies and interventions that incorporate a spiritual perspective or dimension, it is clear that they advocate similar techniques or strategies to enable a person to 'connect with' or shift their consciousness and way of operating. Underlying most of the therapeutic approaches is a call to develop what eastern approaches might term 'wisdom and compassion' via a variety of skillful means, such as developing mindfulness present moment awareness and meditation practices.

There are five general points about the assumptions behind skills and interventions used in a spiritual approach to psychological therapy.

Our essential or true nature is spiritual. With this there is an 'inherent wisdom' and healthy part within a person that knows best – even if the person does not realise this prior to therapy. This has been referred to as the 'self' in transpersonal approaches. This 'self' can be called upon as part of the journey towards health and well-being, and has an inherent knowing about what is required to restore a person to their true nature or well-being. It is this part of a person that needs to be accessed and facilitated within psychological therapy.

Looking for meaning and purpose in distress. The skills that are used when incorporating a spiritual perspective within psychological therapy are the same as those used with other approaches. What is different is the manner in which they are used and the nature of our listening and questioning which aims to facilitate the inner or innate wisdom of a person. We are looking at what is purposeful in the distress for a person and what meaning this may hold for them. It is there to move the person towards health and wholeness.

Seeing pain and problems as opportunities for growth. Most psychological approaches that incorporate a spiritual dimension see a person's distress as signaling something 'greater' that needs attention and as an opportunity for growth and learning.

Spirituality can be a coping strategy. Most of the recent research indicates that those who have a sense of their own spirituality and follow spiritual practices tend to maintain a sense of well-being and are less likely to experience mental health problems. In fact, some research has shown that spirituality can prevent or act as a buffer against a person experiencing further mental health problems.

Many of the skills and techniques utilised in psychological approaches that incorporate a spiritual perspective are used by other approaches. As aforementioned, it is the way in which these are utilised that is key. These include:

▶ reflective questioning

▶ meditation, mindfulness

▶ developing present moment awareness

▶ utilising the 'wise mind' and 'compassionate mind' as means to accessing our 'true nature'

▶ imaging and dream work

▶ active imagination and imaging

▶ guided fantasy

▶ visualisation

▶ body work, breath work and voice work

▶ working with symptoms or symptoms as a symbol

▶ developing and focusing on strengths and virtues (Seligman).

The further reading and references section provide pointers to texts which give further detail on these methods. In particular, see Rowan's (2008) book on transpersonal therapy and the chapter 'Helping people with their spirituality' in Velleman and Aris' (2010) book *Counselling and Helping*.

Tools for the workplace

The various skillful means mentioned in previous sections of the chapter are also useful tools to aid personal development and help others to develop in order to maintain well-being in the workplace. These are listed below:

▶ cultivating mindfulness

▶ meditation

▶ developing compassion

▶ cultivating spaciousness

▶ developing present moment awareness

▶ reflective practice

▶ skillful means of remembering our 'inner true nature' or 'essence'

▶ focusing on strengths and virtues

> **Reflection exercise**
>
> Allow yourself some time to settle into a space that feels nurturing and restful for a few moments. Reflect on the following questions and see what images, senses and phrases emerge.
>
> **What gives me strength in challenging times? What do I call on inside myself when the going gets tough?**
>
> See what arises as you sit with this. What do you feel in your body and where do you feel this?
>
> When you have a sense of this, get some pencils or crayons and draw what comes into your mind, or what has touched you in those moments of reflection. It may be words or an image. However fleeting, put whatever arises down. It may help to share it with someone you know and trust.

Conclusion

As can be seen from this brief overview of some of the key psychological approaches that incorporate a spiritual perspective or are utilising the skillful means associated with a spiritual practice, they are developing and gathering momentum. There is now a considerable evidence base, demonstrating the effectiveness of mindfulness, DBT, CAT, and ACT in particular, for a variety of symptoms and problems that individuals experience. Some approaches are NICE recommended treatments of choice for particular problems within the NHS, as the chapter has outlined earlier. Clearly, further appropriate research and evidence bases need to be developed to validate other approaches, such as spiritual emergency work and transpersonal therapies.

As Rogers said: *'Our experience in therapy and groups involve the transcendent, the indescribable, the spiritual. I am compelled to believe that I, like many others, have under-estimated the importance of the mystical, spiritual dimension.'* (Rogers, 1980)

Perhaps we are now beginning to appreciate the importance of both addressing and incorporating our spirituality in psychological interventions and beginning to understand the crucial role it plays in enabling, maintaining and sustaining our health and well-being.

References

Cortright B (1997) *Psychotherapy and Spirit: Theory and practice in transpersonal psychotherapy*. Albany: State University of New York Press.

Department of Health (2010) *New Horizons: A shared vision for mental health*. London: DH.

Gilbert P (2010) *Compassion Focused Therapy: Distinctive features*. London: Routledge.

Kabat-Zinn J (1990) *Full Catastrophe Living: Using the wisdom of your body and mind to face stress, pain, and illness*. New York: Delta Trade Paperbacks.

Layard R (2005) *Happiness: Lessons from a new science:* London: Penguin.

Lajoie DH & Shapiro SI (1992) Definitions of transersonal psychology: the first 23 years. *Journal of Transpersonal Psychology* **24**.

NIMHE (2005) *Guiding Statement on Recovery: January 2005*. Leeds: NIMHE.

Rogers C(1980) *A Way of Being*. Boston: Houghton Mifflin.

Rowan J (2008) *The Transpersonal: Spirituality in psychotherapy and counselling* (2nd edition). London and New York: Routledge.

Teasdale J (2003) *Mindfulness Based Cognitive Therapy for Depression*. New York: Guilford Press.

Velleman R & Aris S (2010) *Counselling and Helping*. UK: BPS Blackwell.

Further reading

Baer RE (2005) *Mindfulness-Based Treatment Approaches: Clinician's guide to evidence base and applications (Practical resources for mental health professionals)*. London: Academic Press.

Clarke I (2010) *Psychosis and Spirituality: Consolidating the new paradigm* (2nd edition). Chichester: Wiley-Blackwell

Department of Health (2009) *NHS and Well-being Review: The government response*. London: HMSO.

Gilbert P (2009) *The Compassionate Mind:* London: Constable.

Grof S & Grof C (2010) *Spiritual Emergency: When personal transformation becomes a crisis*. Los Angeles: Tarcher.

Hayes S, Strosahl KD & Wilson KG (1999) *Acceptance and Commitment Therapy*. London: Routledge.

Kabat-Zinn, J (2005) *Coming to Our Senses: Healing ourselves and the world through mindfulness*. London: Piatkus.

Linehan MM (1999) *Dialectic Behaviour Therapy*. London: Guildford Press.

Linehan MM & Dimef L (2001) Dialectic behaviour therapy in a nutshell. *The California Psychologist* **34** 10–13.

Linehan MM (1993) *Skills Training Manual for Treating Borderline Personality Disorder*. London: Guildford Press.

Marshall H, Somers B & Gordon-Brown I (2002) *Journey in Depth: A transpersonal perspective*. Leicester: Archive Publishing.

McCormick EW (2010) *Change for the Better* (3rd edition). London: Sage.

Seligman M (2002) *Authentic Happiness: Using the new positive psychology to realize your potential for lasting fulfillment.* New York: Free Press.

Senge PM, Scharmer CO, Jaworski J & Flowers BS (2006) *Presence: An exploration of profound change in people, organisations and society.* New York: Currency.

Shepherd G, Boardman J & Slade M (2008) *Making Recovery a Reality.* London: Sainsbury Centre for Mental Health.

Teasdale JD, Segal Z, Williams J, Ridgeway V, Soulsby J & Lau M (2000) Prevention of relapse/recurrence in major depression by mindfulness-based cognitive therapy. *Journal of Consulting and Clinical Psychology* **68** (4) 615–623.

Thich Nhat Hanh (2007) *The Miracle of Mindfulness.* London: Rider.

Welwood J (2002) *Towards a Psychology of Awakening: Buddhism, psychotherapy and the path of personal and spiritual transformation.* USA: Shambhala publications.

Williams JMG, Segal ZV, Teasdale JD & Kabat-Zinn J (2007) *The Mindful Way through Depression.* New York: Guildford Press.

Websites

Authentic Happiness website available at: www.authentichappiness.org (accessed November 2010).

Mental Health Recovery website available at: www.mentalhealthrecovery.org (accessed November 2010).

Spiritual Crisis Network website available at: www.spiritualcrisisnetwork.org.uk (accessed November 2010).

Jon Kabat-Zinn's website for mindfulness-based cognitive therapy available at: www.mbct.co.uk (accessed November 2010).

Chapter 10

Assessing a person's spiritual needs in a healthcare setting

Sarah Eagger and Wilf McSherry
With contributions from Peter Gilbert and Steve Wharmby

Introduction

This chapter introduces you to the skills, practices and tools required to assess whether an individual has an underlying spiritual need. The area of spiritual assessment is not straightforward and careful thought must be given to the development and utilisation of any spiritual assessment tool. Therefore, this chapter explores some of the challenges and opportunities of using spiritual assessment tools within mental health services. Stoter (1995) argues that spiritual assessment has been largely ignored within health care contexts. Recently, more attention has been ascribed to this concept within health care literature (McSherry & Ross, 2002; Gordon & Mitchell, 2004; Timmins & Kelly, 2008) with psychiatrists (Culliford & Eagger, 2009) and mental health services leading innovation and exploration in this area (Gilbert, 2008).

The authors of this chapter affirm that the implementation and success of any spiritual assessment tool is dependent upon rigorous preparation and planning. The context in which a specific tool is to be used is fundamental to the decision-making process. For example, someone going into a day surgery unit for the removal of an ingrown toe nail would not expect to be subjected to a barrage of questions about what gives their life meaning and purpose. Conversely, these types of questions may be extremely important to someone admitted to an acute mental health unit with depression. This analogy illustrates that there is no such thing as a 'generic' spiritual assessment tool. The 'one size fits all approach' to spiritual assessment is not in keeping with the philosophy of person-centred and individualised care.

McSherry (2010) suggests that there are four areas (see box 1) that practitioners and organisations must consider before routinely assessing patients' spiritual needs.

Box 1: Consideration for spiritual assessment
Conceptual: consideration must be given to the way in which people define, perceive and understand the nature of spirituality.
Organisational: acknowledges the importance of people, places and processes when undertaking a spiritual assessment.
Practical: covers the practical implications when any form of spiritual assessment is introduced.
Ethical: considers any ethical issues and potential dilemmas encountered with any type of spiritual assessment.

These considerations will be used as a framework for discussing spiritual assessment within the remainder of the chapter.

Context

Before exploring the meaning of spirituality there is a need to briefly outline why the area of spirituality has been recognised as a central component within mental health services. The Chief Nursing Officer's Review of Mental Health Nursing (Department of Health, 2006) under Recommendation 10 asserts that all mental health nurses (MHNs) must recognise and respond to the spiritual and religious needs of service users, and that those providing services should ensure all MHNs have accessible sources of information or advice regarding religious and spiritual issues, for example information directories and access to experts and faith community representatives.

Similarly, in the General Medical Council's (2008) guidance on personal beliefs and medical practice asserts: *For some patients, acknowledging their beliefs or religious practices may be an important aspect of a holistic approach to their care. Discussing personal beliefs may, when approached sensitively, help you to work in partnership with patients to address their particular treatment needs.'*

For example, by exploring with an individual what they consider to be their strengths, the person may feel more empowered to participate in the helping and recovery process. Therefore, the strengths perspective:

▶ posits clients' personal and environmental strengths as central to the helping process

▶ encourages us to enquire sympathetically about what gives their life meaning, and about what helps most in times of adversity.

Spirituality and recovery

The National Institute for Mental Health in England's (2005) 12 guiding principles for the delivery of recovery-oriented mental health services affirms the central and pivotal role spirituality can play in recovering from a mental illness.

Third principle

▶ Hope is encouraged, enhanced and/or maintained

▶ Life roles re: work or meaningful activity are defined

▶ Spirituality is considered

▶ Culture is understood

▶ Education needs are identified

▶ Socialisation needs identified

Fifth principle

▶ Recovery is most effective when an holistic approach is considered

▶ Including psychological, emotional, spiritual, physical and social needs

The third and fifth principles highlight that spirituality is an essential component and crucial to the provision of holistic mental health services.

Also, the delivery of such services accommodating the spiritual dimension of individuals can be supported by conceptual models of recovery (Jacobson & Greenley, 2001). For example, the external and internal conditions that directly affect the person.

Reflection exercise

Spend a few moments reflecting on the following conditions and ask yourself how these may apply to mental health services?

External conditions
- ▶ Human rights
- ▶ A positive culture of healing
- ▶ Recovery-oriented services

Internal conditions
- ▶ Hope
- ▶ Healing
- ▶ Empowerment
- ▶ Connection

An early pioneer

One of the early pioneers of spiritual assessment was Ruth Stoll (1979). Stoll's guidelines have been used by many health care disciplines and her model suggests that the nurse should enquire into the following areas.

The person's:

- ▶ concept of deity

- ▶ source of strength and hope

- ▶ significance of religious practices and rituals

- ▶ perceived relationship between beliefs and health.

The model can encourage reflection on the particular narrative of the patient and how meaning relates to their experience of illness. The model can support the exploration of deeper aspects of a person's spiritual life. It might be that there is a need to reframe significant questions concerning the nature and function of a person's spirituality and spiritual experiences within different cultures.

This model may be transposed to mental health services within the UK, but in its original format it may be too focused on religious forms of spirituality and exclude those who express their spirituality in different ways.

Conceptual considerations

The principal purpose of spiritual assessment tools is to establish whether an individual has any underlying spiritual needs. However, before this can be established the assessment tool must be able to accommodate the broad range of meanings, understandings and languages associated with spirituality.

The Royal College of Psychiatrists (2006) define spirituality as: *'In healthcare, spirituality is identified with experiencing a deep-seated sense of meaning and purpose in life, together with a sense of belonging. It is about acceptance, integration and wholeness'*. This definition reveals that spirituality may mean different things for people depending upon factors such as personal belief and faith, ethnicity and cultural group. Therefore spirituality is:

▶ deeply subjective

▶ unique and varied

▶ in a multicultural society there may be no shared definition

▶ a secular version of Judeo–Christian faith dominates.

Despite spirituality having a broad range of meanings, the term has the potential to offend people from some faith traditions and the concept cannot be routinely applied to all people within a secular society where there may be more emphasis on humanistic, existential meaning. Therefore, those working within mental health services must guard against making assumptions about people's understandings of spirituality and their expectations about receiving spiritual care (McSherry & Cash, 2004).

Personal spirituality

Govier (2000) provides a useful framework for ascertaining the religious, spiritual needs, and beliefs of patients. These questions can enable us to clarify and identify our own unique spirituality.

Reflection exercise

Reflect upon the following questions, asking yourself if they tell us about the concept of spirituality.

▶ What gives my life meaning?
▶ What do I believe in?
▶ What do I hope for?
▶ Who do I love and who loves me?
▶ What do I understand by the term 'spirituality'?
▶ What practices keep me well?
▶ How am I with others?
▶ What would I change about my relationships?

By reflecting on your own understanding of spirituality you will recognise that the word is an 'umbrella term' that covers a number of essential aspects of daily life. For example, this may include relationships and connectedness to other people and your own personal beliefs and values. Spirituality for some people is intricately and inextricably linked with what gives their life meaning, purpose and fulfilment (McSherry, 2006; Edwards & Gilbert, 2007). Spirituality concerns the ordinary and the mundane aspects of life; the routines and rituals that provide security and stability and a foundation for life. It is not until these foundations are shaken that individuals may start to reflect on life at a deeper level.

What is spiritual care?

An emerging debate concerns the nature of spiritual care and its relationship with the fundamental care that is provided by healthcare professionals (see Coyte et al, 2007). In the past a reductionist and medical approach to care delivery has been evident. The danger is that spiritual care is seen as something additional and not integral to the caring relationship. This may be evident in the desire to see spirituality as a discrete area of assessment. The Hospital Chaplaincy Council suggests that spiritual care is necessary when a patient, member of staff, or visitor exhibits spiritual pain or distress.

Signs of spiritual pain/distress:

▶ **anger:** directed at God or other people

▶ **bitterness:** what have I done to deserve this?

▶ **regret**: I should have been a better person

▶ **guilt/punishment**: I must have done something wrong

▶ **doubt:** Is there really a God? Really a purpose for existence?

▶ **fear:** I am not sure there is anything after death

▶ **isolation:** my family, neighbours, friends or God etc. have abandoned me

▶ **loss of hope:** I see no future – there is a negative future stretching endlessly ahead of me.

Cautionary debate

A review of this list of potential indicators of spiritual distress demonstrates the duplicity that exists with psychosocial dimension. Clarke (2009) suggests that there is a need for differentiation between the psychological (emotional) and the spiritual dimension. Clarke (2009) suggests that nursing and, indeed, healthcare now have to deal with 'portmanteau' terms, which are difficult to articulate and difficult to put into practice, frequently being indistinguishable from psychosocial care.

While Clarke (2009) raises valuable criticisms about the evolution of the concept of spirituality and the lack of critique; academic debate alone will not provide and equip frontline staff with the practical skills and the tools required to support patients in their struggle to find meaning, purpose and fulfilment. The nature of spiritual care and its relationship with other aspects of the person are still very much in evolution. Therefore, continued debate and dialogue are required so that these concepts have relevance and meaning for all involved in the delivery of care.

Models of spiritual care

Govier (2000) developed a model of spiritual care based on reasoning and reflection, see box 2. This model enables practitioners to undertake a systematic enquiry using observation and questioning to establish whether a person has an underlying spiritual need. The model of spiritual care provides a framework for the delivery of spiritual care. By using reason and reflection this assists the practitioner in partnership with the patient to explore any spiritual concerns. This model is a holistic approach that helps the person to reflect upon and find meaning in experiences. Religion, for some people, is a significant form of spirituality and can be expressed in its own way – not necessarily referring to traditional systems. With regard to reason, humans are essentially meaning-seeking beings who require ways of restoring the quest after meaning has been lost or impaired through illness or disease.

Box 2: Model of spiritual care (Govier, 2000)
Reason and reflection: Do they take time to reflect on life's experiences? How? What motivates/frightens?
Religion: Do they have a religion, useful representative, see a chaplain? For example, how are rituals accommodated in hospital?
Relationships: Most influential, belief in higher being? How does it manifest? Have they ever felt abandoned?
Restorations: Illness affected beliefs? Are they at peace with themselves? Signs of spiritual distress?

Likewise, Cobb (1998), after Lyall (2001), provides a useful model for understanding the nature of spiritual care and importance within health care settings. The broad principles of Cobb's model are summarised.

▶ **Understanding:** A response to the spiritual needs of a person is understood by exploring life events, beliefs, values and meaning.

▶ **Therapeutic support:** Enables a person challenged by illness, trauma, or bereavement to find meaning in their experiences of vulnerability, loss or dislocation.

▶ **Dimensions of illness:** Addresses the dimensions of illness, disability, suffering and bereavement that go beyond the immediate and the physical.

▶ **Healing and rehabilitation:** Contributes to healing and rehabilitation by respecting the integrity of the person and by attending to 'wholeness' in the midst of 'brokenness'.

▶ **Holistic approach:** May incorporate psychological, social and religious dimensions.

▶ **Liturgy and belief:** May incorporate liturgical actions which embody the beliefs of a particular tradition, if appropriate.

Spiritual needs explored

Murray *et al* (2004) indicate that spiritual needs are the needs and expectations which humans have to find meaning, purpose and value in their life. Such needs can be specifically religious but even people who have no religious faith have belief systems that give their lives meaning and purpose. This approach to spiritual needs brings into question the relationship that exists between religious frameworks and more existential-based ones. Narayanasamy (2001) provides a detailed review of the spiritual needs that may be experienced by all human beings. These are summarised in box 3. Through observation and discussion with a patient about their spiritual needs, Hay (1989) suggests that a spiritual diagnosis may be made. This may reveal concerns with the following:

▶ spiritual suffering

▶ belief system problems

▶ religious request

▶ inner resource deficiency.

Spiritual well-being

O'Brien (1998) suggests that spiritual distress may result in spiritual loss, anxiety, alienation and despair. The challenge for those assessing and supporting individuals with meeting their spiritual needs is to restore their sense of spiritual well-being. The difficulty associated with this is how you develop outcome measures that may assist with this activity, since spiritual well-being is not just about focusing on the mental or psychological problems an individual may display. Some of these questions are better understood through reflection on experience and dialogue with a community advocating a narrative approach to care. As indicated, how to assess and measure impact with regards to the restoration of spiritual well-being is not well developed. Perhaps one method is to explore the relationships that exist between spiritual well-being and quality of life.

Box 3: Spiritual needs and prompt questions (Narayanasamy, 2001)
Meaning and purpose: What gives you a sense of meaning and purpose? Is there anything especially meaningful for you now? Do they show any sense of meaning and purpose?
Strength and hope: Who is the most important person to you? Who would you turn to when you need help? Is there anyone we can contact? In what ways do they help? What is your source of strength and hope? What helps you most when you feel afraid or need special help?
Love and relatedness: How do they relate to family and relatives, friends and others, surroundings? Do they appear peaceful – what gives them peace?
Self-esteem: Describe state of self-esteem – how do they feel about themselves?
Fear and anxiety: Fearful or anxious about anything?
Anger: Angry about anything? How do they cope with anger?
Relation with health: What has bothered you most about being ill – what do you think is going to happen to you?
Concept of god: Is prayer or meditation important to you? How would you describe your god or what you worship?
Spiritual practices: Do you feel your faith or religion is helpful to you – would you like to tell me more, or discuss it with anyone else? Are there any religious practices that are important to you? Has being ill made any difference to your practice of praying or other practices? Are there any religious books or symbols important to you? Is there anything we could do to help you with your religious practices?

Organisational considerations

This section introduces you to some of the organisational considerations that impact upon the area of spiritual assessment. However, before this can be achieved there is a need to understand what is meant by 'assessment'. Assessments within healthcare practice can take many different forms and they are used for many different purposes. The danger in creating any form of assessment tool is that it becomes another bureaucratic process that contributes little to the care and recovery of the individual.

Drivers for spiritual assessment

Every organisation, before developing and introducing any form of spiritual or practice assessment, must give consideration to the drivers or motives. If this consideration is not given, then the entire exercise can be a 'red herring' in that individuals, wards and institutions may not fully co-operate in the exercise (for an example from a mental health trust, see Barber, 2009). The result is the development and utilisation of an assessment strategy that, rather than engaging all parties, disengages and has no therapeutic benefit. Therefore, motivation for initial development must be explored.

What is assessment?

The word 'assessment' tends to raise anxiety. As a service user once said: *'They keep asking me questions about myself, but they never tell me anything about themselves!'*

But, in fact, the word 'assessment' originates from the Latin 'to sit beside'. So, assessing someone's strengths and needs isn't a matter of standing over and judging someone, but getting alongside them and seeing where they are at. It is not so much about 'ticking a box' as ascertaining 'what makes someone tick'. As another service user put it: *'We are all primary experts on our own mental health and what works for us ... we can and should value the coping strategies we have developed for ourselves...'* (Coyte et al, 2007).

In terms of mental health services, service users tell us that they want:

▶ to start from where I am! Not where you think I am!

▶ empathy

▶ time (quality)

▶ attendance to emotional needs; culture, identity and dignity

▶ working with, not doing to, to find solutions to practical issues

▶ being seen as having strengths as well as needs.

This list indicates that simply gathering data is not an assessment in itself; the information must be interpreted, organised, integrated with theory and made meaningful. Accordingly, assessment is defined as the process of gathering, analysing and synthesising salient data into a multi-dimensional formulation that provides the basis for action and decisions. Assessment involves comparing results with an accepted standard regarded as representing the 'norm'. Many formats simply screen for spiritual needs and do not ascertain how spirituality functions in the patient's life, for example the use of indicators, questionnaires or value clarification tools (Baldacchino, 2010). When considering spiritual assessment within mental health, attention must be given to the following areas:

▶ providing a guide and systematic approach

▶ ensuring that only relevant information, which will be used is deliberately sought, thus acknowledging the individual's right to privacy

▶ providing a basis for nurse and patient decision-making and goal setting

▶ a focus for nurse and patient to validate the existence of problems.

Practicalities

The following section addresses the practicalities of undertaking a spiritual assessment. The section will deal with the why, when, who and how questions raised by practitioners when undertaking a spiritual assessment. Readers will be introduced to the different forms (classification) of spiritual assessment tools and examples of the different tools will be provided.

Why, when, who and how

There is a need for those considering the use of spiritual assessment tools to reflect on the practical implications. Figure 1 summarises some of the practical issues that will need to be resolved when determining the most appropriate tool and method of choice. Some pointers have been provided under each of the practical steps. Gorsuch and Miller (1999), in addition to the point presented under 'why', provide further explanations about why organisations may undertake a spiritual assessment. These are:

1. Prognosis: How the individual will handle illness or crisis.

2. Context: Explore with the person how illness challenges their belief system. This will be dependent upon good communication.

3. Outcome: Identification of spiritual variables – these may be important mediators of change and outcome, with regard to recovery from mental illness.

4. Intervention: Recognising how an individual may respond to spiritual distress.

The 'How' is covered in a little more detail since this involves the selection and utilisation of specific assessment tools.

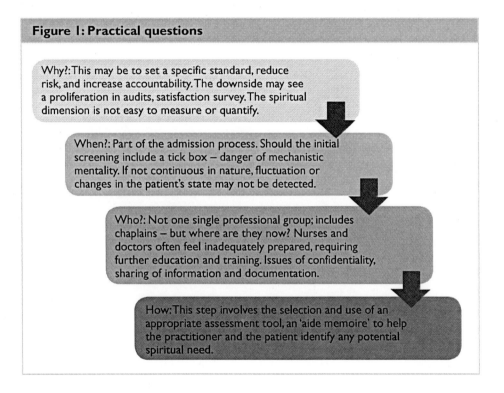

Figure 1: Practical questions

Why?: This may be to set a specific standard, reduce risk, and increase accountability. The downside may see a proliferation in audits, satisfaction survey. The spiritual dimension is not easy to measure or quantify.

When?: Part of the admission process. Should the initial screening include a tick box – danger of mechanistic mentality. If not continuous in nature, fluctuation or changes in the patient's state may not be detected.

Who?: Not one single professional group; includes chaplains – but where are they now? Nurses and doctors often feel inadequately prepared, requiring further education and training. Issues of confidentiality, sharing of information and documentation.

How: This step involves the selection and use of an appropriate assessment tool, an 'aide memoire' to help the practitioner and the patient identify any potential spiritual need.

How

A brief screening will often indicate that a more detailed history is required to establish relevant aspects of the patient's background, specific spirituality or religion-related problems, available spiritual supports and additional spiritual needs.

Various authorities have separately designed guidance on assessing the religious and spiritual aspects of people's lives. As will become clear, they are fairly uniform regarding the topics covered. This allows practitioners to pick for themselves the style with which they feel most comfortable. Guides tend to take the form of an 'aide-memoire' rather than an exact prescription. Box 4 provides a simple classification of the different forms of spiritual assessment tools used by health care professionals.

Reflection exercise

Review the types of spiritual assessment tool available and ask yourself which may be appropriate for use in mental health services.

Box 4: Types of spiritual assessment tool

(Adapted from McSherry & Ross, 2002; McSherry, 2010)

Direct method: Ask direct questions about the patient's religious or spiritual beliefs to elicit information about his or her potential spiritual needs.

Indicator-based models: This reflects the spiritual diagnosis–spiritual distress approach to spirituality (Carpenito, 1983), which identifies certain characteristics that may indicate underlying spiritual distress (eg. expression of concern or anger, resentment and fear about the meaning of life, suffering, and death).

Audit tools: There are increasing attempts to assess the effectiveness of practitioners in providing spiritual care, and many institutions are setting their own standards, actively monitoring and auditing areas of religious and spiritual needs to establish how well they have been addressed.

Value clarification: Likert-type scales reveal the extent to which patients agree or disagree with a particular statement. Tools using these scales are quick to administer and provide quantifiable measures for researchers. They also give useful insights into their own values and perceptions of the concepts being investigated.

Indirect methods: Observational methods gather information from various sources to establish the presence of spiritual needs. Consensus must be reached about who does the observing, what signs are looked for and how they are interpreted, and whether (and how) they are documented.

Acronym-based models: PLAN (Highfield, 1993), FICA (Puchalski & Romer, 2000) and HOPE (Anandarajah & Hight, 2001) all focus attention on specific areas associated with spirituality or spiritual care. They are all quick and flexible and can be incorporated into the general assessment process.

Narrative approaches: Idea of the journey. Talk about spirituality during lifetime through journal, story or art work. May include the development of a spiritual life map.

Your review of the different forms of spiritual assessment tool may reveal that not all are suitable. You may have identified that there is a need for some general enquiry into a person's personal beliefs and values – an initial screening. Importantly, reflection on experience and life meaning should be prior to the specific questions about religion, for example:

▶ what is really important to you in life?

▶ do you have a way of making sense of the things that have happened in your life?

▶ what sources of support or help do you look to when life is difficult?

This type of tiered approach will feel less threatening and intrusive. If necessary, a practitioner may also use one of the acronym-based models that have been developed to assist them with the assessment. For example, box 5 presents the FICA model (Puchalski & Romer, 2000). This model is designed for use in doctor consultation. This type of assessment is open to wider dimensions of spirituality. It may be relevant for those who express no formalised religious orientation including atheists and secular humanists agnostics. It must be remembered that not all patients will have spiritual or religious needs, emphasising the need for sensitivity when introducing such assessments within mental health practice.

Box 5: FICA (Adapted from Puchalski & Romer, 2000)
F–Faith and belief
Do you consider yourself spiritual or religious? or Do you have spiritual beliefs that help you cope with stress? or What gives your life meaning?
I–Importance
What importance does your faith or belief have in your life? Have your beliefs influenced how you take care of yourself in this illness? What role do your beliefs play in regaining your (mental) health?
C–Community
Are you part of a spiritual or religious community? Is this of support to you and how? Is there a group of people you really love or who are important to you?
A–Address in care
How would you like me, your healthcare provider, to address these issues in your healthcare?

Reflective/narrative approaches

It must be emphasised that spiritual assessment is not a one-off activity as White (2006) asserts spirituality as a process of reflection. Therefore, practitioners must be willing to engage with and listen to each individual's own personal life story or narrative. This means that after the initial screening or tier there is a need to explore in more depth with a patient their needs and wants. This may require the practitioner taking a more in-depth spiritual history. A narrative and ongoing continuous approach to assessment where spirituality is part of the healthcare process, depending on the quality of the conversations, not a chart or box that needs ticking. However, these narrative and reflective models of spiritual assessment require:

▶ grounding in reflective learning

▶ a team needing knowledge, skills and confidence

▶ assessment undertaken within the context of a therapeutic relationship

▶ to be based on a dynamic, dialogic, reflective model.

The reflective/narrative approach has the potential to create opportunities to raise and explore deeper concerns about meaning and purpose with an individual. They may lead to a connection without becoming locked into formal assessment process. Use a combination of questions to explore spiritual concerns. They may be used within a multi-professional assessment tool allowing any member of the team to complete and be returned to at different stages.

Reflection exercise

Look at the questions presented in box 6 and ask yourself how you would feel using these within your practice.

Box 6: Reflective/narrative questions for spiritual assessment proposed by White (2006)

Meaning and purpose
▶ What are some things that give you a sense of purpose?
▶ Do you have a specific aim that is important to you at the moment?
▶ Do you believe in any kind of existence after this life?
▶ Has your illness changed your attitude to the future?
▶ What bothers you most about being ill?

Security and hope
▶ What are your sources of strength and hope?
▶ Who do you turn to when you need help? In what ways do they help?
▶ What inner resources do you draw upon?
▶ Who or what do you depend on when things go wrong?

Religion/spirituality
▶ Do you consider yourself to be religious or spiritual?
▶ How does this affect you? Has being ill changed this?
▶ Is prayer helpful to you? Can you talk about how?
▶ Is there anything we can do to support your spiritual/religious practice?

Skills required

By reading through this chapter you will now appreciate that there is a number of fundamental skills required when assessing and supporting individuals with spiritual needs. One of the essential skills is the use of excellent interpersonal and communication skills. Therefore, being a good listener, showing empathy, and being available (presence) are required. These qualities are fundamental because they foster a supporting environment, encouragement and freedom to explore spirituality. There is also a need to adopt a non-intrusive and relaxed approach. It must be remembered that spiritual assessment is not an interrogation, since the focus is on the needs of the individual. The interaction should encourage participation of the individual, meaning language shouldn't alienate but be inclusive, non-threatening and non-judgemental. Crucially, the assessment should be patient-centred. Some recent developments around spiritual assessment advocate a levelled approach, for example with nurses undertaking a generic, initial assessment and a more in-depth assessment, if necessary, conducted by another spiritual care specialist (chaplain or counsellor). However, this competency-based approach to assessment may work well in theory but if not implemented and facilitated with thought and care, it has the potential to fragment spiritual care.

Reflection exercise

Before proceeding with the remainder of the chapter, please read the case study (Gilbert, 2008) and answer the following questions.

Is this the kind of situation that you recognise?

Are staff supported to respond to episodes of distress which have a spiritual component?

How can services prepare and support staff in better ways?

Case study

A young South Asian woman was admitted to an acute ward. She was in great distress, and both medication and a period of restraint were used to calm her down and ensure her safety. During this period of distress she mentioned that she thought she might be possessed by a jinn (spirit).

Several of the nurses on the ward were from the same ethnic and cultural group as the service user and, later on, the chaplain asked them whether they thought that the young service user was experiencing a period of 'spiritual distress'. The nursing staff agreed that they felt she was, and that they had not responded in a way which addressed her spiritual needs. But they were concerned that a more spiritual approach might not have been viewed favourably by the organisation if they had attempted it.

Your reflection may have revealed a number of cultural and organisational challenges that prevent practitioners from assessing and supporting people with their spiritual concerns. People's own fears, taboos and misconceptions around the nature and meaning of spiritual issues can be a major barrier. This is often combined with a lack of knowledge and understanding (education) into the diverse meanings and interpretations of the word 'spirituality'. These factors raise a number of ethical considerations for those providing mental health services.

Ethical considerations

Cobb (1998, p114) provides three broad questions that should be considered prior to the introduction or utilisation of any spiritual assessment tool. These questions provide a useful framework for exploring the ethical implications of undertaking spiritual assessment.

▶ Is the assessment practicable for the type of patients being assessed?

▶ Are the language and concepts used appropriate for all patients?

▶ Is the healthcare professional carrying out the assessment capable of dealing with the immediate consequences of what the assessment may evoke?

These questions demonstrate that preparation, planning, personal and professional development are essential when constructing a spiritual assessment.

Some of the specific ethical questions spiritual assessment raises are associated with competency and educational preparedness of staff to deal with spiritual issues. Walter (2002) suggests that some staff may see spiritual assessment as an opportunity, but others as an unwelcome burden. Therefore, consideration must be given to the practical implications and more importantly to the individual beliefs and ideologies of staff. Thought must also be given to practitioners' personal beliefs and the philosophies associated with these subjects and importantly, do they consider that they have the necessary time and expertise to address such sensitive and personal issues? (See chapters 15 and 16). Some of the general ethical issues are captured under the following:

▶ controversies evoked by the topic of spirituality

▶ not getting it right, treading on holy ground, fear of mismanagement

▶ lack of spiritual confidence

▶ theory practice gap, and why this exists

▶ ethical concerns as to:

  ▶ inappropriate proselytising

  ▶ imposition of religious beliefs or activities (such as prayer)

  ▶ bias against various spiritual perspectives (for some debate, see Ahmed, 2009)

Therefore, some of the barriers or deficits associated with spiritual assessment and spiritual care need to be challenged. These may be the organisational, environmental, economic and educational barriers that inhibit and prevent engagement with spiritual matters. For example, the misconception that spirituality is only appropriate to people who hold and practice a religious belief. Some of the misconceptions and ambiguity around the word spirituality must be explored through ongoing personal and professional development. This may also remove some of the uncomfortable and negativism. For some, as Walter (2002) highlights, may not see spirituality as a welcome opportunity.

Documentation

One area that needs to be considered in the discussion of ethics surrounding spiritual assessment is the issue of documentation. The primary purpose of any assessment is to identify whether a person has any specific needs. From this assessment, needs are documented and a plan of care developed (either electronically or other format) to support the person to meet any identified need. Documentation is important because it provides a detailed, chronological account of the person's psychiatric history, their own personal journey and care delivered. Any care plan produced will take into account all health and social care assessment including the Care Programme Approach (CPA). For example, in one of the authors' trusts they use the CPA and Section 5 of it addresses cultural and spiritual issues. This section includes any religious and cultural needs that the service user believes would make life better.

CPA is a model for delivering patient-focused care and is based on four principles:

▶ a comprehensive assessment of health and social care needs

▶ a single care plan that describes how identified needs will be met

▶ the allocation of a care co-ordinator to oversee the delivery of the care plan and to communicate with all those involved

▶ the review of the process; CPA may be used in conjunction with a spiritual assessment tool to aid the practitioner to engage in a dialogue about spiritual concerns.

Conclusion

This chapter has presented and explored the conceptual, organisational, practical and ethical challenges surrounding the development of spiritual assessment tools. Yet as the final sections of this chapter reveal, the introduction of spiritual assessment tools requires methodical planning, development, implementation and education. Careful consideration must also be given to the ethical challenges that impact upon the area of spiritual aspect. Failure to address the ethical issues will result in the development of spiritual assessment tools that have the potential to be intrusive and offensive to both service users and practitioners.

The material presented implies spiritual assessments may have a therapeutic effect, enhancing the delivery of mental health services by focusing upon the holistic needs of individuals. Furthermore, the entering into a meaningful dialogue with patients improves the channels of communication and establishes a rapport. Clinicians and practitioners regularly discover that taking a spiritual history, at whatever level, by enquiring attentively to patients' primary concerns and motivating factors, deepens rapport and improves the quality of the caring relationship. Feeling valued as individuals, patients often relax and invest further trust in the doctor and practitioner, thus improving the therapeutic alliance.

The exploration of spiritual needs with individuals may identify the person's inner resources that can be utilised during recovery from mental illness. In addition, the introduction of spiritual assessment may raise awareness of the importance of spiritual practices (religious and secular) that individuals draw upon to make sense and find meaning and purpose during times of crisis and need. The use of spiritual assessment tools may assist with making connections to external supports, both directly through local chaplaincy (spiritual and pastoral care) departments, and indirectly from families, friends and liaison with an individual's own religious spiritual leader.

With thanks to Steve Wharmby, senior OT, States of Jersey Mental Health Services, for his kind assistance.

References

Ahmed M (2009) Should I pray or should I go? *Community Care* **1789** 16–17.

Anandarajah G & Hight E (2001) Spirituality and medical practice: using the HOPE questions as a practical tool for spiritual assessment. *American Family Physician* **63** (1) 81–88.

Baldacchino D (2010) Indicator-based and value clarification tools. In: W McShery & L Ross (Eds). *Spiritual Assessment in Healthcare Practice.* Keswick: M&K Publishing.

Barber J (2009) *Handbook of Spiritual Care in Mental Illness.* Birmingham: Birmingham and Solihull Mental Health Foundation NHS Trust.

Carpenito LJ (1983) *Nursing Diagnosis: Application to clinical practice.* JB Lippincott: New York.

Clarke J (2009) A critical view of how nursing has defined spirituality. *Journal of Clinical Nursing* **18** 1666–1673.

Cobb M (1998) Assessing spiritual needs: an examination of practice. In: M Cobb and V Robshaw. *The Spiritual Challenge of Health Care.* Edinburgh. Churchill Livingstone.

Coyte ME, Gilbert P & Nicholls V (2007) *Spirituality, Values and Mental Health: Jewels for the journey.* London: Jessica Kingsley Publishers.

Culliford L & Eagger S (2009) Assessing spiritual needs. In: C Cook, A Powell & A Sims (Eds). *Spirituality and Psychiatry.* London: RCP publications.

Department of Health (2006) *From Values to Action: The chief nursing officer's review of mental health nursing.* London: DH.

Edwards W & Gilbert P (2007) Spiritual assessment: narratives and responses. In: ME Coyte, P Gilbert & V Nicholls. *Values and Mental Health: Jewels for the Journey.* London: Jessica Kingsley.

General Medical Council (2008) *Personal Beliefs and Medical Practice.* London: GMC.

Gilbert P (2008) *Guidelines on Spirituality for Staff in Acute Care Services.* Staffordshire University: CSIP/NIMHE.

Gilbert P, Bates P, Carr S, Clark M, Gould N & Slay G (2010) *Social Work and Mental Health.* Lyme Regis: Russell House Publishing.

Gordon T & Mitchell D (2004) A competency model for the assessment and delivery of spiritual care. *Palliative Medicine* **18** 646–651.

Gorsuch RL & Miller WR (1999) Assessing spirituality. In: WR Miller (Ed). *Integrating Spirituality into Treatment: Resources for practitioners.* Washington DC, US: American Psychological Association.

Govier I (2000) Spiritual care in nursing: a systematic approach. *Nursing Standard* **14** (17) 32–36.

Hay MW (1989) Principles in building spiritual assessment tools. *American Journal of Hospice Care* September/October 25–31.

Highfield MF (1993) PLAN: a spiritual care model for every nurse. *Quality of Life* **2** (3) 80–84.

Jacobson N & Greenley D (2001) What is recovery? A conceptual model and explication. *Psychiatric Services* **52** 482–485. (Accessed online: http://ps.psychiatryonline.org/cgi/content/full)

Lyall D (2001) *Integrity of Pastoral Care.* London: SPCK.

McSherry W (2006) *Marking Sense of Spirituality in Nursing and Health Care Practice: An interactive approach* (2nd Ed). London: Jessica Kingsley Publishers.

McSherry W (2010) Spiritual assessment: definition, categorisation and features. In: W McShery & L Ross (Eds). *Spiritual Assessment in Healthcare Practice*. Keswick: M&K Publishing.

McSherry W & Ross L (2002) Dilemmas of spiritual assessment: considerations for nursing practice. *Journal of Advanced Nursing* **38** (5) 479–488

McSherry W & Cash K (2004) The language of spirituality: an emerging taxonomy. *International Journal of Nursing Studies* **41** (2004) 151–161.

Narayanasamy A (2001) *Spiritual Care: A practical guide for nurses and health care practitioners* (2nd Ed) Wiltshire: Quay Books.

Murray S, Kendall M, Boyd K, Worth A & Benton T (2004) Exploring the spiritual needs of people dying of lung cancer or heart failure: a prospective qualitative interview study of patients and their carers. *Palliative Medicine* **18** 39–45.

National Institute for Mental Health in England (2005) *NIMHE Guiding Statement on Recovery*. London: Department of Health.

O'Brien M (1998) *Spirituality in Nursing*. Boston: Jones and Bartlett.

Puchalski CM & Romer AL (2000) Taking a spiritual history allows clinicians to understand patients more fully. *Journal of Palliative Medicine* **3** 129–137.

Royal College of Psychiatrists (2006) *Spirituality and Mental Health* (Help is at Hand Series leaflet). London: Royal College of Psychiatrists.

Stoll R (1979) Guidelines for spiritual assessment. *American Journal of Nursing* **1** 1572–1577.

Stoter D (1995) *Spiritual Aspects of Health Care*. London: Mosby.

Timmins F & Kelly J (2008) Spiritual assessment in intensive and cardiac care nursing. *Nursing in Critical Care* **13** (3) 124–131.

Walter T (2002) Spirituality in palliative care: opportunity or burden? *Palliative Medicine* **16** 133–139.

White G (2006) *Talking about Spirituality in Healthcare Practice*. London: Jessica Kingsley Publishers.

Chapter 11

Children and young people's well-being

Rebecca Nye

When Ryan was seven years old he came home from school to find his mum dead. She had committed suicide. Now eight, he has never spoken about her or her death at school, something all too apparent to his teachers and classmates who sense he is increasingly weighed down by carrying this unspeakable pain. One day, as part of their religious education lesson on parables, the teacher tells a story to the children. The children sit in a circle to focus on the objects used to tell the story quietly. It is a reflective storytelling style so the story is not overshadowed by the storyteller's persona or the distraction of audience participation. The story describes the 'kingdom of heaven' as being like when a person searches and searches for a great pearl, and on finding it, he gives up everything for this. As the story ends the teacher invites the children to comment on the character's behaviour. Most say he must have been crazy to give up so much for apparently so little. There's a lot of laughter and ridiculing of this silly man. Then the teacher asks *'is there anything you'd give up everything for?'* Again, most are negative, but Ryan speaks up. *'Yes, my mum is that pearl. I'd give up everything to have her back'.* All seem aware of the breakthrough Ryan's comment represents, as well as its poignancy, and there's a prolonged moment of stillness and respect. Finally, the boy nearest to Ryan reaches out to pat Ryan's arm.

Mia is 12, has been losing weight and looks permanently tired and anxious. The school nurse is aware that her dad has chronic alcoholism and that things must be hard at home. As they chat, Mia says she can cope so long as she 'does prayers and stuff' every night to ensure that her dad doesn't have a 'bad day'. She worries that sometimes she just falls asleep before she's done enough, *"cos if I manage about an hour or more, my dad can be quite good the next day'*. Mia also mentions it's easier to stay awake on an empty stomach, suggesting she is deliberately restricting her food intake. She justifies this saying, that it *'makes prayers better too doesn't it, like fasting and stuff that my friends do at Ramadan. I know what they mean, it really is like you are closer to God that way'*.

As these two cases suggest, spirituality can be a potent reality in childhood. It is certainly not something that is for 'adults only', nor something that occurs only to children with obvious religious backgrounds. The crucial primary response we can make is to assume spirituality does feature in children's lives, and that to ignore that reality can negatively impact children's well-being.

These cameos also highlight that spirituality is not simply a panacea or a 'short cut' to well-being. Sometimes, as in Ryan's story, spirituality is part of the coping, recovery or adjustment process in a positive way. For others, like Mia perhaps, spirituality can seem to contribute to the stressors and disorder in a young person's life. The experience of spiritual distress as a child will be explored towards the end this chapter too.

Treading sensitively through this can feel like walking through a minefield. When spirituality, often out of the blue, is expressed to us in some way, we may be unsure about 'where to start' or how to 'say the right thing' to the child. But the general taboo around intruding into the 'private' territory of religious belief and cultural practices can feel even stronger when our clients are children: we worry that we may be insensitive to the child's family, community or culture, or over-influence a child in terms of our own beliefs. We may tend to steer away from this area with the child, but follow it up indirectly with adult family members instead. It is important to be aware of our instinctive avoidance of this area, and any inclination to ignore the feelers children put out about spiritual things – experiences, thoughts, behaviours or motives. Ultimately, this avoidance sends children messages which can undermine our promises to listen and to care generally.

This chapter will equip you to overcome that temptation to avoid or pass over spirituality in working with children. It will provide a brief guide to research findings which establish common features of natural childhood spirituality and to explore some of the ways these contribute to children's well-being. It will also address the various ways a child's context – their family, community, culture, (both religious and non-religious) – can affect the child's natural spirituality.

Children's spirituality: who has it?

In 1990, psychiatrist Robert Coles (1992) published a landmark account of conversations with a wide range of children from many faiths and cultures. The book's title was *The Spiritual Life of Children*. Then, and to some extent still today, the title had a certain shock value. It raises immediate questions.

▶ Can children have spiritual lives? If so, from what age?

▶ What kind of children? Do they need to be religious?

▶ In what sense are they 'spiritual'? Is it about what they say, what they believe or having certain experiences?

▶ Are children aware of this? Does it 'count' if they are not?

▶ Do they seek it, or does it just happen to them?

These questions highlight some of the assumptions many people make about children and the quality of their experience. There's a tendency to assume that 'if there is anything spiritual on', it is either because it has been drummed into them (eg. indoctrination) or they are simply very unusual.

However, a detailed series of case studies of 40 'ordinary' school children in the UK, most of whom had no family faith background, yielded a rich variety of spiritual experiences, spiritual views and self-taught spiritual practices drawing on not only some religious knowledge, but also ideas from science, stories and films, and significant relationships (see Hay & Nye, 1998). In fact, children's spirituality can have a particularly authentic quality to it because it arises out of everyday moments and isn't necessarily yoked to a particular kind of language or faith, as Louise's example below illustrates. Their spirituality is not only connected to deliberately 'spiritual' places, actions or statements such as a church or temple, ceremonies such as weddings and funerals, or restricted to religious statements of belief or traditional spiritual narratives. They are as likely to find any aspect of their environment spiritually stimulating, provoking awe (which can be a kind of fear) or wonder, or prompting an intuitive (but powerfully intense) awareness of transcendence.

> For Louise, 10, at playtime on a sunny day, the blue of the sky was 'holy', and the greenness of grass was a kind of metaphysical mystery ('where does green even come from?').
>
> Recalling her experience of gazing through her brother's telescope, she remembered very powerful feelings: 'It all has a meaning, but you can't think of the meaning … all of the … um … growing, flying and just imagining things. And it all just fits into "one" and it's just like a big explosion in your mind.'

Nevertheless, the assumption that spirituality is not a normal feature of childhood, arising in ordinary moments of children's lives, means that children (and those who care for them) can worry about their mental and emotional stability when addressing things from a spiritual perspective.

Nadeem, 10, explaining why he'd never mentioned his spiritual ideas and feelings with his family or friends: *'Because they might think I'm stupid or something … it's embarrassing'.*

'It's one of those things you can't explain … it really doesn't make sense to other people.' (Anya, 11)

'Perhaps they [my family] *do it too* [pray] *themselves, but they'd tease me if they knew I did.'* (Seema, 10)

'And sometimes I think about which God's real … and after the universe … what is the universe? Is it going on forever … [it] gets annoying trying to think about it … you think your brain's gonna get all scrambled.' (Tim, 10) (quotes from Hay & Nye, 1998)

So paradoxically, although spirituality is often about sensing a deep sense of connectedness (to God, to self, to others or to nature), there's an inherent loneliness in this realm of experience for children – 'no one else thinks or feels like this'.

'Sometimes I feel very lonely when I am alone with God because I can't see God and I can't hear God; I just think about God, and I feel really, really lonely.' (Beth, 10)

So, in answer to the sorts of questions posed above, numerous recent studies have systematically documented that:

▶ children can and do experience spirituality in words and feelings, affecting thoughts and behaviours

▶ this is ubiquitous among all kinds of children

▶ this is largely spontaneous and natural.

In other words, childhood spirituality is 'normal', and possibly more prevalent than in adulthood. Large scale studies in Finland found 60% of 11-year-old children and 80% of seven-year-old children reported having experienced a sense of divine presence at least once in their lives (see Tamminen, 1991). And it is common for adults to report that the most vivid spiritual events of their lives occurred in childhood, though expressing this or finding anyone to take this seriously was very hard (see Robinson, 1983).

While studies of very young children are harder to undertake, from a psychological perspective younger children may have heightened perception and capacity for spiritual experience eg. for feelings of awe, wonder, sense of mystery or value, a search for meaning and pattern, or experiences of feeling totally overwhelmed (see Kimes Myers,1997). The difference for the younger child is that they normally lack a recognisable language to frame this to themselves, let alone express it (see Watts, et al, 2002). It is interesting to speculate whether early non-verbal expressions, including peaceful contentment, infant rage, tantrums, fascinations and fears might be symptoms, sometimes, of early spiritual encounter. Certainly, in some African cultures, many signs of infant distress are interpreted as spiritual unease ie. a kind of existential angst or adjustment to 'being alive' rather than automatically put down to physical causes like teething, hunger or tiredness (see Gottlieb, 2006).

The functions of childhood spirituality

Coles (1992) explained this prevalence of childhood spirituality as a natural response to living their lives, and that this serves an important function.

'Children try to understand not only what is happening to them, but why; and in doing that, they call upon the religious life they have experienced, the spiritual values they have received, as well as other sources of potential explanation.' (Coles, 1992)

It can help them to make meaning, find resolution, or cope. Another way of seeing this is to assert that spirituality helps meet particular kinds of need in childhood, to process things more effectively. This highlights the importance of supporting (not sidestepping) the child's instinct to process life events 'spiritually' ie. their need to work on the big picture existential issues that lie behind prime facie happenings – such as 'who am I?', 'am I free or controlled by things?', 'is there any meaning to this?', 'what's the point or purpose of being?', 'what about good and evil?', 'what about power and dependency?', 'is anything permanent – does everything end?' and so on.

Spirituality is also inherently developmental: it can often move people on, help them to grow or transform. As Miller states *'spirituality moves the individual toward knowledge, love, meaning, peace, hope, transcendence, connectedness, compassion and wholeness'* (Miller, 2003). Since so much about childhood involves change and growth, it makes sense that spirituality can play an especially important function in the most developmental periods of our lives, and that its suppression or malfunction can cause serious harm.

Without support and interest from others that their spiritual ideas, intuitions and questions are worthwhile, children not only feel this is a lonely area, but can learn to suppress this, with potentially devastating effects on their ability to wrestle with life for themselves. Deprived of opportunities to explore or share this with others, children have *'to travel too alone and too far in their spiritual journeys'* (Derezotes, 2006). These connections are important for those in helping professions. Paying attention to spirituality may facilitate both the child's and practitioner's own understanding of their reality – appreciating the myriad ways they address the big 'why' questions (verbally or otherwise) especially in response to complex life events.

In Ryan's example above, the 'spiritual' story functioned as a way to say something about the proportions of his loss, his love and his needs, and what seemed the first chance for explicit peer support. But it seems there is an important general benefit (or cost) to the child's well-being here too. By having an 'open door' policy on spirituality as a normal and necessary part of children's ways of processing experience, children might feel encouraged to use this additional route to expressing complex emotional needs and reactions. In other words, this is not just about something that comes up sometimes, or in certain cases, and requires a rather specialist set of procedures. Rather this is something that matters all of the time, and requires a protocol and style to reflect that.

Reflection exercise

Influential development psychologist Erik Erikson suggested *'the most deadly of sins is the mutilation of a child's spirit'*. Why do you think encouragement or hindrance of spirituality could affect a child so much?

Think of a recent encounter with or observation of a child. Can you identify any 'big issues' they may have been wrestling with? How was this evident – in words, play, behaviour, silence?

Working with children's spirituality

It is one thing to accept that spirituality plays an important part in children's mental health, but another to know how to handle this in your practice. Spirituality in childhood does not mean simply finding out what a child's beliefs are, or even less merely gathering information about what their family view is on key spiritual issues. To know 'they are Jewish' or 'they are atheists' suggests that a fixed set of conclusions characterises both the child and the adults in their lives – spirituality is more fluid than this. The key features of children's spirituality (see figure 1) remind us that this is not something that will appear 'on demand', especially in a time-limited meeting. It can be characterised by flashes of insight, intensity and clarity on one hand, and incomprehension, indifference and uncertainty on the other. Sometimes the tide is in, sometimes it's out.

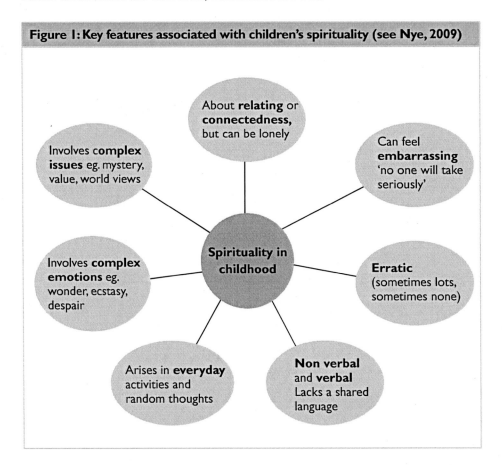

Figure 1: Key features associated with children's spirituality (see Nye, 2009)

The complexity of spiritual ideas and emotions can seem a barrier too, especially for adults who might (wrongly) assume that children can only process what they can verbalise. For example, even without traditional spiritual vocabulary, children frequently develop or intuit their own concept of 'God', ie. they may have a developing internal, non verbal frame of reference that may be vibrant and sophisticated compared to their formal comprehension. And while so much about spirituality revolves around a sense of connectedness of the child's self to 'more than just me', there is the fear that no one else experiences that, so it could be defensively guarded.

A useful first step is to operate in ways that respect, rather than try to overrule, these qualities. Using the letters of SPIRIT as a mnemonic is a helpful guide to what facilitates spirituality in most practice settings. Note: most good practice in mental health encounters, especially with children, should aspire to create these sorts of therapeutic conditions.

S – Space

Creating a feeling of 'safe space', avoiding physical or emotional crowding or intrusion; aesthetically 'warm, cared for' rooms are preferable to clinical, paying heed to wider environmental influences (war, family conflict, urban desolation) which could depress or uplift someone's 'spirits'.

P– Process

Absence of time-pressure to 'produce' a result. Allowing time for insight or questions to arise, comfortable with silence.

I – Imagination

Being deliberately open to creative, perhaps unusual ways of expressing inner life, through art, movement, play, drama etc.

R – Relationship

Being sensitive to issues of perceived authority and judgement, aiming for a style that offers the child the confidence to be and speak for him/herself.

I – Intimacy

Supporting vulnerability; the need for privacy – sharing issues with others only with permission and when really necessary; sensitive to fact that shared spirituality may expose child's most inner core of hurts, struggles and insights to themselves and to you.

T – Trust

Being comfortable in yourself with your range of knowing and not knowing, trusting the child, trusting the process.

Specific tools

Clearly, the ineffability of spirituality is exaggerated for children. Equally, the adult capacity to appreciate what is said by children about this as part of a discussion is often stretched to its limits. Transcribing conversations offers a valuable way to discover almost missed comments or notice hidden threads – 'big questions' in an apparently erratic chat about not much at all.

Stories

Stories (both from various spiritual traditions and fairytales and myths) allow children to raise, or simply find recognition of, spiritual issues such as redemption, birth and death, chaos and order in the widest sense (see Crompton, 1998). Often relating to stories 'about others' can reduce the embarrassment factor. Stories, songs and music can also help to hold the complexity of spiritual feelings for children (eg. delight, despair, adversity, courage) and responses, and act as sources of comfort, strength or illumination in themself. That is to say, the story may be more effective than anything a practitioner's carefully worded response could offer. Children's desire to have certain stories (or films) repeated over and over may point to spiritual processing of key existential issues – a 'self-help' remedy for their mental well-being.

Bhagwan suggests *'the greatest sacred stories are our own'* (Bhagwan, 2009) and encourages the practice of helping children to tell, write or make visual representations of their own life story, including those elements that transcend their immediate existence – the 'before me, beyond me' connections to the past and possible future.

Rituals

Rituals are clearly important ways that people process life events at a spiritual level. For example, these can help to address issues of loss, grief and hope (such as at a funeral), or more generally offer ways to connect with others in experiences of spiritual life, including responses of wonder, reverence, comfort, gratitude, protection and uncertainty (eg. Shabbat, Puja or Holy Communion). Children can benefit from being part of rituals as they offer a predominately non-verbal and shared (not lonely) approach to this area of experience. The repetition of action and signs also supports a more gradual kind of processing, rather than a 'now I get it' kind of understanding, which discussion tends to demand. Equally, it is worth paying attention to any rituals the child has created – possibly another clue to their well-being (or not, as in Mia's case at the beginning of this chapter), and to the success of self-administered spiritual 'therapy'.

Creative arts

Creative arts, including art, movement or poetry, can help express those 'hard to communicate' aspects of spirituality non-verbally (see Broadbent, 2004). Also, silence and meditative techniques can have a role too (see Galanki, 2005; Goodman, 2005).

Children can also be encouraged to create something tangible, which may become an important symbol of their situation, with a capacity to hold together the emotional complexity of that more effectively than words, and with more permanence than conversation. This approach works well in work with bereaved children who can be invited to represent the complexity of their grief with layers of coloured sand – even very young children find this a way to articulate the mix of 'sad' emotions and 'happy' memories, as well as a physical referent to what is now intangible (grief) and absent (the person who died).

Again, children may already have their own important symbols that support their spiritual processing. For example, a terminally ill child treasured a 'guardian angel' trinket her aunt had given her. From the aunt's point of view, this was a source of comfort and protection for the girl. But in fact, the girl was frustrated that her family could not face talking to her about dying, and so privately this angel became the focus for her thoughts, questions and feelings about 'becoming an angel' herself – in fact her 'death' symbol.

Spiritual distress

As the previous example serves to remind us, negative, and even bleak experiences, are part of children's spirituality range. Sometimes these can even be important causal factors in their mental ill health. Distressing or anxiety-provoking aspects can include fear, terror, despair, panic and unworthiness. The embarrassment 'only I feel or think like this' factor is heightened in these forms, giving children even greater reason to suspect they are going mad. Common types of negative spiritual issues among children include fixations about death or obsessions about specific religious ideas (at least their own interpretation of those) such as sin, lack of perfection, the reality of evil (the devil, witches, ghosts, hell), or the sinister omniscience of God 'watching them'. However, 'diffuse' spiritual unease is also possible.

The desire to protect children from negative emotions can mislead some to regard childhood as a rather anodyne period, devoid of the most profound struggles associated with adult spiritual distress – the 'dark nights of the soul'. However, in his influential psychological model of the lifecycle, Erik Erikson (2008) identifies key existential conflicts and resolutions faced at every developmental stage. This reminds us that, if anything, the potential prevalence of spiritual crises is greater for children as they work their way through developing a sense of hope, a sense of will, of purpose, of competence and fidelity decisions via struggles with trust, autonomy, shame, doubt, initiative, guilt, inferiority and identity. In children, the forms these crises adopt can hide the profundity or sense of ultimacy being faced, though at least by adolescence we accept (or remember) that the struggle to find our identity is not trivial at all. To date, a lot of the research literature about spiritual distress in childhood is in fact gathered from adults' recollections. What these accounts share is a sense that, had they expressed this as children, the scale of their distress would have been dismissed.

The implications for mental health services here are fairly clear: don't underestimate the degree to which children face spiritual angst, and the potential for this to have a life-long negative legacy on well-being if ignored. Research on the collateral spiritual distress suffered by children with suffering physical illness tells a similar story (see Pridmore & Pridmore, 2004; Erickson, 2008). The need to provide the space, process, imaginative strategies, relationship, intimacy and trust (SPIRIT) to help children process these in cases can be vital. Eaude (2009) makes the case that supporting agency may be an important factor in the relationship between child mental and physical health and spiritual well-being. In other words, that rather than protecting or distracting children from suffering, it can be important to enable children to face, for themselves, aspects of their life circumstances that take them deep beneath the surface issues of this crisis or that ailment.

However, there is evidence that many of the same tools that foster a child's engagement with 'positive' spirituality (stories, rituals, symbols etc), can trigger distress too, especially when the material is unfamiliar or culturally distant. Ipgrave (1995) described how some Muslim children feared the demons and ghosts in Christian graveyards, but not Muslim cemeteries; similarly secular children can find visits to churches with crucifixes disturbing, especially as sometimes the timing of school holidays means the end of the Easter story is not heard at all.

Conclusion

This chapter has focused on how spirituality can affect children's well-being and how adults with responsibility for children's mental health can best respond to this. Other chapters address mental health in a variety of adult contexts, and yet one might bear in mind that children, and their spirituality, still feature in those lives too. Indeed sometimes 'a child has the ability to inspire others, create change and provide vision for others' (Harris, 2007). This is to say, a child can be an agent of transformation often providing a kind of transcendence or breakthrough to others in difficulty too – a theme in fact of more than one spiritual tradition.

References

Bhagwan R (2009) Creating sacred experiences for children as pathways to healing, growth and transformation. *International Journal of Children's Spirituality* **14** (3) 225–234.

Broadbent J (2004) Embodying the abstract: enhancing children's spirituality through creative dance. *International Journal of Children's Spirituality* **9** 97–104.

Coles R (1992) *The Spiritual Life of Children*. New York: Houghton Mifflin.

Crompton M (1998) *Children, Spirituality, Religion and Social work*. Aldershot: Ashgate.

Derezotes D (2006) *Spiritually Oriented Social Work Practice*. New York: Allyn & Bacon.

Eaude T (2009) Happiness, emotional well-being and mental health – what has children's spirituality to offer? *International Journal of Children's Spirituality* **14** (3) 185–196.

Erickson D (2008) Spirituality, loss and recovery in children with disabilities. *International Journal of Children's Spirituality* **13** (3) 287–296.

Galanki E (2005) Solitude in the school: a neglected facet of children's development and education. *Childhood and Education* **86** 573–580.

Goodman T (2005) Working with children: beginner's mind. In: CK Germer, CD Siegel & PR Fulton (Eds) *Mindfulness and Psychotherapy*. New York: Guildford Press.

Gottleib A (2006) Non western approaches to spiritual development among infants and young children: a case study from west Africa. In: P Benson, P King, L Wagener & E Roehlkepartain *Handbook of Spiritual Development in Childhood and Adolescence*. London: Sage.

Harris K (2007) Re-conceptualising spirituality in the light of educating young children. *International Journal of Children's Spirituality* **12** 263–275.

Hay D & Nye R (1998) *The Spirit of the Child*. London: Harper Collins.

Ipgrave J (1995) God and Guna: The religious education of Muslim children. Unpublished report cited in M Crompton (1998) *Children, Spirituality and Social Work*. London: Ashgate.

Kimes Myers B (1997) *Young Children and Spirituality*. London: Routledge.

Miller G (2003) *Incorporating Spirituality in Counselling and Psychotherapy*. Hoboken, NJ: John Wiley & Sons.

Nye R (2009) *Children's Spirituality: What it is and why it matters*. London: Church House Press.

Pridmore P & Pridmore J (2004) Promoting the spiritual development of sick children. *International Journal of Children's Spirituality* **9** (1) 21–38.

Robinson E (1983) *The Original Vision: A study of the religious experience of childhood*. New York: Seabury Press.

Tamminen K (1991) *Religious Development in Childhood and Youth: An empirical study*. Helsinki: Suomalainen Tiedeakatemia.

Watts F, Nye R & Savage S (2002) *Psychology for Christian Ministry*. London: Routledge.

Chapter 12

Dementia and spirituality: a perfume always remembered

Ben Bano, Susan Mary Benbow and Kate Read

Introduction

In chapter 1 Peter Gilbert draws on a definition of spirituality developed by the Royal College of Psychiatrists (Cook *et al*, 2009) to expand the concept of spirituality as relating to a person's inner spirit – their experience of being human. Spirituality gives meaning and purpose to our lives and our relationships with others, and sustains us through challenging times. Spirituality may relate to organised religion, but this is not exclusive.

What is spirituality in relation to a person with dementia? Many definitions of spirituality have been offered in recent years. There is recognition that spirituality involves the qualities which are deepest in us and provide us with purpose and meaning in our lives. This is particularly important in old age when some of us need an opportunity to look back and reflect on what we have done with lives. One helpful definition of spirituality is: *'The personal quest for understanding answers to ultimate questions about life, about meaning, and about relationship to the sacred and transcendent, which may (or may not) lead to or arise from the development of religious rituals and the formation of community.'* (Koenig *et al*, 2000)

Elizabeth Mackinlay provides another definition: *'That which lies at the core of each person's being, an essential dimension which brings meaning to life. It is acknowledged that spirituality is not constituted only by religious practices, but must be understood more broadly, as a relationship with God, however God or ultimate meaning is perceived by the person, and in relationship with other people.'* (MacKinlay, 2001)

How might we apply this understanding to the world of a person with a dementia, in the face of the seeming disintegration of both physical and mental faculties? A traditional view of dementia sees the self deteriorating as dementia attacks the mind, and people retaining a form of social behaviour despite their actions becoming meaningless. People with dementia are labelled as 'dementia sufferers', even though not everyone with dementia necessarily suffers. In fact, some people with dementia can be filled with – and radiate to others – a sense of great peace and joy. As Barbara Pointon, in chapter 5, movingly puts it: *'To stand stripped of everything the world values and to see each other as we really are is a very precious and humbling experience, and one which I would never have encountered if it was not for the ravages of dementia. Paradoxically, Malcolm's "losses" have turned into "gains"*.

Personhood and identity

To be a spiritual being requires an acknowledgement of ourselves as unique beings, with strengths as well as deficits and with our individual choices and preferences. Hence to promote the spirituality of someone with dementia we need to promote their personhood. Over recent years there has been a fundamental shift in the way we see people with a dementia, due not least to the influence of the late Tom Kitwood, who challenged the prevailing traditional model of dementia.

Kitwood reminded us that we have to see the person as a whole and that a person with a dementia functions in a world that is social as well as physical. This is why he stressed the need for a person with a dementia to be seen as a person first rather than someone afflicted by declining physical and mental functioning. Kitwood defined the concept of personhood, which he saw as: 'the morality of accepting and acknowledging the right of each person within the care relationship to be accepted as a person with the same needs, worth and well-being as other members in the relationship' (Kitwood, 1997).

A focus on the personhood of a person with dementia enables us to focus on their qualities as a living being rather than as someone who has a terminal condition, symbolising a living death. A focus on personhood counteracts a perception that as dementia advances we lose any hope of having a meaningful existence. As Goldsmith (2004) reminds us, comments such as *'The brains of these people are virtually dead. All they need now is quietness and physical care'* are being challenged by those who believe in the potential of people with dementia.

Kitwood's views on personhood led to a focus on person-centred care. The core of the philosophy of person-centred care is based on:

▶ a focus on the person with dementia as much as on managing the symptoms of dementia

▶ getting to know the person, and then thinking about how their dementia is affecting them

▶ valuing people who are at risk of being vulnerable.

How do we promote the personhood and the spiritual identity of someone whose mental and physical faculties may appear to be fragmenting and ebbing away? In line with Gilbert's question in the first chapter, we need to ask what gives a person with dementia a sense of purpose and meaning. This is relevant not just in working with a person with advancing dementia, but equally in working with a person who may have just been diagnosed with a dementia and who may have a sense of hopelessness and worthlessness after the diagnosis.

Kitwood's approach reminds us of the importance of considering the whole person when seeking to understand the personhood and identity of a person with dementia. Personhood can be lost in dementia as the psychological defences which enable us to cope with anxiety and adverse life events are broken down. People with dementia may have difficulty in making sense of their life story as they have difficulty in filtering out challenging times in looking back at their life. Social interactions each day, important for all of us, can lack meaning and satisfaction.

We need to remember that it is often when someone has been diagnosed with a form of dementia that feelings of vulnerability and uncertainty can come to the fore. In particular, for people diagnosed at a relatively early age there will be a lack of self-worth, hopelessness and anxiety that one's faculties will inevitably decline.

> ### Box 1: Promoting the personhood and spirituality of a person when a diagnosis of dementia has been made
>
> People with a diagnosis of early dementia may feel excluded and marginalised from discussions about them and the support they may need in the future.
>
> ▶ A person with early dementia may be feeling very vulnerable, particularly after they have been diagnosed. Feelings of a lack of self-worth and of being a burden might come to the fore.
>
> ▶ It is important to acknowledge and work with these feelings.
>
> ▶ The person may need encouragement in maintaining activities which enhance their self-worth.
>
> ▶ Where appropriate, faith communities have an important role in ensuring that people at this stage feel included and that the practice of the person's faith is encouraged.
>
> ▶ Care givers can also feel vulnerable. It is important to acknowledge their feelings.

Promoting personhood and spirituality as dementia advances

In line with the principles of person-centred care we need to acknowledge the importance of other people in helping to preserve the personhood and identity of the person with advancing dementia. As Radden and Fordyce (2006) point out: *'Others must remember, reinforce, and reinscribe the identity of the person with dementia ... we must preserve the person's identity as the person's own grasp on it weakens.'*

The promotion of someone's personhood as dementia advances is closely linked to understanding the spiritual journey we each make during our lives. This includes an understanding of what has given and continues to give purpose and meaning in our lives. For someone with advancing dementia, reminiscence work can focus not just on memories of the past, but on their own part in those memories. We need to remember that just as for the rest of us, the spiritual journey of a person with dementia may or may not include a religious belief. In the third section of this chapter we will consider some ways in which personhood and spirituality can be promoted in dementia.

Working with caregivers

Those close to a person with a dementia may only see the loss of functioning in their loved one. They may see this as inevitable and have difficulty in seeing the potential for 'self-hood' in their loved one. It is unrealistic, and possibly unhelpful, to promote a positive image of a person with dementia without giving permission to those involved to articulate deep and often conflicting feelings about their loved one. They may have difficulty in acknowledging the personhood of their loved ones and see only their physical and mental diminishments. They may feel bad or guilty because they have not lived up to their own expectations. They may find themselves in the difficult position of caring for someone who has neglected or abused them in the past. We need to acknowledge the need for formal caregivers, such as support workers and those working in care settings such as residential and nursing homes, to promote an image of dementia based on person-centred care. Later in this chapter we will look at some of the ways this can be done.

Understanding and assessing spiritual needs

Spirituality can be assessed as part of a more holistic assessment and two tools which might be useful in doing this are: Maslow's Hierarchy of Needs (Maslow, 1987) and the Social Role Inventory (O'Brien, 2006). Maslow's Hierarchy of Needs (Maslow, 1987) is represented as a pyramid, see figure 1. The base is a person's physiological needs but, moving up the pyramid, some people add spirituality as the pinnacle of the pyramid.

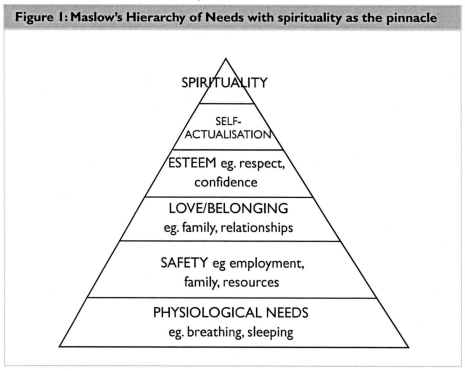

Figure 1: Maslow's Hierarchy of Needs with spirituality as the pinnacle

SPIRITUALITY

SELF-ACTUALISATION

ESTEEM eg. respect, confidence

LOVE/BELONGING eg. family, relationships

SAFETY eg employment, family, resources

PHYSIOLOGICAL NEEDS eg. breathing, sleeping

(Adapted from Maslow (1987))

The Social Role Inventory (O'Brien, 2006) is a tool which develops a profile of the roles a person is performing (or might perform) across eight different areas, which are:

▶ home and neighbourhood

▶ family and friends

▶ work

▶ learning

▶ spiritual/religious

▶ community association/citizenship

▶ sport/fitness

▶ creative expression.

In each of these areas assessment involves considering the constraints facing the person in performing that role and reflection on that person's individual interests, skills and talents. Importantly, it also requires the person to be considered within their community, in relation to the people around them. In this way it places spirituality and religious practices within the context of the various roles that an individual undertakes and it leads to reflection on how the person can be supported to continue to develop that area of their life.

The two tools address spirituality as part of an holistic assessment but there are also specific tools which address spirituality, both in quantitative and qualitative measures.

Various quantitative tools measure aspects of spirituality and faith. Hill and Hood (1999), in Measures of Religiosity, document 126 different measures of religion, faith, belief and spirituality dating back to the 1950s. The System of Belief Inventory (Holland et al, 1998) is a 15-item tool measuring personal spirituality and religious behaviours: it has been used in research with people with dementia (Katsuno, 2003). The Royal Free Interview for Religious and Spiritual Beliefs is a well-known and well-respected instrument (King & Speck, 1995; King et al, 2001; King et al, 2006), which has been used in a memory clinic population of people with dementia and their carers (Jolley et al, in press). There is a short self-report version (King et al, 2001) which takes about 15–20 minutes to complete.

Qualitative methods have also been used to explore aspects of spirituality. They have the advantage of not imposing a structure in the way that quantitative tools inevitably do. Katsuno (2003) combined qualitative and quantitative measures to study 23 people with mild dementia attending a day centre in the USA. 19 reported they viewed religion as important in their daily lives. The main theme identified was faith in God, consisting of six related categories: beliefs, support from God, sense of meaning/purpose in life, private religious practice, public religious practice, and changes due to dementia.

Personal testimonies also contribute to our understanding. Robert Davis, a Methodist minister, wrote an account of changes in his faith and understanding through the progress of Alzheimer's disease (Davis, 1989), which has contributed to the understanding of spirituality and dementia. Robinson (2008) has written about her spiritual journey in *The Friend*.

Morgan (2010) also describes how her spirituality helps her, describing faith as part of the '*essence of you, like a perfume always remembered*'. Many people trace the origins of their spiritual awareness or faith to their early years, but some link it to life-changing experiences related to their illness or the illness of a loved-one (Nightingale, 2003).

'I am enfolded in love; the love of my beloved family, the love of my friends, both in and outside the (Quaker) Society and most of all the love of God. Love so immense it shields me, strengthens and grounds me.' (Robinson, 2008)

The opportunity for individuals to practise their faith and nurture their personal spirituality may provide them with coping resources, social support, comfort and strength (Stuckey & Gwyther, 2003). Therefore, physical and mental health service providers need to take spiritual and religious needs into account in planning holistic care. Friedli (1999) argues the importance of spirituality in physical and mental well-being.

Any assessment of an individual's spiritual needs cannot be reduced to simply asking whether or not the person does or does not have a religious belief. Koenig (2008) describes taking a spiritual history in mental health practice. The Spirituality Special Interest Group of the Royal College of Psychiatrists has a number of useful resources on its website, including a guide to assessment designed for use in mental health (Eagger, 2009). Culliford and Eagger (2009) also give useful practical advice on how to take a spiritual history. They distinguish two types of questions and two areas of spiritual practice. See box 2.

Box 2: Taking a spiritual history

Two types of questions useful in taking a spiritual history

1. What helps you most when things are difficult (eg. when facing severe illness, major loss, important challenges)?

2. Do you regard yourself as being religious or spiritual (or both)?

Two categories of spiritual practice

1. **Mainly religious:**
   ▶ belonging to a faith tradition
   ▶ taking part in forms of worship, sacred music
   ▶ taking part in prayer, meditation
   ▶ reading religious writings.

> **2. Mainly non-religious/secular:**
> ▶ appreciation of the arts
> ▶ engaging in contemplative reading
> ▶ engaging in acts of compassion.
>
> (From Culliford & Eagger, 2009)

There are more detailed approaches to taking a spiritual history using mnemonics which make them easily memorable for practitioners. See box 3 for details of two approaches.

> **Box 3: Mnemonics for spiritual assessment**
>
> FICA (Puchalski & Romer, 2000)
>
> F – faith and belief
>
> I – importance to the current circumstances
>
> C – community
>
> A – how should this be addressed in their health care

Hodge (2005) has described spiritual life maps as another useful tool for spiritual assessment (with the advantage of visual impact). They also facilitate the move on from assessment to intervention or support.

Assessment of spiritual needs should not ignore the spiritual needs of carers and family members. Within the same family there may be a range of religious and spiritual needs and in planning care for a person with dementia the needs of their carer and other family members should not be neglected, indeed in supporting a carer to continue in their caring role, attention to their spiritual needs may be vitally important. Hodge (2001) has described spiritual genograms and these may have a useful role.

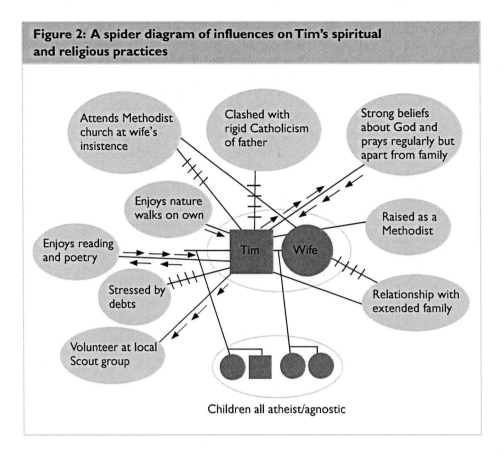

Figure 2: A spider diagram of influences on Tim's spiritual and religious practices

Figure 2 is an example of a spider diagram. This one was drawn by a man called Tim who was asked to think about influences on his spirituality and his religious and spiritual practices during an episode of depression. The arrows show the direction of energy flow and the crossed lines indicate conflicts. This exercise gave Tim some ideas of the possible ways he could relieve sources of stress and obtain more support.

Reflection exercise: spiritual history

Imagine you are taking your own spiritual history. Draw a spider diagram or a family tree to highlight spiritual and religious influences and practices in your life.

Now reflect on the exercise. What can you learn from this about how you might take a spiritual history from people with dementia and their families?

Developing a high quality environment in dementia care

Dawn Brooker (2004) built upon Tom Kitwood's work as she drew together the VIPS Framework as an attempt to synthesise existing evidence and to define the essential elements of person-centred dementia care. The acronym VIPS was used to summarise the defining elements of person-centred care as follows.

V A value base that asserts the absolute value of all human lives regardless of age or cognitive ability.

I An individualised approach recognising uniqueness.

P Understanding the world from the perspective of the service user.

S Providing a social environment that supports psychological needs.

Applying the tool to describe person-centred care in practice (Brooker, 2007) reiterates that consideration and support of people's spiritual needs is intrinsic to delivering each of the elements of the VIPS framework. So what does positive person-centred dementia care feel like and how does spirituality contribute?

Reflection exercise

How would you describe high quality person-centred dementia care?

You may wish to consider this quotation from Eileen Watford of Guild Care which David Sheard cited in his article in the *Journal of Dementia Care* (2008): *'Feels like home, sounds like being among friends, looks like fun. Feels warm, gives a sense of attachment, is secure and happy with contentment and love all around.'*

What evidence would you look for to see that people's spiritual needs were being supported?

How could attention to spiritual needs be evidenced in each of the VIPS elements?

Considering spirituality emphasises the intrinsic value of each individual.

Stuckey and Gwyther (2003) argue strongly that spirituality has a key role in keeping practitioners true to person-centred care: people are more than cognitive ability or memories. So what needs to be considered in developing and delivering spiritually enhancing dementia care?

In the first section we considered the importance of promoting personhood and spirituality in dementia. Box 4 shows some practical ideas on promoting personhood and spirituality in dementia.

Box 4: Ideas for promoting personhood and spirituality in dementia

▶ Families and friends can play a key role in helping to understand the life story of a person with dementia and what has meant most to them, but they need to be asked!

▶ Personhood and identity in dementia if we treat the person with respect and dignity. Communication needs to be simple, but never at the cost of treating the person as a child.

▶ A memory box with treasured objects and possessions can be helpful in providing a reminder of what has meant most to the person with dementia.

▶ Not all memories are helpful. We need to be sensitive to the fact that like any of us some memories can be difficult or painful. Just as for anyone, the religion of a person with dementia can have negative as well as positive effects.

▶ A person with advancing dementia needs the presence and involvement of other people to remind them of their personhood and identity – not just relatives and pastoral visitors but staff who can take a real interest in them as a person with wishes and choices. As Radden and Fordyce (2006) put it: '*Others must remember, reinforce, and reinscribe the identity of the person with dementia … we must preserve the person's identity as the person's own grasp on it weakens…*'

▶ A person with dementia may have had some difficult religious experiences. They may want to express their religious beliefs in a particular way – there is no 'one size fits all'.

▶ Everyday tasks and care routines can often have a real spiritual significance. Careful attention to cultural needs in preparing and serving meals, time taken to ensure that washing and dressing is a meaningful experience, are just some ways of promoting personhood and identity in care settings.

▶ A person with advancing dementia often has a great sense of the present, even if they may not remember what they did a few minutes ago. This sense of the present can be a deep source of satisfaction, enhance the personhood and identity of the person with dementia, and be the source of a profound spiritual experience.

Promoting personhood and spirituality through positive person work

In order to promote the personhood and identity of a person with dementia as well as promoting their spiritual needs we need to interact with them in a way which does not mirror what Kitwood described as the malignant social psychology of social interaction often experienced by a person with dementia. Kitwood described the need for positive person work for people with dementia and describes the interactions which maintain personhood and well-being in a person with dementia. Box 5 describes some of these interactions with particular relevance to care settings and how they may have a spiritual component.

Box 5: Spiritual components of positive person interactions	
Positive person interactions	**Some spiritual components**
Celebration: being alive with joy and gratitude.	Celebrating major religious feasts, for example Easter or Diwali
	Marking joy and gratitude through a religious service
	Dressing in some 'special' clothes
Creation: for example dancing, reading, talking and listening activities.	Enjoying a visit to the garden and picking flowers
	Remembering special occasions such as a wedding or first Communion
	Helping a person to recall familiar prayers and hymns
Recognition: recognising and accepting the uniqueness of the individual with dementia.	Listening to spiritual music together
	Using a memory box containing reminders of the spiritual journey of a person with dementia
	Watching or looking at pictures of birds or animals
Timalation: providing pleasurable activities, for example through using senses to stimulate the body.	Hand massage
	Foot washing
	Listening to familiar music
Validation	Understanding and accepting the reality of someone's experience at an emotional level. Valuing the emotional experiences of the person with dementia and being with the person through those experiences

The key to positive person work is communication. Consideration of spiritual needs is often rushed, either because staff members are uncomfortable raising issues or lack confidence about the specifics of the individual's faith, beliefs and practice. So communication on spiritual issues needs careful attention to dementia friendly practice.

Some of the key guidelines in respect of communication are:

▶ make it clear that you are prepared to spend time with people

▶ take it at their pace

▶ time conversations to the part of the day and length best suited to each person

▶ be prepared for the conversation to skip about

▶ try for a style of questioning that works well for the person (usually short is better)

▶ give the person time to think and respond (avoid rushing in too soon)

▶ be ready to rephrase questions

▶ use words that express respect and understanding

▶ pay attention to non-verbal communication

▶ give the person your genuine undivided attention

▶ recap at intervals both to confirm understanding and to prompt detail or a different memory.

Building up a full life story or history is the key to understanding each person's spirituality and gives scope to enhance spiritual well-being. Some details may be gathered from the person but often involvement of family, friends and colleagues is required. Life story work is central to person-centred care and an excellent way of working purposefully with the person to maintain their sense of self and relationship with the world and loved ones. It is also a vehicle for talking about the part formal religion has played in the person's life, what has guided them at different stages of their lives, what currently gives life meaning and their hopes and fears for the future.

> **Reflection exercise**
>
> Are you and your colleagues aware of the individual life histories and key stories of proud times for each of the people you work with?
>
> How do you use that knowledge to support people's spiritual needs?
>
> How could that knowledge be used more effectively?

There are many excellent resources to support life story work including Age Exchange (http://www.age-exchange.org.uk) and the Life Story Network (http://www.lifestorynetwork.org.uk).

In drawing together life histories it is important to pay attention to the spiritual dimensions throughout the person's life in order to tune in to the elements which are key to experience and expression now. A person may be recorded as having no current religious belief but have very strong and positive memories of attending Sunday school, so activities that draw on hymns and readings from that time may bring feelings of safety and reassurance.

> **Reflection exercise**
>
> To gain some insight into how knowledge of the person's earlier spiritual grounding can be key to stimulating engagement and a sense of comfort and safety seek out a copy of Naomi Feil's moving interaction with Gladys Wilson (available on DVD – 'There is a Bridge'. Extract available at: http://www.memorybridge.org/video9.php

Approaches and activities to address spiritual aspects of care plans for a person with dementia must grow out of each individual's assessment, including their life story. Elements to consider include the following.

Enabling attendance at familiar places of worship

While there is evidence that people with dementia often cease to attend places of worship, research (Snyder, 2003) suggests that this is often linked to social embarrassment, fear of forgetting parts of the ritual, or not remembering faces and names rather than because the experience of worship is no longer meaningful. Sensitive support could restore a sense of belonging to a faith community as well as enabling participation in worship.

Facilitating faith communities to lead worship within day and residential/nursing home settings

Again, this needs insightful facilitation aimed at meeting needs of people who are too frail to attend their previous preferred place of worship. The need for sensitivity is complex: to ensure that those who wish to attend are enabled and that those who do not wish to participate have the scope to opt out without embarrassment. It is also a skilled piece of work to identify leaders from the range of faith communities to match the needs of the people cared for and to engage with those leaders so that they have the necessary understanding of dementia to make their communication effective.

Private spiritual practices

For some people individual prayer or listening to a service, sacred readings or singing hymns is very meaningful. Sometimes this need can be met by thoughtful use of DVDs, CDs, TV or radio. For others support in the lifelong rituals of prayer, whether at significant times during the day or at bedtime, may be needed. It is important to be vigilant for the person who can no longer do this for themselves but gains comfort from the practice. As one of the participants in a study by Snyder (2003) said: *'I am frightened that the day will come when I will no longer be able to think of God's everlasting promises. Then I will have to rely on my dear friends in Christ to keep me close to the Lord and comfort and reassure me with simple scripture passages and prayer.'*

The conversations are needed early in the journey so that there is confidence in providing what is meaningful and important throughout.

Reflection exercise

Iris is an 85-year-old woman with advancing dementia and has been in a specialist EMI unit for the last six months. She is confined to bed and has entered the non-verbal stage of dementia. Familiar hymns arouse a flicker of interest in her. The activities organiser in the home has been encouraged by her manager to spend time with Iris in her bedroom. As she gently holds Iris's hand, the staff member sets a calm and peaceful atmosphere away from the bustle of the home and plays a CD of familiar hymns. When 'Songs of Praise' is on, Iris is unable to watch but shows though expressions her recognition of some of the hymns on the programme.

Think of any people with advancing dementia you are working with.
How could you use this sort of approach to help them?

Sensory reaffirmation

For some, the full ritual of worship may be too taxing even when offered at home, but a particular piece of music may evoke a feeling of peace or of previous happy days. Likewise someone may be moved by a particular style or piece of music either because of its significance or intrinsic beauty.

A piece of art or photographs may have similar significance and be used to great effect.

Natural world

Communing with nature is the preferred way that some people attune themselves to a relationship with their God. For others nature itself provides them with their sense of meaning and place within the order of things. Again, understanding of the person's life story provides the key to significant places that create a sense of communion. This may be facilitated through planned visits, which give scope for later reminiscence, but may also be supported through use of photographs and DVD. For some people the feel of soil in their hands and the opportunity to contribute to growing plants and tending a garden provides a similar connection with creation and the life cycle.

'...in the evening, at sunset, when I spotted [climbed] on a mountain and looked at the valley up which I had just climbed ... and I stopped and realised that's why I come here, and I always cried. It's so beautiful. That is religion. That's my religion.' (Snyder, 2003)

Relationships

Relationships are significant to most people; providing meaning and purpose to their lives, but also from a symbolic perspective of reinforcing their contribution and their being. So key to maintaining well-being and a sense of self is to make meaningful relationships with people and to help them maintain relationships with those who have been important in their lives and whom they love. In a recent interview a wife spoke movingly of the day centre staff who ensured that her husband bought her flowers and a card on her birthday. In this way he regained his role of loving husband

and for a few moments she had back the caring man she had married 40 years ago. Making family and friends welcome, facilitating visits when necessary, sustains a crucial sense of the self as loved and loving.

Key messages

For health and social care workers:

▶ people with dementia have spiritual needs which should be addressed as part of person-centred care

▶ there are various different tools and approaches which can help in assessment

▶ a comprehensive and sensitive spiritual care will lead on to practical care planning from which the person with dementia may gain much strength, comfort and support

▶ alongside the spiritual needs of the person with dementia, health and social care workers should recognise and address the spiritual needs of carers and be aware of their own spiritual needs.

For staff in the care sector:

▶ the spiritual needs of people with more advanced dementia are equally important and can be approached in practical ways such as those suggested above; understanding and meeting spiritual needs is particularly important in end of life care in dementia

▶ addressing spiritual needs is an important part of holistic person-centred care.

For families:

▶ family members can help meet the spiritual needs of their relatives with dementia who are in a care setting by helping the staff to understand the things which mean most to their relative

▶ those working with carers and other family members should be alert to understanding and addressing their spiritual needs as well.

Conclusion

People with dementia often have a profound need to express their spirituality and need the help of other people in maintaining their personhood and identity at a time when they might be disintegrating physically and mentally. There are practical ways to understand and assess spiritual needs and to provide spiritual care for people with dementia as they progress along their journey. These are readily embedded in person-centred care and offer simple but powerful ways of enhancing the experience of people with dementia, their family carers and the staff working with them.

References

Brooker D (2004) What is person-centred care for people with dementia? *Reviews in Clinical Gerontology* **13** (3) 215–222.

Brooker D (2007) *Person-centred Dementia Care: Making services better.* London: Jessica Kingsley.

Cook C, Powell A & Sims A (2009) *Spirituality and Psychiatry.* London: Royal College of Psychiatrists.

Culliford L & Eagger S (2009) Assessing spiritual needs. In: C Cook, A Powell & A Sims (Eds). *Spirituality and Psychiatry* (pp 16–38). London: Royal College of Psychiatrists.

Davis R (1989) *My Journey into Alzheimer's Disease.* Wheaton: Tyndale House.

Eagger S (2009) *A Guide to the Assessment of Spiritual Concerns in Mental Healthcare.* Available at: http://www.rcpsych.ac.uk/pdf/A_guide_to_the_assessment_of_spiritual_concerns_in_mental_healthcare.pdf (accessed November 2010).

Friedli L (1999) A matter of faith. *Nursing Standard* **14** (3) 24.

Goldsmith M (2004) *In a Strange Land: People with dementia and the local church.* Nottinghamshire: 4M Publications.

Hill PC & Hood RW (1999) *Measures of Religiosity.* Birmingham, Alabama: Religious Education Press.

Hodge DR (2001) Spiritual assessment: a review of major qualitative methods and a new framework for assessing spirituality. *Social Work* **46** 203–214.

Hodge DR (2005) Spiritual life maps: a client-centred pictorial instrument for spiritual assessment, planning, and intervention. *Social Work* **50** 77–87.

Holland JC, Kash KM, Passik S, Gronert MK, Sison A, Lederberg M, Russak SM, Baider L & Fox B (1998) A brief spiritual beliefs inventory for use in quality of life research in life-threatening illness. *Psycho-Oncology* **7** 460–469.

Jolley DJ, Benbow SM, Grizzell M, Willmott S, Bawn S & Kingston P (2011) Spirituality and faith in dementia. *Dementia*, in press

Katsuno T (2003) Personal spirituality of persons with early stage dementia. *Dementia* **2** (3) 313–335.

King M & Speck P (1995). The Royal Free Interview for Religious and Spiritual Beliefs: developments and standardization. *Psychological Medicine* **25** 1125–1134.

King M, Speck P & Thomas A (2001) The Royal Free Interview for Spiritual and Religious beliefs: development and validation of a self-report version. *Psychological Medicine* **31** 1015–1023.

King M, Jones L, Barnes K, Low J, Walker C, Wilkinson S, Mason C, Sutherland J & Tookman A (2006) Measuring spiritual belief: development and standardisation of a beliefs and values scale. *Psychological Medicine* **36** (3) 417–425.

Kitwood T (1997) *Dementia Reconsidered: The person comes first.* Buckingham: Open University Press.

Koenig HG (2008) Religion and mental health: what should psychiatrists do? *Psychiatric Bulletin* **32** 201–203.

Koenig HG, McCullough ME & Larson DB (2000) *Handbook of Religion and Health.* New York: Oxford University Press.

Mackinlay E (2001) *The Spiritual Dimension of Ageing.* London: Jessica Kingsley Publishers.

Maslow AH (1987) *Motivation and Personality* (3rd revised edition). Hong Kong: Longman Asia Ltd.

Morgan K (2010) *Meeting with God.* Manuscript in preparation.

Nightingale M (2003) Religion, spirituality and ethnicity. *Dementia* **2** (3) 379–392.

O'Brien J (2006) Reflecting on Social Roles Identifying Opportunities to Support Personal Freedom and Social Integration. Available at: http://www.inclusion.com/socialroleinventory.pdf (accessed June 2010).

Puchalski C & Romer A (2000) Taking a spiritual history allows clinicians to understand patients more fully. *Journal of Palliative Medicine* **3** 129–137.

Radden J & Fordyce J (2006) Into the darkness: losing identity with dementia. In: J Hughes, S Louw & S Sabat (Eds). *Dementia, Mind, Meaning and the Person* (pp 71–88). Oxford: Oxford University Press.

Robinson S (2008) Dementia: my worst nightmare. *The Friend*, 21st November 2008. Available at: http://thefriend.org/magazine/issue/488 (accessed July 2010).

Sheard D (2008) Less doing: more being person-centred. *Journal of Dementia Care* **16** (1) 15–17.

Snyder L (2003) Satisfactions and challenges in spiritual faith and practice for persons with dementia. *Dementia* **2** (3) 299–313.

Stuckey J & Gwyther L (2003) Dementia, religion and spirituality. *Dementia* **2** (3) 291–298.

Further reading and resources

Age Exchange is at: http://www.age-exchange.org.uk

Caritas Social Action Network (www.csan.org.uk) has produced a DVD called 'It's Still ME, Lord...' on spirituality and dementia, which addresses many of the issues raised in this chapter.

The Life Story Network is at http://www.lifestorynetwork.org.uk

There is a Bridge. Extract available at: http://www.memorybridge.org/video9.php

Chapter 13

Mental health, dignity and palliative care

Andrew Goodhead and Malcolm Payne

Introduction

This chapter explores end-of-life and palliative care services as locations for work on issues of mental health and spirituality. We refer particularly to the concept of 'dignity' as a way of understanding the intersection of these issues.

The first section describes current end of life and palliative care policy and practice, and the place of mental health within it. We argue that spirituality has for good reason been an important aspect of addressing good mental health at the end of people's lives and during the bereavement of their carers and families. This is because facing the end of life raises uncertainties about the experience of life that people have had and the need for hope about the future of the personal world that the dying person is leaving. The second section illustrates with a case study how mental health issues may exclude people from spiritual resources in their lives and reduce their resilience in coping with uncertainty and loss later in life. The third section examines 'dignity work' in health and social care and how this connects with spirituality and mental health care. The fourth section proposes that spiritual aspects of end-of-life care focus on, and aim to help people resolve issues about hope and uncertainty; 'dignity work' is a helpful way of conceiving spiritual care practice in this context. We conclude by arguing that we can transfer to other areas of practice the idea of 'dignity work' as a method of spiritual care practice in end of life and palliative care.

End of life and palliative care as settings for spiritual and mental health care practice

This section explores end of life and palliative care and the difference between them. It then goes on to examine why spiritual care engaging with mental health, psychological, psychiatric and social care are important aspects of end-of-life and palliative care services.

Palliative care for people who are dying with advanced disease, together with their carers, families and communities, is a specialist multi-professional practice, developed from services for people with cancer, and other serious diagnosed illnesses (Reith & Payne, 2009). Advanced disease is a disability or illness that has progressed towards an 'end stage' in which symptoms of the condition threaten the life of a patient, having a major impact on patients' health and capacity to carry on normal life. Palliative care starts from medical and nursing care, especially help with pain and symptom control for the individual patient. This is combined with concern for the psychological, social and spiritual issues that arise for someone who is dying and the family and community around them. Palliative care is a well-established element of healthcare services internationally, and is considered by the World Health Organization to be a human right for people with advanced illness (WHO, 2009).

End of life care is the provision of care services wider than palliative care for people who are approaching the end of life. It has developed more recently, from a recognition that most people come to a phase of life in which they become increasingly frail, either mentally or physically, and sometimes suffer a combination of chronic illness and disability, even though they may not have an identifiable serious disease. During this phase of their lives, people may not need or receive extensive specialist medical and nursing help, but their families and people around them and non-specialised health and social services in their community need to focus not only on the daily pressures of dealing with increasing frailty, but also the reality that this signals the approach of the end of life (Reith & Payne, 2009).

Palliative care is practised in a number of different settings. General or non-specialised palliative care is provided by primary health care teams, led by general practitioners, where patients with identifiable advanced disease are cared for at home, with periodic out- or inpatient treatment in hospital. Specialist palliative care has a number of elements. Home care is provided by visiting community nurse specialists acting as part of teams including consultant palliative care physicians and a range of health and social care specialists. The aim is to provide advice and support for patients being cared for at home, their families and carers and for non-specialised professionals in primary care services. Many general hospitals and hospitals have palliative care teams, typically comprising a consultant palliative care physician, specialist nurses and sometimes a social worker. These teams advise practitioners in other specialties in, for example, renal, heart and lung conditions, where life is threatened by a medical condition. Some hospital palliative care teams provide inpatient palliative care; alternatively, they may rely on local hospices. Comprehensive palliative care services are provided in many areas in the UK by hospices, following a model pioneered in the UK initially at St Christopher's Hospice, in south London. This includes inpatient, outpatient, home and day care, although not every hospice will provide the full range of these services.

Mental health care is important within palliative services for four main reasons.

▶ Many palliative care patients suffer from anxiety or depression, either about the impact of major illness on their lives or because of their concerns about approaching death.

▶ Some patients experience physical changes approaching the end of life that lead to important psychological symptoms. For example, some cancers spread to affect the brain (brain metastases).

▶ Some people approaching the end of life become comatose or lose mental capacity and require psychiatric or other assessment of their capacity to make decisions about their personal affairs or medical treatment.

▶ Research on dying and bereavement processes has led to the recognition that death can lead to psychological distress and social problems because of the loss of significant attachments among dying people and their families. Social and psychological help in palliative care and bereavement services have developed to help families move through dying and bereavement processes.

Such issues have led to specialist forms of social work (Monroe & Sheldon, 2004; NASW, 2003) and psychology (British Psychological Society, 2008). Guidance produced by the National Institute of Health and Clinical Excellence (NICE, 2004) acknowledged the roles of social work and psychological care in palliative care, and debate continues about the interaction of these professional practices.

Spiritual care has also been an important element of palliative care (NICE, 2004) for three reasons. First, dying is an important social transition in the lives of individuals and their families. It raises religious or spiritual issues for them. For example, they look back on their life to see what they have achieved and whether this has importance or meaning for them, and whether they have contributed well to society, their families or other personal relationships. They may experience dread, guilt or other profound emotions as they look back on their lives and forward to the end of their lives. In particular, we argue, dying people and their families often need to explore uncertainty about how and when their life will end and hopes and fears about the future of their family, community or the things they have been committed to in life. Spiritual care has developed concern for the meaning of these feelings and life experiences to the dying person and those close to them. Consequently, it has come to be considered an important aspect of palliative care services.

Second, spiritual or religious commitment has been found to benefit people's survival and resilience in the face of major illness (Dein & Stygall, 1997; Tarakeshwar *et al*, 2006). This appears to be the case both for people who have a conventional religious commitment and also for people who have a strong adherence to an alternative philosophical view. Help to resolve spiritual issues is therefore thought to benefit patients by helping them to live longer and die well, with less distress and emotional turmoil than they might otherwise experience.

Third, spiritual care implements the concerns of some health and social care practitioners who are motivated by religious or spiritual commitment to focus their work on the end of life as an important part of life that enables them to work with spiritual issues in their professional practice.

Including spiritual interventions in palliative care links closely to psychological and social care. Powerful emotions may be disturbing to patients and people around them and may require psychological or psychiatric interventions. Similarly, worries about past and present family and other social relationships may lead to need for social work and social care assistance. An organisational study of a hospice suggests that many practitioners find that spiritual, psychological and social care interventions are hard to tell apart in every day practice (Payne, 2004). Price *et al*'s (2006) survey of UK and Ireland hospices suggests that while social work practitioners are major contributors to psychological care, some psychologists and psychiatrists also work in UK hospices and nursing and spiritual care staff make important contributions to psychological care. A US study similarly suggests that there is a wide range of professional involvement in psychological and social interventions in palliative care (Adler & Page, 2008).

Connecting loss in mental health with end of life care

This section discusses, using the case study 'Joan and praying for the dead', how loss and its mental health consequences may have a social impact for individuals and communities. That sense of loss and its consequences may recur powerfully in end of life and palliative care, as people face further loss of health and the impending loss of their life. Patients and their families may face significant uncertainty and lose hope for the future.

In the case study, Joan's religious commitment to being a church member was a potential support in living with her mental illness, and the minister of the church that she attended tried to help her with the problems of her life. However, her mental illness led to her behaving in church services in ways that members of the church saw as socially inappropriate. The congregations of most urban churches include people with mental illness or learning disabilities whose behaviour is regarded as socially inappropriate in many social settings, including the public setting of a church service, where there are norms of behaviour. Because this is hard to manage, people like Joan may be socially excluded, and lose some of the potential benefits of their religious or spiritual commitment. Moreover, churches and their members may fail in their commitment to include and support members of their community.

Case study 1: Joan and praying for the dead

Joan was of Northern Irish Protestant descent. She had come to England with her husband and they had settled on the outskirts of a large city. In her mid-50s, Joan's children had left home. She was a member of the local Methodist church, although she had a Presbyterian background. She also had mental health 'issues'. The church minister was used to her regular phone calls to his home and to his visits to her home being conducted on the doorstep as she half opened the front door. To other members of the church, her 'issues' centred on the way in which worship was conducted and her belief that the church was, despite the reality of commitment to Methodist practices, 'going to Rome'.

A trainee minister takes up the story. *'I had a placement in a church in the suburbs of Bristol. The suburb, a quiet, genteel enclave of semi-detached and detached post-war housing, had a thriving Church, to which I was attached. My experience of its life reflected the suburb exactly; quiet, middle class, reserved and unused to challenge. One Sunday morning, during the prayers in a service I was leading, Joan stood up and began to loudly castigate me for praying for the dead and insisting that this was a practice of the Roman Catholic Church, which was, in her view, not a Christian Church, but an agent of the devil. Once she had finished speaking, Joan left the service. She subsequently wrote to the college where I was training, expressing her view of my conduct of the service and reiterating her belief. The college tutor, to whom it was sent, thought her letter was nothing more than ramblings worthy of disregard and humour.'*

The church as a body was unable to accept how Joan's mental health issues impacted on their communal life; they were excluding, and her attendance at church dwindled. Members described her as an example of the extremity of Northern Irish Protestant views. Her dignity as a person and as a Christian was diminished by the Church community to a problem of her upbringing over which she had no control. Joan was treated not a person, but a nuisance by church members, even though the minister tried to maintain contact with and help her.

In this case example, we can see a number of consequences of behaviour that may be symptomatic of mental illness. What may be genuinely held beliefs were rejected as 'ramblings' and laughed at; church members failed to respond to challenge in a positive way. Racist assumptions developed that these beliefs were the result of cultural and ethnic factors. Socially inappropriate behaviour was defined as a nuisance and led to exclusion, rather than being tolerated as a manifestation of genuine, if unusual, beliefs or as the consequence of illness. Members of the church community might, instead, have organised to help Joan participate appropriately in some activities, or manage her behaviour in public settings.

A significant factor is that Joan was affected by loss. She lost the stability that came with good mental health, and this in turn led to her loss of the potential support of the church community and the professional support of the minister. All these factors in her life might give her resilience, the capacity to bounce back from the difficulties that affected her. Such difficulties affect us all, but losing resilience because of her mental illness meant that Joan was at greater risk than many others. She lost a social support that might have enabled her to deal with uncertainties in her life and hope for engagement with others in spiritual aspects.

Loss is a major issue in palliative care services, since people with advanced illness have lost their health and may expect to lose their lives. Loss often destroys people's identity as coping people, because it reduces their sense of hope that things will be alright, and hence their security and resilience (Flaskas *et al*, 2007). When things are going well, people are able to tell themselves that they are managing in spite of the difficulties, and they become hopeful of the future; their self and their family identity becomes a coping, hopeful identity. Loss trips this into despair and they oscillate between despair at the loss and hope that things will work out. The dual process theory of bereavement (Stroebe & Schut, 1999) describes this oscillation in families and individuals who have experienced the death of a loved one, but it also affects many people in loss situations.

Dignity in health and social care

What is 'dignity work'? This section examines the importance of dignity in health care as well as in end of life and palliative care. It considers, first, important sources for the emphasis on dignity in health care and then identifies crucial elements of dignity that practitioners in end of life and palliative care need to tackle.

WHO's (2009) conception of palliative care as an important human right emphasises the human rights basis of palliative care practice. The United Nations Universal Declaration of Human Rights (UN, 1948), accepted for more than 60 years by most nations in the world, is founded on fundamental human dignity. Its first provision sees dignity as the foundation of humanity, freedom, equality and justice:

'Whereas recognition of the inherent dignity and of the equal and inalienable rights of all members of the human family is the foundation of freedom, justice and peace in the world.' (UN, 1948)

If we take this view, dignity is not just a feeling that people have about how they are treated by others; it is the basis of equality and freedom, and most states have committed themselves to uphold human dignity. Knowing that our human rights are acknowledged in any society is an important basis for certainty about our place in the world and our acceptance by the people around us.

Incorporating dignity into health and social care policy has been an important aspect of the 'modernisation agenda' for public social and health care provision, a policy initiative of the Labour government in power in the UK from 1997 onwards. The political impetus lies in a view that people in a consumer society are used to having a high degree of individual choice, and public services have to respond to an expectation of a higher degree of individuality. This is reflected in the title and approach of the government's green paper on health and social care, *Independence, Well-being and Choice* (Department of Health, 2006a) and the subsequent white paper *Our Health, Our Care, Our Say* (Department of Health, 2006b). The incorporation of the European Convention on human rights into UK law in the Human Rights Act 1997 directed further attention to the implications of meeting requirements to respect dignity for care services. These developments therefore emphasised the importance of autonomy and participation as integral to dignity and to how public services should be provided.

The Dignity in Care campaign of the English Department of Health (2009), launched in 2006, led to the development of the Dignity Challenge, which formalised the concept of dignity into health and social care services. It involves knowledge and skill development by various organisations, publishing toolkits to encourage development of best practice, appointing 'dignity champions' throughout the country and promoting public debate about dignity through local and national events and the television personality Sir Michael Parkinson becoming a 'dignity ambassador'.

The aim of the challenge was to improve the quality of care services available to people; reducing abuse, increasing respect and choice, maintaining independence and alleviating loneliness. The challenge sought to ensure dignity was an issue for best practice. A survey of public opinion identified major uncertainties about dignity in the public's mind (Department of Health, 2006c) and the Dignity Challenge sought to secure service improvements to respond to this (SCIE, 2009). Most of these aims were set for care homes, and supported by action from the care home regulators, but have wide application in health and social care. For example, a well-conducted study by the Royal College of Nursing (Baillie *et al*, 2008), based on responses from more than 2,000 nurses, identified caring activities that might compromise dignity, people vulnerable to loss of dignity and how nurses protect dignity through privacy, good communication and the way in which they provide physical care, by trying to 'dignify' care activities wherever possible.

Dignity and mental health in end of life and palliative care

This section brings together issues about responding to mental health and dignity issues in end of life and palliative care settings. We argue that by incorporating 'dignity work' as part of spiritual care, these settings can help people to resolve uncertainty and hope issues in their personal and family lives.

The Dignity Campaign and Challenge sought to improve the level and nature of care for people receiving mental health services, in the same way as with other health and social care service users. Because, as we have seen, a palliative setting aims to secure care for people at a particularly uncertain stage in the lives of families and individuals; dignity and respect in dealing with mental health issues becomes even more important. The incorporation of spiritual care in end of life care means that it also needs to be an important aspect of best practice in caring. In palliative care, dignity has historically been central to the quality of care provided to patients and to the support of their families through the delivery by both professionals and volunteers, of spiritual care. Palliative care was strongly influenced by the ideas of Cicely Saunders, founder of St Christopher's Hospice and pioneer of the modern hospice movement. Saunders traced her ideas back to her early experience as a medical social worker, of helping David Tasma, a Jewish, Polish refugee, isolated and dying, stripped of his dignity, in a central London hospital. What made him human, his beliefs, practices and need to find meaning in the present were ignored in this conventional healthcare setting as his life ended. Saunders listened to his story, ensured that she remained present with him in his suffering, returning to him a sense of value in his life. Their mutual sharing of the idea of a place in which dying people might be cared until death allowed Tasma to plan for a future he would not live to see. This attention and engagement met his spiritual needs for dignity and hope, encapsulated by Saunders in the phrase *you matter because you are you; you matter to the last moment of your life*.

Chochinov and colleagues (2005) have recently built on this historical commitment by creating a psychotherapeutic intervention, dignity therapy. This allows patients to discuss issues in their lives that matter to them and contributions to their families or work roles that they would want others to remember. After discussion, a formal document is created to be 'bequeathed' to their family. Initial studies (Chochinov *et al*, 2005; McClement *et al*, 2007) showed a favourable response from both patients and family members. Studies in the UK and Canada are being developed to explore the value of this psychotherapeutic approach, and Ferrell (2005) argues that this has the potential to develop a 'science' of spiritual care. These developments suggest that our approach to dignity work as a facet of spiritual care, rather than as a psychotherapy, may have a wide application.

The government's *End of Life Care Strategy* (Department of Health, 2008) is a current example of how that historical commitment to dignity chimes with government policy and human rights. Among other proposals, it seeks to offer to people the 'right' to make choices about the dying process. Dignity is promoted, for example, by patient autonomy in making advance care plans (Henry & Seymour, 2007) in which people set out how they want to be cared for as they lose their capacity for independence in the approach to death. Although they usually do this in consultation with relatives and health care providers, having a process for making decisions autonomously enhances freedom, a practical implementation of the UN declaration. The professional is not the prima facie decision maker; the patient decides, sometimes long before events take place. Thus, the need to be heard and, for an individual's wishes to be met remain as important as they did for David Tasma.

End of life and palliative care services, therefore, need to maintain and, wherever possible, enhance patients' dignity by the care from staff and volunteers willing to stay with that individual and respond appropriately to a wide range of needs, including the spiritual. The role of chaplaincy and other resources for spiritual care in palliative settings is to enable appropriate expression of religious and spiritual beliefs. A referral by a ward or home care nurse could ensure a patient, struggling to find a place to make religious or spiritual meaning of their life, of present uncertainty or future hope, is enabled to do exactly that.

Case study 2: David and his family describe a situation in which some of the family's religious beliefs conflicted with the work of a hospice.

Case study 2: David and his family

David, aged 37, was admitted to a hospice ward with advanced cancer and severe pain. He was unmarried, with two children, both under 18. He had siblings and an extended family, many of whom came to his single room at the hospice at David's admission. The first task of the team was to address his pain to ensure he was comfortable. Several family members crowded into David's room, including a cousin, Danny. Danny was a practising Christian, attending a black Pentecostal church. He was also the oldest male relative on the ward and took a role of speaking for the family and for David who was unable to communicate.

The chaplain picks up the story. *'I was called to David's room, because of complaints from other patients about the level of noise emanating from the prayers being said in David's room. Some patients and staff felt that the extent of religious activity was irrational, and was obstructing the normal work of the hospice and the peace of other patients and their families.*

'The prayers centred on physical healing. When I entered David's room, Danny was present, together with David's siblings, pastors from the church and the church's bishop. Immediately, I was asked about my own view on miraculous physical healing. This question was "testing" me to find out whether I believed that God could make a person, suffering from a life-threatening illness, physically better through saying prayers, laying hands on a person and exhorting God to make someone well. A tenet of Pentecostal belief is the ability of God to perform miraculous healing, as described in the Bible, in the modern age. I stated my belief that God can heal people. However, that healing may be to enable people and their families to recognise death is approaching; to "put things right"; or that

death itself can be healing, bringing freedom from pain and suffering. I was then, as I expected, challenged that I didn't believe the Bible. I remained in the room, offered the family and church leader use of the chapel to pray in and was allowed to pray with David and the gathered family. I prayed for David, that he would be free from pain; for his family, that they would be able to support each other and for the gift of the Holy Spirit, to bring peace and God's blessing on the whole family. These interventions sought to establish a valid position, what might perhaps be described as a spiritual care alliance with the family, acknowledging their views while asserting through action the existence of alternatives.

'Danny's role as spokesman increased over the ensuing days and he actively challenged staff, who followed a well-established policy of reducing David's discomfort by withdrawing intravenous fluids and nasal gastric feeding. Danny felt that maintaining fluids and feeding would "enable God to carry out his healing". I maintained contact with the family members, being given a wary welcome.

'On the Saturday following David's admission, I was called into the hospice twice, in the morning and evening, to support the staff as noise levels had increased again in the room. To deal with this, I encouraged family members to use the chapel. In the evening, Danny became insistent on feeding and fluids being given to his cousin, again to enable God to heal David. Danny's request was carefully declined by medical and nursing staff, at which point he indicated he would contact the press, as the hospice were "killing David". I suggested a family meeting would help, to explain the medical and nursing issues and to explore the spiritual issues.

'Late in the evening, an on-call doctor, a senior nurse and I sat with around 40 relatives in the chapel. We talked with them about David's care since admission and the plans for ongoing care. Reasons for withholding fluids and feeding were explained. The meeting concluded with the majority of family members understanding the hospice's rationale for care. Danny continued to maintain that not enough was being done to help God's healing and that I, the chaplain, did not believe the Bible.

'In the ensuing few days, the family were calmer and accepting of David's condition. I spoke to two of David's sisters who had, before the family meeting been unable to express their own view that David was dying. David's cousin, Danny ceased to be the self-appointed spokesperson for the family.'

This is another situation in which apparently irrational behaviour is associated with spiritual commitment and with different cultural expectations. In case study 1, Joan was diagnosed mentally ill, and her behaviour, although deriving from her religious commitment, was classified as part of her illness and of her ethnicity. In a similar way, behaviour that came from Danny's religious commitment was also seen as irrational and a 'nuisance', although it was also attributed to cultural differences between the family, other patients and their families and staff.

'Dignity work' helps us to understand these spiritual care interventions. David, different members of his extended family, Danny, other patients and their families and staff all had a range of religious, spiritual and non-spiritual beliefs and views. The first approach of the chaplain was to dignify the range of beliefs and the expression of them. He sustained the right of other beliefs to be heard, by expressing a different view of healing and by engaging in prayer with the family; this activity and his commitment to faith himself were important.

Dignifying one set of views does not 'undignify' other views and responsibilities. There was a medical responsibility to maintain David's dignity by ensuring that he received appropriate treatment in his best interests. David could not make decisions about his care needs and the medical team had a legal duty to provide care in his best interests. Moreover, the dignity of members of the family who dissented from the certainty of Danny's presentation of belief, also needed to be maintained. Some were excluded by gender discrimination, a failure to accord them human rights. The spiritual care intervention here involved providing a physical and social space where many people could be involved in discussion, without interfering with the operation of the ward. By using a faith context, the chapel, and developing a transparent discussion that presented professional medical and nursing opinion and encouraged the expression of a wide range of views, the chaplain accorded dignity to professional information and spiritual beliefs that were excluded by Danny's attitudes to them. This was given greater authority because he was an ordained minister with the professional duty and social right to be engaged in spiritual issues.

Spiritual and religious belief is both personal and cultural and this interaction often leads to uncertainty. Danny's view had every right of expression and maintaining his dignity also required that his voice be heard and respected. However, allowing other voices from the family expression meant that it did not override all other voices and allowed the uncertainties to be understood. This was particularly important when David was not able to articulate for himself what measures he wanted hospice staff to take. Had Danny's view been allowed to dictate the care for his cousin, David's dignity would have been ignored at a point in favour of Danny's certainty, when his dignity was the most important care aim of all staff involved and also of the family and of Danny.

Conclusion

The importance of uncertainty in religion and spiritual thought is profound; faith means that we believe what we cannot know. However, in providing care, we cannot allow faith to overcome uncertainty. This is particularly important in end of life and palliative care because when we die and how is always uncertain; how we should respond to illness and death is culturally determined, but is also a personal response. According dignity to people in caring situations means acknowledging uncertainty.

In this chapter, we have examined the role of spiritual care and mental health care in end of life and palliative services. Approaching the end of life raises issues about how to respond to mental health difficulties. We may learn about dealing with uncertainty and spiritual distress from working with people approaching the end of their lives and transfer this to other settings. We have argued that the challenge of trying to achieve dignity in care is an important way of respecting and valuing people facing uncertainty and spiritual distress.

References

Adler NE & Page AEK (Eds) (2008) *Cancer Care for the Whole Patient: Meeting psychosocial health needs.* Washington DC: National Academies Press.

Baillie L, Gallagher A & Wainwright P (2008) *Defending Dignity: Challenges and opportunities for nursing.* London: Royal College of Nursing.

British Psychological Society (2008) *The Role of Psychology in Palliative Care.* Leiciester: British Psychological Society.

Chochinov HM, Hack T, Hassard T, Kristjanson LJ, McClement S & Harlos M (2005) Dignity therapy: a novel psychotherapeutic intervention for patients near the end of life. *Journal of Clinical Oncology* **23** (24) 5520–5525.

Dein S & Stygall J (1997) Does being religious help or hinder coping with chronic illness? A critical literature review. *Palliative Medicine* **11** (4) 291–298.

Department of Health (2006a) *Independence, Well-being and Choice: Our vision for the future of social care for adults in England* (Cm 6499). London: TSO.

Department of Health (2006b) *Our Health, Our Care, Our Say: A new direction for community services* (Cm 6737) London: TSO.

Department of Health (2006c) *'Dignity in Care' Public Survey: Report of the survey.* (Gateway number: 7213) London: Department of Health.

Department of Health (2008) *End of Life Care Strategy: Promoting high quality care for all adults at the end of life.* London: Department of Health.

Department of Health (2009) *History of the Campaign and Progress to Date* [online]. Available at: http://www.dhcarenetworks.org.uk/dignityincare/DignityCareCampaign/?parent=3571&child=6361 (accessed November2010).

Ferrell B (2005) Dignity therapy: advancing the science of spiritual care in terminal illness. *Journal of Clinical Oncology* **23** (24) 5427–5428.

Flaskas C, McCarthy I & Sheehan J (Eds) (2007) *Hope and Despair in Narrative and Family Therapy.* London: Routledge.

Henry C & Seymour J (2007) *Advance Care Planning: A guide for health and social care staff.* London: Department of Health.

McClement S, Chochinov HM, Hack T, Hassard T, Kristjanson LJ & Harlos M (2007) Dignity therapy: family member perspectives. *Journal of Palliative Medicine* **10** (5) 1076–1082.

Monroe B & Sheldon F (2004) Psychosocial dimensions of care. In: N Sykes, P Edmonds & J Wiles (Eds). *Management of Advanced Disease.* London: Arnold: 405–437.

NASW (2003) *Standards for Social Work Practice in Palliative and End of Life Care.* Washington DC: National Association of Social Workers.

NICE (2004) *Guidance on Cancer Services: Improving supportive and palliative care for adults with cancer.* London: NICE.

Payne M (2004) Social work practice identities: an agency study of a hospice. *Practice* **16** (1) 5–15.

Price A, Hotopf M, Higginson IJ, Monroe B & Henderson M (2006) Psychological services in hospices in the UK and Republic of Ireland. *Journal of the Royal Society of Medicine* **99** 637–639.

Reith M & Payne M (2009) *Social Work in End-of-Life and Palliative Care.* Bristol: Policy Press.

SCIE (2009) *SCIE Practice Guide 09: Dignity in care* [online]. London: Social Care. Available at: http://www.scie.org.uk/publications/guides/guide15/index.asp (accessed November 2010).

Stroebe M & Schut H (1999) The dual process model of coping with bereavement: rationale and description. *Death Studies* **23** (3) 197–224.

Tarakeshwar N, Vanderwerker L, Paulk E, Pearce M, Kasl S & Prigerson H (2006) Religious coping is associated with the quality of life of patients with advanced cancer. *Journal of Palliative Medicine* **9** (3) 646–657.

UN (1948) *The Universal Declaration of Human Rights* [online]. Available at: http://www.un.org/en/documents/udhr/ (accessed November 2010).

WHO (2009) *Palliative Care* [online]. Available at: http://www.who.int/cancer/palliative/en/ (accessed November 2010).

Further reading

The following four books provide broad introductions to spiritual care practice in health and social care.

De Boulay S with Rankin M (2007) *Cicley Saunders: The Founder of the modern hospice movement.* London: SPCK.

Greenstreet W (Ed) (2006) *Integrating Spirituality in Health and Social Care: Perspectives and practical approaches.* Oxford: Radcliffe.

Hollis S (2006) *Religions, Culture and Healthcare.* Oxford: Radcliffe Publishing.

Robinson S, Kendrick K & Brown A (2003) *Spirituality and the Practice of Healthcare.* Basingstoke: Palgrave Macmillan.

White G (2006) *Talking about Spirituality in Health Care Practice.* London: Jessica Kingsley Publishers.

This is a well-established introductory book on spiritual care with dying and bereaved people.
Speck P & Ainsworth-Smith I (1999) *Letting Go: Caring for the dying and bereaved.* (2nd Ed) London: SPCK.

This collection looks at spiritual care issues with dying and bereaved people at a more advanced level.
Rumbold B (Ed)(2002) *Spirituality and Palliative Care: Social and pastoral perspectives.* Melbourne: Oxford University Press.

This book explores further some of the issues discussed in this chapter about the intersection of intercultural and spiritual care issues.
Narayanasamy A (2006) *Spiritual Care and Transcultural Care Research.* London: Quay.

A discussion of psychological care and social work in end-of-life care, which incorporates the role of spiritual care.
Reith M & Payne M (2009) *Social Work in End-of-life and Palliative Care.* Bristol: Policy Press.

Chapter 14

Death – the ultimate challenge

Margaret Holloway

Introduction

The association between the study of spirituality and the study of death has long been noted. At first sight, this is unsurprising. In situations of existential challenge, people become more than usually aware of the more intangible, some would say 'spiritual' dimension, and most concern themselves, if not with 'ultimate' concerns, then at least with those things which infuse their everyday lives with meaning. Most religions suggest that dying provides the opportunity for new spiritual insight (Department of Health, 2009). Why then does the title for this chapter suggest that, in fact, death presents the ultimate challenge to spirituality, dignity and mental health?

We start to understand this challenge a little more when we look at some common definitions or attributes ascribed to spirituality. In contemporary debate, most suggest that it has to do with meaning and purpose; that it concerns relatedness; that it calls into play one's moral sense; and that this is all bound up in what it means to be human – the 'wholeness' of our humanity. Moreover, spirituality is both experienced and practised – the being and the doing are intrinsically related to each other. So how can this rich dimension of life survive in dying, which progressively takes away the capacity to experience and engage with living, ultimately taking away life itself? One clue may lie in an aspect of spirituality about which commentators are not entirely agreed, including on its significance – the notion of transcendence.

This chapter will explore this central paradox of death – 'the philosopher's touchstone' – as we tease out the meaning of spirituality for the dying person, their family, friends and those carers relating to them through their dying process. We shall then look at understanding and responding to spiritual need and the implications of this for quality, holistic end of life care.

The meaning of death

Philosophers and theologians suggest that we cannot think about life unless we grapple with the fact of death. Death is the ultimate challenge to any notion that human existence, both individually and as a community, has purpose and meaning (Feifel, 1959; Jaspers, 1967; Jungel, 1975). When I first started to research spiritual issues in death, dying and bereavement, I realised early on that the way in which we make sense of death on a personal level is of immediate importance to how we as professional carers approach our work with dying and bereaved people. To an extent, this is what underlies the frequently repeated maxim in palliative care training, that working with death requires us to confront our own mortality. It is far more than that, however. Working with dying people and their families, before and after the death, requires us to not only think about the fact that we will die, but to consider what that actually means for how we live and what sense we make of everyday interactions and occurrences. This, in turn, brings us back to the meaning of death.

As health and social care workers, we have tended to neglect the philosophical underpinnings for what we do, which may be one of the reasons why – in palliative and end of life care at least – we often struggle with the ethical questions which confront us on the front line of practice. In a lecture which focuses on the art of dying – Edwin Pugh, a palliative care physician, reminds us that it is the philosophy of care which we must get right if our excellent innovations in end of life care are truly to result in better deaths for dying people and those around them (Pugh, 2008). Philosophers and theologians, on the other hand, have given much thought over the centuries to trying to understand death, in ways which at first sight (to me at least) can seem far removed from the realities which confront practitioners and clinicians.

These musings group into three approaches to understanding death, only one of which seems to me to have genuine integrity in the face of the human realities of dying and bereavement, although we see examples of both the other two approaches in the literature about the management of end of life care (Lloyd, 1995; Holloway, 2007a). The first approach takes a positive tone, reflected in the familiar claim that death is the final stage of growth (Kubler-Ross, 1975). Images such as light and moving on and concepts such as autonomy and freedom predominate. By contrast, a second set of approaches sees death in negative terms, so much so that it robs from life all meaning, and at its most extreme treats death as senseless tragedy. Elements of this approach can be seen in some of the arguments for euthanasia (Neuberger, 2006), particularly where personhood is seen to have already departed leaving an existence without the capacity to be truly human (Harris, 1995). The third approach, however, argues that the only authentic way to approach death is to hold its positive and negative elements together in dialectical tension:

'Light in light is invisible ... but light in darkness gives great light and hope.' (Indian guru quoted in Maguire, 2001, p136)

Such an approach recognises but is not overwhelmed by the pain of death – in all its physical, psychological, social and spiritual manifestations – and sees the way to hope, peace and reconciliation, those features so commonly associated with 'the good death' and 'positive spirituality', as being through the pain not avoiding its encounter. Hans Kung, a Catholic theologian (although this philosophy is by no means confined to the Christian or any other religion) points out that:

'...resurrection-faith is not to be had by passing over suffering, concrete conditions, opposition and antagonism, but only by going through all these... The cross is 'surmountable' only in the light of the resurrection, but the resurrection can be lived only in the shadow of the cross.' (Kung, 1984, p147)

I suggested earlier that my own initial response to these theoretical positions was to question whether or not they had relevance in the organised health systems of today, where we continually strive to make dying a managed process. I hope to show in this chapter that they are without doubt of contemporary relevance and should form part of the bank of resources on which the frontline worker may draw. For the time being, let me suggest those modern equivalents that readers with any familiarity with death will have heard in common parlance (table 1).

Table 1: Typology of concepts of death		
Concept	**Traditional academic meaning**	**Contemporary lay translation**
Death as light	In death is achieved ultimate fulfilment, it is essentially the consummation of the life.	'I've grown through this.'
Death as darkness	Death destroys the meaning in life; tragedy and suffering are senseless.	'It's such a waste, it doesn't make sense.'
Death as mystery	We cannot fully understand death.	'I just go with the flow now.'
Death as end	Death must be simply and pragmatically accepted.	'That's it, no sense worrying about it.'
Death as transition	Death is a stage which moves our existence on.	'It wasn't really him lying there, only his body.'
Death as limit	Death should be seen as a boundary which bestows meaning on life.	'It concentrates the mind, makes you realise what's important.'
Death as borderline situation	Death pushes us to the limits of personal resources in which ultimate freedom may be achieved.	'I've reached my limit.' 'There's no going back now.'
Death as the only truly personal act	In dying we exercise ultimate freedom.	'I've got to do this one on my own.'
Death as passivity	Acceptance of our own experience of death.	'It comes to us all.'
Death and life together make sense	Each must be examined and understood in relation to the other.	'If you didn't have death, you wouldn't have life.'
Death as natural event	Mortality is the natural condition of human existence.	'She was ready to go, it was like her time had come.'
Death as unnatural event	Death is sometimes violent and premature.	'He was snatched away, snuffed out.'
Death as hope	In death is healing and release.	'He's at peace now.' 'I'm going home.'

(Adapted from Holloway (2007a))

The contemporary need to conceptualise death

Perhaps the next question to ask ourselves, however, is whether there is any more to these comments than their face value? In other words, people feel the need to say something in the face of death but this doesn't necessarily imply any deeper thinking about its meaning, or any need to think about its meaning. In my research, I have found surprisingly strong evidence that in our consumerist, technologically-dominated society, people facing their own death or the death of someone close to them are concerned, to a greater or lesser degree, to place their personal experience in some wider spiritual and philosophical context. Importantly, this appears to be regardless of their stated position of belief or no belief. In a study completed in the UK in the early 1990s, I found five categories of response among a mixed sample of people who knew that they were dying and people who had been bereaved in the preceding 6–18 months. These were:

▶ people who were drawing on, perhaps returning to, beliefs acquired in childhood

▶ people for whom this experience represented a crisis, including sometimes of faith, and were establishing or at least searching for new beliefs and values in order to deal with the crisis

▶ those who demonstrated a mature faith, developed and adapted over life, which was their foundation for dealing with their illness or loss

▶ those who affirmed a humanistic frame of reference which guided them through this experience

▶ and, finally, those who appeared to have no philosophical frame or spiritual resources and demonstrated a high degree of distress and disorientation. (Lloyd, 1996)

The interesting finding from this research was not so much that spiritual and philosophical issues played a part in facing death, but the degree to which they pre-occupied most (though not all) of the respondents and the significance which they accorded to this aspect.

Some 15 years later, in another UK study exploring evidence and shape of spirituality in contemporary funerals, similar patterns of 'belief' emerged, but what became apparent, although it was not in itself the focus of the study, was that the recently bereaved have a strong need to conceptualise death (Holloway *et al*, 2010a). People expressed views about death, falling into categories which reflected those derived from my original review of the academic literature (see table 1).

A relatively small number were firm in their materialist view of life:

'My personal opinion is, that when you are dead, you are dead.' (Holloway *et al*, 2010a, p183)

Rather more reflected the idea of death as transition:

'...and I can't remember the words, but where it comes over as saying, you know, I haven't left you, I'm in the room next door.' (unpublished data)

In quite a few cases this was combined with firm notions of dualism – the Platonic notion of the soul as distinct from the body (Jackson, 2001):

'When the hearse pulled up initially I got a knot in me stomach and I just went over to it and stared at it, I thought, it's a box ... the person inside it is me mother, but whether you're religious or not religious it's just a shell.' (p195)

Others reflected eco-spiritual ideas found in the spirituality literature, in the following case combining it with that hopefulness expressed in one philosophical approach (see table 1):

'I don't believe that you can die and your energy or your soul whatever you want to call it can just disappear. I think it is somewhere... I don't know where but you can't destroy energy.' (p145)

Interestingly, for those people of firm religious faith (and they were in the minority as in my earlier study) they tended not to articulate their ideas about death so much as to refer to and draw on the structure of their belief system, for example, through the Christian belief of the resurrection. For the most part, however, the bereaved people in this study expressed their spirituality and spiritual needs through the ways in which they tried to make sense of the death and infuse it with meaning, drawing on a whole range of resources, some of which were of personal significance and some drawing on snippets of particular traditions, including religious.

Responding to death

What, then, are the implications of this and other research about spirituality in the face of death for our response as professional carers to the dying person and those closest to them? There is little evidence of people in the UK holding to systematic belief systems except in the case of adherents to minority religions – including fundamentalist Christian denominations (Brierley, 2000). There is, however, considerable, and still growing evidence of widespread acknowledgement of a spiritual dimension to life which is closely associated with those things which provide meaning, purpose and represent our 'take' on life (Holloway & Moss, 2010). If facing death causes both carers and those cared for to consider its relationship to life, and if the meaning we find in life reflects our understanding of death, then it follows that this broader spiritual dimension is present in all our interactions with people who are dying or bereaved. That follows whether the individual believes that in death they will go to their maker, or whether death is seen as the final stop but that what will continue is memories and the contribution of that person's life to those that remain, as individuals and as a human community. Our response as carers cannot, however, be a blanket 'one size fits all' as sometimes seems to be the case when simple statements about offering spiritual care are made.

Recent evidence from the UK suggests that while the importance of spiritual care at the end of life has been recognised by healthcare organisations and offering spiritual care is seen to be a legitimate and indeed expected role for all frontline workers, those workers themselves are frequently uncertain about entering into such 'holy ground', partly through fear of giving offence but often because they feel they do not have the knowledge and skills to work with spiritual need (Holloway *et al*, 2010b). Even ministers of religion may express doubts about what is an appropriate role for them in secular health care organisations and wary of appearing to proselytise at such a vulnerable time (Lloyd, 1995; Holloway *et al*, 2010a, 2010b; Nolan, 2010).

Certain concepts and approaches elicit common accord, however. These are those which link understandings of spirituality and approaches to spiritual care with the core philosophy of palliative and hospice care: that each person should be supported in their own unique pathway towards death, that they continue to live until they die and that supportive care centres around the relief and control of pain (in all its manifestations) so that the essence of the person may be freed up to live their life in its final stage and to prepare for their death in the manner which for them provides peace, meaning and sustenance (Puchalski *et al*, 2006). For some hospice workers, this of itself is spiritual care (Sinclair *et al*, 2006). It belongs to an approach which sees holistic care as being about wholeness, where healing may come through death (Grad, 1980; Holloway & Moss, 2010). Others prefer a more explicit recognition of the role and task. In a systematic review of the literature Holloway *et al*, (2010b) found evidence that most workers preferred to think of themselves as companions in the end of life journey, offering spiritual support through their attentive presence, including sustaining the person through their spiritual struggles and sharing with them in their experiences of joy. This practice has been variously termed creating and holding a 'safe nurturing space' (Hegarty, 2007); being prepared to enter into the 'weak places' of the other person (Cornette, 2005); being a 'supportive presence' (Callahan, 2009) and 'sharing the journey' (Wright, 2001).

The model of spiritual care which I have developed from research in this specific field of dying and bereavement takes this last approach as its name – The Fellow Traveller Model – suggests (see Holloway and Moss, 2010 for a full exposition of this model). In palliative and end of life care we join people at the end of their journey if we measure it by chronological time, yet in relationships, meanings and coming to terms with themselves, the end of life may represent the part of their journey in which they cover the most ground. Being able to transform and transcend their situation, so that the illness does not define who they are or dictate how they go on, is a powerful indicator of spiritual strength and growth, whatever the internal and external resources drawn upon. We are privileged as carers if we are able to share and assist with this journey.

We have said little so far about spiritual pain and distress, although the early part of this chapter suggested that only an approach to death which holds together both the darkness and the light can have true integrity for the palliative and bereavement care worker. Spiritual pain is sometimes described in terms which overlap with deep emotional conflict or psychological distress. Undoubtedly this is the case, but I have argued elsewhere that spiritual pain is properly designated as such only if its source is a spiritual or religious issue (Holloway, 2007b; Holloway & Moss, 2010). Sometimes this source is the person's religious history, and it is in reconstruction of their own self-narrative that healing of the spirit is to be found, even as physically they are beyond cure. People who evidence deep alienation from everyone and everything around them, and those who express existential despair, profound hopelessness, helplessness and absence of meaning as they approach death, discomfort us as carers and challenge our cherished notions of the 'good death' (Lloyd, 1995). This is pain which cannot be controlled by drugs and neither can it be ignored. Indeed, there are many examples where physical pain remains resistant to pain relief until the issues causing pain deep inside the person are resolved (Gordon, 2001). Even our 'talking therapies' may be made redundant as the person slips into unconsciousness or otherwise withdraws into their dying world. Yet spiritual care is still possible.

Case study: Sandra Walker

Sandra was not known to the hospice when she was admitted from hospital. She was a woman in her 50s suffering from an inoperable brain tumour. By the time she was admitted she had already lost her sight. Maureen, the chaplain, was called in by the nurses because of Sandra's extreme agitation, screaming, calling out and making pronouncements of a religious nature – 'I'm going to burn in hell'. Sandra and her husband, David, belonged to a Christian evangelical church. They had a young teenage daughter, Holly, and Sandra also had an adult son and daughter from her first marriage with whom she was in contact, although they did not live locally.

Sandra was visited by her family and members of her church, who between them kept up a vigil by her bedside. One brother, Steve, was not a member of the church but another brother and sister-in-law were very active members. When church members visited they spent the time praying for Sandra's healing, singing and playing rousing religious music. They told Sandra that God would be very disappointed in her if she died. David kept himself apart from these conversations. Sandra's agitation increased during and after these visits. She appeared to be in spiritual anguish. Eventually, after the nursing staff said that they would exclude any visitors except close family, David intervened and asked the church friends to refrain from this behaviour. They then ceased to visit.

Maureen was kept at bay by the church visitors, some of whom were very hostile to her. David was courteous, but very guarded. Occasionally he spoke about how he had not coped very well with his first wife's cancer. David said that Sandra had had a very troubled life. Her first husband abused her physically and eventually ran off with her sister. When David and Sandra's daughter was very young, Sandra had sustained serious injuries in a road traffic accident which resulted in her being in a wheelchair for a long time.

Maureen saw her role as trying to provide comfort for Sandra. She did not attempt to engage in spiritual ministry through conversation (and Sandra lost all speech in the end) but by gently holding and stroking Sandra's face, repeatedly assuring her that she was 'safe and secure'. This was the only thing which calmed Sandra, and the nurses, who had felt there was little they could do for Sandra, began to do the same. Maureen also suggested peaceful music in place of that played by the visitors. When Sandra died, a fortnight after her admission, she was peaceful and accompanied only by her brother Steve. David was not there, although he had planned to be and was initially distressed that she had slipped away while he had gone home. Maureen was in the hospice and saw Sandra shortly before she died.

Maureen was not consulted about the funeral arrangements but she did attend. To her surprise, she found it a 'low key but uplifting' occasion. Maureen had not known it, but Sandra had been a singer and made some recordings which were played, as well as her older daughter singing songs she had written. Tributes were paid to Sandra by family and friends and David did a reading.

Conclusion

It has been suggested (Narayanasamy, 2004) that spiritual integrity is evidenced in people who are sufficiently comfortable in themselves to be able to reach out and provide comfort to others, whatever their personal circumstances; spiritual distress, on the other hand, is illustrated by people who complain that they are 'not themselves' and are at a complete loss to know how to deal with the situation in which they find themselves. We find the extremes of both in people at the end of life, and in the people who care for them. Probably most people show elements of both as they struggle to deal with fear, pain, loss and the unknowns which attend the dying process. The remarkable thing is that so many transcend and transform their situation, finding their ultimate healing in death itself. So death is not so much the ultimate challenge to the dying person's spirituality as the ultimate paradox – that it is in nurturing hopefulness and resilience in living, and all those aspects of life that make it worthwhile, that we are enabled to let go and give ourselves to death. The challenge is to us as carers: can we stay with the person, sustain the spirit, as they travel a road which for some may be through a dark valley and for others, the home strait.

References

Brierley P (2000) Religion In: A Halsey & J Webb (Eds) *Twentieth Century British Social Trends.* London: Macmillan.

Callahan AM (2009) Spiritually sensitive care in hospice social work. *Journal of Social Work in End of Life and Palliative Care* **5** (3) 169–185.

Cornette K (2005) For whenever I am weak, I am strong. *International Journal of Palliative Nursing* **11** (3) 147–153.

Department of Health (2009) *Religion or Belief: A practical guide for the NHS.* London: Department of Health.

Feifel H (Ed) (1959) *The Meaning of Death.* New York: McGraw-Hill.

Gordon T (2001) *A Need for Living: Signposts on the journey of life and beyond.* Glasgow: Wild Goose Publications.

Grad B (1980) Healing and dying. *Journal of Pastoral Counselling* **15** 50–54.

Harris J (1995) Euthanasia and the value of life. In: J Keown (Ed) *Euthanasia Examined: Ethical, clinical and legal perspectives.* Cambridge: Cambridge University Press.

Hegarty M (2007) Care of the spirit that transcends religious, ideological and philosophical boundaries. *Indian Journal of Palliative Care* **13** (2) 42–47.

Holloway M (2007a) *Negotiating Death in Contemporary Health and Social Care.* Bristol: Policy Press.

Holloway M (2007b) Spirituality and darkness: is it all sweetness and light? unpublished paper in Making Sense of Spirituality conference. University of Hull, Scarborough.

Holloway M, Adamson A, Argyrou V, Draper P & Mariau D (2010a) *Spirituality in Contemporary Funerals.* Hull: Department of Social Sciences, University of Hull.

Holloway M, Adamson A, McSherry W & Swinton J (2010b) *Spiritual Care at the End of Life: A systematic review of the literature.* London: Department of Health.

Holloway M & Moss B (2010) *Spirituality and Social Work.* Basingstoke: Palgrave Macmillan.

Jackson R (2001*) Plato: A beginner's guide.* London: Hodder & Stoughton.

Jaspers K (1967) *Philosophical Faith and Revelation.* London: Collins.

Jungel E (1975) *Death, the Riddle and the Mystery.* Edinburgh: Saint Andrew Press.

Kubler-Ross E (1975) *Death: The final stage of growth.* Englewood Cliffs, NJ: Prentice Hall.

Kung H (1984) *Eternal life?* London: Collins.

Lloyd M [M Holloway](1995) *Embracing the Paradox: Pastoral care with dying and bereaved people.* Contact Pastoral Monographs No 5. Edinburgh: Contact Pastoral Limited Trust.

Lloyd M [M Holloway] (1996) Philosophy and religion in the face of death and bereavement. *Journal of Religion and Health* **35** (4) 295–310.

Maguire K (2001) Working with survivors of torture and extreme experience. In: S King-Spooner & C Newnes (Eds) *Spirituality and Psychotherapy.* Ross-on-Wye: PCCS Books Ltd.

Narayanasamy A (2004) Spiritual Care. The puzzle of spirituality for nursing: a guide to practical assessment. *British Journal of Nursing* **13** (19) 1140–1144.

Neuberger J (2006) *The Moral State We're In: A manifesto for a 21st century society* (Updated edition). London: Harper Perennial.

Nolan S (2010) Beyond Recovery: chaplains working with people navigating (redundant) hope and no hope. Unpublished paper in Spirituality in a Changing World, 1st International Conference of the British Association for the Study of Spirituality, Windsor, UK.

Pugh E (2008) *Memento Mori: Personal reflections on achieving a good death in today's society.* Occasional paper 1, University of Teesside.

Puchalski C, Harris M & Miller T (2006) Interdisciplinary care for seriously ill and dying patients: a collaborative model. *The Cancer Journal* **12** (5) 398–416.

Sinclair S, Raffin S, Pereira J & Guebert N (2006) Collective soul: the spirituality of an interdisciplinary palliative care team. *Palliative and Supportive Care* **4** 13–24.

Wright MC (2001) Chaplaincy in hospice and hospital: findings from a survey in England and Wales. *Palliative Medicine* **15** 229–242.

Chapter 15

Educating for spiritual care

Bernard Moss, Janice Clarke and Ivor Moody

Introduction

This is the first of two linked chapters which explore issues around education and training for spiritual care. In this chapter we will be exploring some of the opportunities and dilemmas in an educational context; chapter 16 will look in more detail at some training issues.

In a telling phrase, Dr Rowan Williams (2009) talks about *'the freedom to respond to the beautiful and the puzzling and the tragic, to all the things that we do not have the power to manage'*. These words are powerful pointers to the territory of spirituality, or rather they are signposts to a wide range of experiences, intuitions, insights, convictions, beliefs and world views that we neither wish, nor are able, to manage or control, but which nevertheless deepen and enrich our humanity. These are the 'territorial signposts' for our discussion about spirituality.

This manual explores the significance of spirituality for mental health, and especially the contribution it can make to a person's recovery and continuing journey. This emphasis upon spirituality should come as no surprise to us, for we would argue that each and every human being needs a sense of purpose and of being valued. We all need a world view that sustains us in times of difficulty, stress and crisis (Moss, 2005); we all need to feel supported, nourished, encouraged and upheld when the going gets tough. These are all important facets of spirituality in our view. In this sense, people's need for spirituality on the journey of recovery from an episode of mental distress is no different from any other person's need, except that the need here may be more acute and focused. The tragedy is, of course, that it has proved necessary for this claim to be made both by, and on behalf of service users and carers, as if somehow it had been assumed that their spiritual needs had been previously neutralised by their encounter with mental distress.

The importance of this insight cannot be underestimated. Spirituality is at the heart of what it means to be human – it is not a minority interest of a fanatical few. To understand spirituality is to understand what it means to be vibrantly alive; it is neither restricted to, nor exhausted by, an understanding or experience of religious faith and belief. It is, in part, to use Gilbert's (2005) memorable phrase, *'what makes us tick'*. This means that any discussion about education with regard to spirituality must not be restricted to one section of the community, such as those who are experiencing mental distress or those who are charged professionally with the task of caring for, treating and supporting them, important though that is. Education about spirituality is an activity and a commitment which is life-enhancing for everyone, not a minority sport like rock climbing or scuba diving, which may quicken the pulse of the enthusiast, but will leave the majority of the population unmoved. It is something which profoundly affects everyone. To explore education for spiritual care, therefore, we need first of all to look in the mirror at ourselves.

Mirror, mirror on the wall...

It can be a discomforting moment to see ourselves in the mirror, especially first thing in the morning before (for some women at least) the 'lippy' is applied, or (for some men at least) the persistent overnight stubble is removed. Having dealt with these glaring early-day challenges, we then feel more equipped to face the world. Or at least that is the hope.

But a deeper gaze can be no less disconcerting, no matter what time of day it occurs. The famous oracle at Delphi, according to ancient Greek tradition, greeted its enquiring visitors with the welcoming strap line 'know yourself' (gnothi seauton). The message was clear: without a deep sense, knowledge and appreciation of who we really are, no exploration of other problems in the world is likely to be successful. Certainly in any people-work, where we try to help, support and journey with people encountering particular difficulties, we have to be acutely aware of who we are – with all our prejudices and 'baggage' – so that we do not become part of the other person's problem, rather than contributing to an answer, or at least offering a constructive way forward. If we stay with Gilbert's phrase for a moment – that spirituality is what makes us tick – we realise that this gazing into a mirror of self-awareness is not some narcissistic self-indulgence, but a necessary precondition for any involvement in people-work. Two examples illustrate this point powerfully.

> A social work student learning and practising her basic communication skills was faced with someone who, in a role play setting, wanted to talk about the impact of domestic violence upon her life. The student's immediate reaction to this was tentatively to say, 'OK', and then she immediately began to ask a series of other unrelated questions about this person's life. When challenged afterwards by the trainer, she said 'Oh, I can't be doing with that sort of issue – it's too painful and difficult'.

> A mental health worker was visiting one of his service users who was just emerging from an episode of psychosis. The service user began to 'praise God' for her 'deliverance' and wanted her worker to join her in a prayer of thanksgiving. The worker was acutely embarrassed, and beat a hasty retreat, finding anything which explicitly raised questions about religion to be way outside his comfort zone. It was only later in the day that he realised how rejecting and un-affirming his attitude had been.

In both of these examples it was the workers' discomfort that prevented them from really hearing what the service user wanted to say. In both of these examples the workers needed to look long and hard in the mirror, to learn how to know themselves a bit better to prevent their discomfort from getting in the way of best practice.

The first major challenge educationally, therefore, is how to quicken people's self-awareness and to develop an appreciation of their own spirituality. If we cannot own and explore our own spirituality, the chances are that we will not be able to do so with others. And if service users who have experienced mental distress are demanding that their spirituality – which sometimes, but not always, will also involve their religious needs – is taken seriously as part of their journey to recovery, then without a willingness on the workers' part to enter this territory, best practice will be impossible. This is clearly an individual responsibility that each of us needs to take seriously.

This insight, however, leads us to a deeper underlying issue which needs to be explored, once we have taken on board the need to foster and develop our own spirituality. It is captured in the question, 'Is it possible to be neutral when you teach spirituality? Furthermore, is spirituality neutral?' These are important and challenging questions for educators and trainers to face. At one level there is an immediate response which warns us against trying to proselytise, either in a secular or religious way. It is just as unacceptable for a people-work professional who is a militant atheist to seek to persuade a service user to accept the tenets of that position, as it would be for a devout Christian or Muslim to seek to convert a service user to their faith. Professional values and codes of practice are specifically designed to protect vulnerable service users against this sort of oppressive exploitative behaviour. Our spirituality, whether or not it has a religious framework, is ours to own but not to foist onto others.

But this is not the same as saying that spirituality is neutral. Anyone holding a deeply religious faith will say that this profoundly affects who they are and the values they hold, and that it will also unavoidably impact upon how they treat others. Members of the British National Party would also claim that their allegiance to this political viewpoint necessarily affects how they regard and treat certain minority groups in UK society. It cannot be otherwise. Across a wide range of moral and ethical issues we all locate ourselves at some point on the spectrum, and this will at times impact upon our professional practice. Nurses who are morally or religiously opposed to abortion, for example, are allowed to opt out of such procedures precisely because of their convictions on this subject. Such convictions shape the world view that each of us holds, and which our spirituality expresses (Moss, 2005). In other words, our spirituality is both an expression of the world view we have chosen and also informs and influences it. We would argue that it is incumbent upon people-work professionals and others who seek to help or support vulnerable people, especially those experiencing mental distress, to recognise their own spirituality and the ways in which it informs their approach to others. It may not always be necessary explicitly to mention this to a service user, although at times it will be; but it must always be fully acknowledged by the professional people-worker.

If that is true in a practice setting, it is also true in an educational context when such issues are being explored. Again, it is not for the educator to foist their opinions and beliefs upon their students, but it is appropriate at times to share details of their own journey and world view, not least because the idea of being an expert in this field is far less easy to define. There is every chance, for example, that some students will have a deeper and more mature spirituality than those who are seeking to teach them. In such circumstances the educator needs to create a safe exploratory environment where everyone, including the educator, can feel safe to explore these issues and the impact they have upon their world view and professional practice. Indeed if educators do not 'come clean' and explore some the dilemmas or viewpoints that their faith-position (whether secular or religious) can create, then they are 'modelling' a learning style that does not fit with the teaching of and learning about spirituality.

If this is a challenge or dilemma for educators working in a specifically secular role, it is no less so for colleagues who are clearly identified as coming from a religious background, such as chaplains. The educational challenge of teaching spirituality is something that chaplaincy services are actively exploring, as evidenced elsewhere in this manual (chapter 21). Moody (2010), for example, grapples with how his own institution is trying to engage with the teaching of spirituality, and how to deliver a credible insight into ways in which '*an understanding of spirituality might contribute positively and holistically to the academic and personal preparation of … students to embark upon their chosen professions*'. Again, the self-awareness of the teaching team was a crucial *sine qua non*, although the challenge they face in having a clear religious identity is no less acute. Moody discusses the ongoing struggle of chaplaincy team members, for example, to try and make sense of the relationship between their spiritual and professional lives, which was sometimes projected onto a much larger canvas by some students who in turn were also trying to make sense of a powerful 'calling'. These students struggled at times to reconcile and understand what is often a difficult relationship between their training to acquire expertise in a particular caring profession and the fact that, in former lives, they had been recipients, or victims, of it[1].

Here, in a 'mirror image' between staff and students, the understanding and experience of spirituality was far from neutral. It is not so much a question of having to justify the position one has adopted on such issues, but being willing (whether as a staff member or a student) to be open and honest about how they see the territory that opens up for them. Exploring this territory is clearly a challenging task. For those seeking to enter a career in people-work, however, such challenges lie at the heart of their education, not least in order to help them to engage confidently and competently with service users for whom this is important territory.

Clearly, chaplaincy services have a key role to play, as Moody suggests. But if issues involving spirituality (and religion) are left to the professional 'experts' there is serious risk that others involved in the educational process will opt out at this point. It may well be, as Tomalin (2004) suggests, that *'religious and cultural literacy [is] a key employability skill'*, and that chaplaincy has found a niche in the academic market because, as she points out, even though *'religious diversity issues cut across all academic disciplines ... [due to the] rigid boundaries that exist between academic disciplines, **tutors do not know how they can build these issues into their courses'**.* (our emphasis)

But the challenge of exploring and teaching spirituality across all professional people-work disciplines cannot be left to a small dedicated cadre of so-called 'experts'. If it is that important, then it needs to be owned and 'delivered' by mainstream course tutors who are willing to take risks with their students on the educational journey they are undertaking together.

Teaching spirituality: a generic approach or should it be discipline-specific?

At this point, of course, a further challenge emerges, which again can be captured in the question: should the teaching of spirituality be 'discipline focused? Are the needs of, say, nursing, medical, social work, and mental health students sufficiently similar to allow for a generic educational 'package' to be put together that can be used and applied by any people-work education course? Or are the needs, and the understanding of spirituality, so distinctive within each professional group that they need to devise and deliver their own unique approach? It is to this complex question that we now will turn.

A generic definition of spirituality that will fit all shades of belief, whether religious or non-religious, is increasingly recognised as a chimera, an unrealistic notion (Swinton, 2006). Spirituality is to be understood, we suggest, far more as a signpost or gateway word, pointing us to territory we need to explore, than being a tightly defined phenomenon. However, the idea that spirituality can be taught in the same way to people in widely varying disciplines is still with us. Spirituality, as has been stated above, is a collection of ideas, concepts and experiences which apply themselves to different individuals in different ways. For one person, their spirituality may be powerfully bound up with nature and the earth, expressing itself most clearly through experiencing nature at its fullest in a forest walk miles from anyone, in lonely solitude. Another person may find their spiritual fulfillment amongst their friends and family. For some people their spiritual life is discovered through the spirituality of a religion, whereas for others religion plays no part in their life: their spirituality is about the strength of their individual identity. For some, their spirituality is about reaching out beyond themselves in service and caring and in the quest for social justice. In this sense, therefore, there are as many understandings of spirituality as there are people to experience them.

Similarly, it may be that spirituality has a different relevance whether you are a nurse, a social worker or a doctor. While there will be fundamental tenets which can be applied to any discipline, each discipline will also have its own emphasis in terms of meeting spiritual needs and its own opportunities to offer 'spiritual' care. The fundamental tenets may be about forming authentic, honest relationships; about respecting individual beliefs, and understanding what 'life-events' or challenges to their previously chosen world view may trigger spiritual questioning and the need to discover, or remember, their own spiritual supports. In this sense, then, there may well be core elements of spirituality that can be taught 'across the board'. This approach could well include the idea that practitioners need to understand their own spirituality in order to help another, as this is also common to all professions. Learning about spirituality, its expression and also its relationship to religion is necessary, therefore, no matter what profession you belong to. Other basic notions might include an understanding of the goals people aim for, which might help someone to be able to cope more easily with the current crisis, be it illness, bereavement, fear of death, loss of home or independence. From a professional perspective, the goal might be to become a companion for someone who is asking some big questions of life, looking for a meaning, or wondering what their past life has been about. This is a notion developed by Holloway and Moss (2010) in exploring the role of the 'fellow traveller' to help social work practitioners to understand their role with people who are grappling with deep existential questions.

However, while the fundamental goals and principles may be the same across many professional disciplines and discourses, the problems and opportunities which social workers and nurses encounter, for example, are different. The current preoccupation in health with inter-professional learning – different professions learning together in order to break down barriers between them – could mitigate against professions being able to explore the potential of the opportunities in their own daily work to help spiritually. This is especially true if different professional groups have not done some initial core preparatory work about spirituality to help them understand its relevance to their own professional role. Therefore, it seems important to explore what the various opportunities may be for different disciplines, with some questions about what should be taught and who should teach it. This section will conclude, therefore, with some thoughts about a different and more integrative way to include spirituality in education programmes.

Spirituality education in nursing: a working example

Where other professions tend to be based around interventions, nursing is based around continuous care. While a social worker, physiotherapist or a doctor may be responsible for a person for short intermittent periods while an intervention is made and a task performed – an examination, a therapy, a home visit to assess a situation or evaluate a new situation, for example – the nurse's contact tends to be more constant, at least while the patient is under their immediate care in a hospital or residential setting. Nurses may work 8–12 hours at a time with a group of patients, returning day on day. A nurse is there at night, at meal times and certainly for general nurses is also involved in all the intimate bodily care of the day: washing, toileting, mobility. Nurses have been described as the glue which keeps the system together, often co-ordinating all the other services and filling in the gaps that the therapists, social workers and medics do not reach, and replacing them, as far as they are able, when they are not there. While other workers move in and out of patients' lives when the need arises, the nursing team tends to be the constant factor. This is part of the uniqueness of the nurse's role, in the same way as other disciplines will have their own unique aspects. This constancy creates a particular set of circumstances which are opportunities to offer spiritual support and to have an impact upon the person's spirituality therapeutically. Models of the person which view the spirit, mind and body working in communion and interpenetrating each other suggest that working on the physical and material plane with people in a valuing and caring way can affect their spirit (Clarke, 2010) and different disciplines have different opportunities for this kind of care. In addition, when patients make themselves vulnerable and exposed, perhaps in receiving help with washing and toileting, they may reach spiritual crossroads in themselves which do not emerge in other circumstances. The nurse in these situations is immersed in the most taboo areas of life, giving care which others do not see. They are able to use touch and presence which profoundly affects a person's view of themselves and their value, either for good or ill. Relationships of trust can be built in such moments which can elicit the sharing of thoughts and feelings normally kept hidden. The nurse is particularly privileged, therefore, in being able, at times at least, to encounter the deep core of a person, with its strengths, beliefs, fears and vulnerabilities.

For the mental health nurse, the situation is similar. While there may be less physical care, there can be the overseeing of the person's hygiene and their daily routine; the question of whether a person is neglecting their physical needs is part of the nurse's assessment and responsibility. The nurse therefore can often be more of a constant presence than, for example, the psychologist or psychiatrist, and can gain a much more rounded overview of the person's health and well-being, physical, mental and spiritual.

Mental health care also brings with it its own problems borne out of its specialist focus. Mental health nurses are well used to working with the non-physical aspects of the person but usually within a biomedical framework. There has always been an issue with interpreting what was pathological from what was 'normal' in psychiatry, a dilemma that is of less importance to most practitioners. Understanding a person's concerns hermeneutically, as Swinton (2001) has attempted to do, (so that it is the meaning the person ascribes to their symptoms that is significant and not just the symptoms themselves), can bring the spiritual dimension of the person, which shapes identity and meaning, into sharper focus. In this more subjective model, where the nurse is considering the whole person, not as a combination of parts but as a unity, where each of the parts interrelate with and influences the others, the spiritual meaning that a person gives to their experiences becomes crucial to understanding their situation.

The influence of a person's spirituality on the manifestation of their symptom picture will be much more powerful in mental illness than in physical illness. Therefore, the practitioner's role is very different in mental health where, in addition to helping someone to discover or rediscover their own spiritual support structures, the practitioner may also be using their knowledge of spirituality to aid diagnosis and influence treatment. This may mean having to 'enter into the life world' of clients (Swinton, 2001, p135). Swinton describes how using empathy in encounters with clients to appreciate and understand the experience of paranoia and psychosis, a basic skill in mental health care, is a spiritual skill. Delusions may have an element of truth in them; they may also manifest ideas that are similar to religious ideas and use religious imagery. Thus the skill of empathy and the ability and confidence to enter into the delusional world of clients to understand the delicate interplay of person, history, experience and pathology is particularly important in mental health care. It is also imperative that professional workers are able to recognise when genuine, authentic religious experiences and beliefs are being presented, so that they are not dismissed as being part of the problem rather than being part of the journey to recovery. In all spiritual care the ability to discern clearly, and also to suspend one's own belief system to see the world as our clients see it, is important, but in mental health care this is central. To help mental health practitioners and general nurses to become skilled spiritual enablers in their own contexts is therefore a specialist concern.

Most studies enquiring about nurses' knowledge of spirituality, however, reveal that nurses feel ill-prepared to include spirituality in their work and would like more education to help them to do so (McSherry, 2000). However, it should not be forgotten that this is often the outcome of studies with nurses on any subject, be it diabetes or bereavement. More education is what they usually demand, and education comes to be regarded as a panacea to cure every problem. One of the co-authors remarked that, *'as a Master's lecturer I can't remember a theoretical or empirical essay or research study written by a student which did not conclude that more education was required on their particular specialty'*. As Papadopoulos and Copp (2005) have identified, even nursing lecturers feel that they need more preparation to teach spirituality. Similarly, what her study does not explore, is that if you asked the same lecturers about the other subjects they teach, they might say they are equally unprepared. Satisfying all the clamouring voices, suggestions and competing demands in overcrowded courses makes design of pre-registration curricula particularly challenging for nursing academics. Consequently, a two-hour session on spirituality in a three-year programme is the norm, with possibly an additional session in a module about palliative or end of life care. Getting staff released from practice to attend teaching sessions is a near impossible task as Julian Raffay has spoken about in his account of a training course in chapter 16.

Case study: inter-professional education

In 2008, Ivor Moody, then the chaplain of Anglia Ruskin University (Chelmsford campus), joined an education task group set up by the Essex Palliative Care Network, to demonstrate and encourage an awareness of the role of spirituality in the caring environment, and to ensure a system for its delivery was in place – a task which had been required of the Network by the National Institute for Clinical Excellence (NICE).

Rapidly, it became clear that throughout Essex, in various clinical environments and teaching establishments, there was already much good practice going on in this area, but that there did not seem to be much streamlining and co-ordination going on between the various courses and study days which were being offered.

Moody realised that the process of collating resources and the creation of a more unified approach to the teaching of spirituality could be fed back into the teaching of undergraduates in the Faculty of Health and Social Care at Anglia Ruskin University, and which might address what was the norm at Anglia Ruskin; usually a two-hour session on spirituality (if you were lucky) in a three-year course, often dropped 'stone-like' into a pool, and often inappropriately placed at the end of the course. This might ensure that students would not only have a more integrated approach to the application and significance of spirituality for their various branch programmes, but that, at least for the first two years after they qualify, if they secured a clinical post in the county (which proves true for the vast majority), that spirituality training would continue, nurturing them in their transition from a student experience into a work-based one.

Moody, a senior lecturer from the Faculty of Health and Social Care and staff from the Mid-Essex PCT (including two from the Macmillan nursing service) came together to begin the process of devising a spirituality input for nursing undergraduates spread over a three-year programme in three, two hour slots, and which would run on into their clinical practice, utilising expertise and experience both from within the university and from within various care and teaching centres around Essex.

In May 2009 the first group of 75 first year students had their introduction to spirituality and nursing care soon after starting their course, delivered by a mixture of community based clinicians and Anglia Ruskin teaching staff, and initial feedback from the students was extremely positive. It is hoped that this will be the first cohort, when they graduate in 2012, to have had experience of this new way of presenting and understanding how spirituality may be embedded and applied to situations of nursing care, both in their undergraduate studies and as ongoing training once they have qualified.

What and how?

Further questions arise about what to teach and how to teach it. We have already suggested in this article some core themes and issues that are common to many helping professions, but the challenge comes in applying these general themes to the specific requirements and demands of a particular profession such as nursing or social work. One important question raised here is whether one can teach spirituality without teaching about a particular spirituality; in other words, how neutral can you be about a subject that can be so personal and subjective? The philosopher Santayana said that, 'Any attempt to speak without speaking in any particular language is no more hopeless than the attempt to have a religion that shall be no religion in particular...' (Santayana, 1954, p180). So it may be just as hopeless to speak about spirituality without speaking of some spirituality in particular. As suggested earlier, teachers may do better to try to inspire with the strength and passion of their own spirituality while showing knowledge and respect for other spiritualities, rather than trying to present a bland 'neutral' approach. As one co-author has commented:

'We are always so worried about proselytising, that we are often fearful of talking about our own world view and spirituality, but perhaps we ought to credit our students, service users and patients with the intelligence to make up their own minds.'

A 'secular' spirituality can be just as fervently dogmatic as any religious standpoint: secularity is no guarantee of neutrality. Nurses with faith beliefs can feel beleaguered in classes and clinical environments where the prevailing assumption is a kind of secular dogma (Fawcett & Noble, 2004). Similar experiences from social work students are also evident in the literature (Channer, 1998). Student nurses tend to feel strongly that their own views on the subject should be acknowledged in teaching (McSherry *et al*, 2008). In departments of theology, academics have struggled for much longer than in departments of health with the question of how to teach spirituality and how to achieve the degrees of critical distance which need to be achieved when teaching their own and others' spiritual beliefs (Liebert & Deeter Dreitcer, 1995). It is an issue with which social work academics also grapple as they seek first to introduce, and then to debate, the ways in which an understanding of spirituality can enrich and deepen best practice (Holloway & Moss, 2010). A respectful acceptance of other people's world views, whether religious or secular, is essential therefore both in teaching and practising spirituality, but it does take some humility (Clarke, 2006).

This is the confusing territory that spirituality can take us into. To view it only as a way to form personal identity, for example, can marginalise the belief held by many people that spirituality is about a relationship with some sacred or non-material essence. A teacher, therefore, has to accord equal respect to each viewpoint, a tall order when you are also trying to imbue your teaching with inspiration from your own experience. This is one reason why teachers of spirituality need to develop their own self-awareness so that they are fully aware of their own spiritual beliefs and where their own prejudices and sore points can help them to develop the humility required to maintain this necessary delicate balance. It is not surprising, therefore, that lecturers hesitate to enter into teaching in this area, and feel unprepared to do so (Papadopoulos & Copp, 2005).

Alongside this sits the questions about whether all spiritualities are equal and whether we can begin to explore the concept of authentic and inauthentic spirituality. Are some expressions of spirituality life-enhancing whereas others can be destructive, life-denying, oppressive and discriminatory? Is there a litmus test we can use to evaluate truth claims and the impact of certain types of spirituality? This is clearly firmly within the territory of any educational programme about spirituality. It is an issue that requires more detailed treatment than is possible in this chapter, but its relevance is central to mental health and well-being. If one person's spirituality leads them into patterns of behavior that cause harm to others, then clearly this is a matter of concern. In our teaching and educating about spirituality we must acknowledge the 'darkness' that is implicit, and sometimes explicit, in some forms of spirituality (Satanism is one example that springs to mind here). Here again neutrality is impossible, because the very categorisation of authentic/ inauthentic is itself a value judgement. But in social work at least this is a mainstream activity, and the value base of anti-discriminatory, anti-oppressive practice (Thompson, 2006) provides a very clear litmus test or bench mark against which various spiritualities can be evaluated (Moss, 2005; Holloway & Moss, 2010). Theologians will also be familiar with this territory as they place the interpretative template of good and evil over the tapestry of human behaviour.

This is not some academic casuistry: far from it. This dimension of our teaching and educating around spirituality challenges us all, whatever our professional allegiance may be, to develop a world view that can make some sense of glory, mystery, creativity, grandeur and sacrificial caring, as well as pain, abuse and oppression. It challenges us all to make sense of the enigma variations in what it means to be human. It includes the flickering candles of hope we hold for, and with, people in distress (Moss & Gilbert, 2007) and the searing searchlight that must be played upon child and elder abuse, and the scandals of serious neglect in our hospitals. In short, the teaching of spirituality brings us face to face with human nature with all its potential for good and evil, and if we fail to recognise these dimensions in our teaching we are failing to do justice to the complex concept of spirituality.

It seems reasonable, therefore, to see spirituality as integral to teaching about any topic. If the way to offer good quality care could be seen as attending to the spiritual element in any situation, any relationship and any assessment, then there would only be a limited need to deliver special courses and training sessions. This is not to underestimate the value of using online learning, prescribed reading, lectures, discussion groups and discussion of cases in clinical practice teams. There is always a tendency among practitioners, however, to think that learning has to be the result of formal education programmes. Yet in this area more than in any other, practice educators and team leaders could enable learning in practice by encouraging a focus on spiritual issues in any clinical or practice situation, whatever the professional discipline may be. This approach would have the advantage of embedding spiritual care in practice, and applying it to specific situations, so that practitioners in any discipline can be helped to see the need, the potential and the opportunities for spiritual growth and support in the kind of encounters they deal with every day.

Triggers to thought about spiritual issues are all around us, and online resources or reading of short texts could provide the spark to ignite awareness, discussion and application. Furthermore, we suggest that Julian Raffay, writing in this volume, is right to say that in order to develop practice so fundamentally we need to tackle the whole system of an organisation. His idea of 'spirituality champions' seems particularly helpful. Although spirituality needs to be owned, celebrated and explored by everyone, there also need to be interested individuals who could have an eagle eye for where the 'spiritual gaps' and 'spiritual opportunities' are in each environment, each team and each relationship.

Conclusion

Spirituality is a subject unlike any other, and it needs imaginative and creative new ways to pass on its message to practitioners and to inspire them to see its potential. It would be unrealistic to think that NHS or social work managers are going to release staff to learn about spirituality unless they themselves understand its significance and importance, but even then making time to release staff will always be a challenge. Therefore, if we cannot find new and pragmatic ways to engage with the spiritual and teach about it, spirituality runs the danger of becoming a memorable fad in a few years time – and its loss would be incalculable. It is to meet some of the training challenges implicit in all of this that we turn to our next chapter.

Footnote

Recently a group of new midwifery students was asked why they had chosen their subject; nearly all of them linked their desire to study midwifery with their own experiences of childbirth, and to have the chance, now, to make some intellectual sense of what for them had been intense and in many cases traumatic experiences.

References

Channer Y (1998) Understanding and managing conflict in the learning process: Christians coming out. In: V Cree & C McCaulay (Eds) *Transfer of Learning in Professional and Vocational Education*. London: Routledge.

Clarke J (2006) Religion and spirituality: a discussion paper about negativity, reductionism and differentiation in nursing texts. *International Journal of Nursing Studies* **43** 775–785.

Clarke J (2010) Body and soul: using theology to understand the spiritual relationship between body and soul. *Journal of Mental Health, Religion and Culture*, accepted for publication.

Fawcett TN & Noble A (2004) The challenge of spiritual care in a multi-faith society experienced as a Christian nurse. *Journal of Clinical Nursing* **13** 136–142.

Gilbert P (2005) In: ME Coyte, P Gilbert & V Nicholls (2007) *Spirituality, Values and Mental Health: Jewels for the journey*. London: Jessica Kingsley.

Holloway M & Moss B (2010) *Spirituality and Social Work*. Basingstoke: Palgrave Macmillan.

Liebert E, Deeter Dreitcer A (1995) The spirituality of the teacher. *Teaching Spirituality: The Way supplement* **84** 38–46.

McSherry W (2000) Education issues surrounding the teaching of spirituality. *Nursing Standard* **14** (42) 40–43.

McSherry W, Gretton M, Draper P & Watson R (2008) The ethical basis of teaching spirituality and spiritual care: a survey of student nurses perceptions. *Nurse Education Today* **28** 1002–1008.

Moody I (2010) Curriculum matters: assessing a method of ministry for chaplaincy in a 'new' university'. *Discourse, Learning and Teaching in Philosophical and Religious Studies* **9** (2) 227–242.

Moss B (2005) *Religion and Spirituality*. Lyme Regis: Russell House Publishing.

Moss B & Gilbert P (2007) Flickering candles of hope: spirituality, mental health and the search for meaning. *Illness, Crisis and Loss* **15** (2) 179–191.

Papadopoulos I & Copp G (2005) Nurse lecturers' perception and teaching of spirituality. *Implicit Religion* **8** (1) 22–39.

Santayana G (1954) *The Life of Reason*. London: Constable.

Swinton J (2001) *Spirituality and Mental Health Care: Rediscovering a 'forgotten' dimension.* London: Jessica Kingsley.

Swinton J (2006) Identity and resistance: why spiritual care needs 'enemies'. *Journal of Clinical Nursing* **15** 918–928.

Thompson N (2006) *Anti-Discriminatory Practice*. Basingstoke: Palgrave Macmillan.

Tomalin E (2004) Supporting cultural and religious diversity. *Discourse* **4** (1) 77–82.

Williams R (2009) Lecture at Rikkyo Gaukin University on the occasion of his conferment of a honorary doctorate (21/9/2009).

Chapter 16

Valuing staff and training for spiritual care

Katja Milner and Julian Raffay

Introduction

'It doesn't interest me what you do for a living. I want to know what you ache for, and if you dare to dream of meeting your heart's longing...
It doesn't interest me who you know or how you came to be here. I want to know if you will stand in the centre of the fire with me and not shrink back.
It doesn't interest me where or what or with whom you have studied. I want to know what sustains you, from the inside, when all else falls away.'
(From *The Invitation* © Oriah Mountain Dreamer (1999). All rights reserved. Printed with permission of the author. (www.oriah.org))

This is an excerpt I (Katja Milner) use to begin staff training sessions. This is a poem about spirituality without mentioning the word spirituality and for me it is a poem about the breadth and depth, power and vulnerability of human experience.

Healthcare staff are in a very privileged yet challenging position in society to be caring for and facilitating the recovery of people with many different life experiences, challenges, strengths, backgrounds and belief systems. They are expected to provide care which fits around the individual needs of the service user within a healthcare system which is often contradictory in its principles and their application. In addition, on-going tensions, changes and economic and political pressures can leave staff confused, stressed, disillusioned or, worse still, burnt out. These kinds of issues are curiously missing from many targets and policies, and yet their significance and impact on the effective functioning of the healthcare system itself cannot be underestimated.

This chapter explores some of these issues and outlines a training programme that supports staff well-being and effective practice by helping practitioners to connect with their own inner values. It then goes on to examine general spiritual care training approaches and how they can be embedded effectively and systemically into the organisation. This leads on to some final considerations about the role of leadership in the process of promoting spiritual awareness and understanding in staff and healthcare organisations.

The missing link

Do you feel valued? Will you, as you progress through your career, perhaps working with people who have reached one of the most painful and difficult points of their lives, feel like a valuable and valued member of your collective group of professionals, all inputting their specialist knowledge, skill and care? The answer to this question probably lies in a combination of factors and also most likely will have a significant impact on your current or future job satisfaction, sickness levels, well-being and competency at work (Brown, 2003; 2008; Smith, 2001).

Considering the fact that we are human 'beings' and not human 'doings' (or machines, computers or slaves), it is a wonder the degree to which the heart, soul and vitality of a person gets left out, forgotten, ignored or conveniently pushed aside in many mainstream organisational, political and economic structures and processes. Perhaps this is a by-product of our current stage of social evolution. Perhaps we have become so used to thinking in a certain way, including about ourselves, that we have forgotten how valuable we all are. Certainly the media does a good job in encouraging us to feel like we can never quite be beautiful, strong or 'celebrity' enough. Our education systems and most professional training programmes tend to value theory over intuition, science over spirit, reciting others over expressing ourselves. And so we come to work and here we learn how to apply all this learning and be the best productive unit of person that we can. The problem is that we are human. We are not some mere biological programme which can be trained to tick boxes, jump through hoops and climb all the right ladders with a smile on its face. We all have idiosyncrasies, weaknesses, strengths, parts that reach out with excitement and empowerment and parts that curl inwards in fear or in shame. This, I would argue, is what makes us beautiful, what really makes us have value.

Unfortunately, in an increasingly business (and now perhaps economic fear) driven world, still entrenched in the limitations and dogma of the traditional medical model and economic system, valuing the people who drive and power this system does not tend to get mentioned much in government policy or within organisational practices. This is a generalisation and there will be cases where this does occur, especially on a smaller scale between individuals and teams who do care, because they are caring people and have not fallen prey to the dehumanisation process which seems too often to occur as structures get bigger and more quantitative.

Even the contemporary policy drivers in health and social care which focus increasingly on the individualised needs and holistic care of the service user, tend to omit the 'staff' part of the 'effective care' equation. They assume that practitioners will automatically be equipped with the most sophisticated powers of humane values, reflective practices, holistic attitudes and emotional intelligence. Many people are, but this should not be an assumption nor something which is taken for granted or seen as a commodity which can be endlessly and seamlessly taken or given. For these abilities to be learned, nourished, promoted and valued, they need to be present in the educational, professional and organisational structures and policies of the profession. Even the 'recovery' approach, with its emphasis on the experiences and values of the service user and the ability of staff to value and inspire hope in the people they work with (Basset & Repper, 2005) tends to take for granted where staff themselves can go to feel valued, to gain hope and to feel nourished in a sometimes tireless and thankless role.

'Healthcare professionals are somehow expected to be calm, compassionate, and caring, but very little is done to enhance and strengthen those natural qualities through experiential learning in their training. Paradoxically, these natural qualities may be trained out of us! Caring, as well as competence, are the two pillars of good medical practice and should be equally emphasised in any education programme.' (The Janki Foundation for Global Healthcare, 2004, p6)

The cost of ignoring staff well-being, of taking their care for granted, is staff stress, low morale, illness and burnout. Much has been written about the high levels of stress and unhappiness in health professionals and the effects it has on practice (Firth-Cozens, 1999; Appleton *et al*, 1998). The day-to-day business of taking care of people who are ill or very needy is often inherently distressing. In addition, the increasing rate of change in society and organisational structures and greater service user expectations have imposed an additional burden that can lead to a state of chronic tiredness and demoralisation, or burnout. This can have devastating effects, including depression, higher suicide rates and dependence on alcohol and drugs, negative attitudes towards service users and low self-esteem (Hawton *et al*, 2001; Patani *et al*, 2001; Pines & Aronson, 1998).

So what is it to value someone? More importantly perhaps, what is it to value ourselves?

Reflection exercise

What did you do well yesterday? What qualities did you show whilst talking with others?

What positive thoughts did you have about yourself yesterday?

Is it challenging to be positive about yourself? If so, why?

Why is it useful to have positive thoughts about oneself?

(Adapted from 'Valuing the self' exercise, The Janki Foundation for Global Healthcare, 2004)

'Values can be said to underpin everything we do and say in our work and life... If we lose sight of our values, we may begin to experience a loss of meaning in what we do and who we are, leading to a diminished sense of self-esteem. Our work suffers, and we begin to suffer at work and, inevitably, in our personal lives.' (The Janki Foundation for Global Healthcare, 2004, p51)

Values can be described as our core beliefs or principles by which we live or aspire to live. The problem with the word 'value' is that it is often misused by businesses and organisations: 'We value our customers' or 'We value excellence'. But for values to be meaningful they must be owned at a personal level and genuinely applied and integrated into what we do. They must come from the heart, not just the head.

The great news is that the more we value ourselves the more we learn to value others and become more effective and productive as individuals, teams and as organisations. This, in turn, perpetuates well-being, health and vibrancy and this energy is what can effectively and healthily drive us and the system we work in, rather than that which is rooted in performance anxiety, competition, fear of failure and desire for status over others.

'As above, so below' as the ancient Hermetic saying goes. What is genuinely effective for us as individuals applies also to the wider team, organisation, and even culture and society, and vice versa. We are not being selfish when we look after and take care of ourselves. For when we do this, when we truly learn to reflect on our own truth, our personal growth, our health and well-being, how we are feeling and why we do what we do, then we equip ourselves with the tools, compassion and energy to be a real team player, to give of ourselves, and to sit alongside another when they are at their most confused and distressed.

Values in healthcare

A student giving feedback in a recent training session that I (Katja) co-facilitated said that they had gone to lectures on spirituality which had left them just as confused about the meaning of this concept as before the session. What was the difference in this particular training session? The opportunity to learn through experience, encouragement of exploration and personal discovery, time and space for open reflection and sharing and the realisation that spirituality, by its very nature, cannot be grasped by the intellect alone.

This training was implemented, in a successful collaboration of spiritual care and chaplaincy team staff from South Staffordshire and Shropshire, Birmingham and Solihull and Nottinghamshire Healthcare NHS Trusts, to give people learning experiences which allowed them to reflect deeply and personally on the concept of spirituality. To grasp what is meaningful and valuable to them and how connecting with these experiences, reflecting on them and sharing them with the group can inform, inspire and develop their work practice.

The training programme was an adaptation of the 'Values in Healthcare' approach, a modular training programme of personal and team development for students and practitioners throughout the healthcare services. This innovative approach was set up by a healthcare charity called the Janki Foundation for Global Healthcare who are dedicated to positive human development and to the research and promotion of a spiritual model of modern healthcare. In 2000 The Foundation invited a group of professionals from various backgrounds in healthcare, medical education and training to share ideas about the issues facing healthcare professions. They were concerned about how the spiritual dimension of 'whole-person' medicine could be integrated into current healthcare provision and training. They concluded that the key issues were spiritual in nature and that healthcare professionals needed to find meaning and purpose in their work, to reconnect with their personal values and to create a positive vision of their future. They went on to devise a programme called 'Values in Healthcare' to help workers identify their values and develop ways of reflecting on and applying them in their professional and personal lives.

Reflection exercise

Think of the songs you love, or the poems, books or paintings that are important to you. What feelings do they evoke? What values are reflected through them?

Look back on your working life and reflect on a 'high point', a time when you worked at your best, a time that was significant or meaningful to you, when you felt most alive, creative or effective. What made it a successful or memorable experience?

What felt truly special about it? What values does this reflect in you?

(Adapted from 'My favourite things' and 'A high point in my working life' exercise, The Janki Foundation for Global Healthcare, 2004)

There are three main principles underlying the Values in Healthcare programme.

1. **Physician heal thyself** – the idea that practitioners cannot aim to heal others before nurturing and healing themselves. Instead of only focusing on clinical skills, this approach emphasises the importance of self-care and supports the development of healthy practitioners with raised morale and renewed sense of purpose so that they are then enabled to provide effective and holistic care to others.

2. **Learning through experience** – highlighting the importance of experiential learning, of turning our attention inwards and of exploring through direct experience. This is done by allowing time for silence, reflection, meditation and sharing, in a supportive environment rather than through traditional didactic instruction.

3. **Relevance to work** – the emphasis on reflection, action planning, review and evaluation is very applicable to practice. In addition, working with values can help prevent burnout and practitioners who are healthy are more likely to provide enhanced quality of care for service users. Organisations can also benefit from a clear values-base and by encouraging a culture of care.

To facilitate participants' engagement with their inner exploration and to help them apply their insights to a wide range of situations and problems, the Values in Healthcare programme introduces seven 'spiritual tools' for learning. These are meditation, visualisation, reflection, listening, appreciation, creativity and play. These tools represent an intelligent, tangible and practical application of spirituality often lacking in healthcare education and practice. They are intended to help develop a deeper and broader capacity for reflection and insight, more sophisticated ways of thinking and problem solving and the emotional intelligence so important in effective healthcare practice, personal development and well-being. They have also been used by people with severe illness and disability to help develop coping strategies as described in Jan Alcoe's self-help book *Lifting Your Spirits* (Alcoe, 2008). Here she used the seven tools for her own sustenance and healing after being diagnosed with cancer and wrote this book because of the benefits she derived and because of the lack of any guide of this kind for people with serious illness.

I have found the tools useful in mental healthcare settings as part of my own role as a spirituality healthcare worker, developing programmes and activities akin to 'spiritual interventions', which are accessible to people with a diverse range of beliefs and backgrounds and are safe and relatively simple to practice. Clearly such tools and related interventions including the Values in Healthcare approach itself are in need of research and an evidence base so that they can become more fully integrated into mainstream education and practice. Some research has already been conducted to show the beneficial effects of educational programmes in managing stress (Nishiuchi *et al*, 2007; Krasner *et al*, 2009) and that organisations are more successful if employers help their workers manage stress (Jones *et al*, 1988). However, research into spiritual care and training requires attention generally and is explored further in chapter 2.

The Values in Healthcare programme is delivered via a pack of materials and comprises seven modules. These are values, peace, positivity, compassion, co-operation, valuing yourself and spirituality in healthcare.

Each module consists of a combination of group learning activities utilising the different spiritual tools and can be used flexibly as standalone workshops or incorporated into other training programmes. Packs include detailed facilitation guidelines, and facilitator training programmes are offered twice a year (see website www.jankifoundation.org for more details).

Since its launch in 2004, the Values in Healthcare training has been well received and adopted by health professionals, with more than 300 facilitators trained worldwide. The strong vision, intelligence and enthusiasm behind this unique approach is ensuring its steady growth in the UK and across the world and in a climate of ever-growing stress and pressure is highly pertinent and timely.

Embedding training

Imagine that you have just put on a series of Values in Healthcare workshops which have been highly successful. Imagine that you have got 10% of the workforce to attend and have somehow managed to avoid exhausting your staff team in the process. You could reasonably pat yourself on the back. You would, however, almost certainly be aware that you have only just started out on the hard path of getting spiritual care embedded into day-to-day clinical activity.

It is a hard path and will at times call for nothing less than courageous leadership but, to the extent that you succeed, you will bring to client care (and staff well-being) something almost beyond measure. There may be some who will oppose you but most will simply be too busy with their targets to engage with you. Getting staff released from busy wards may yet prove your greatest challenge. Any apparent rejection is likely to make you anxious but Koestenbaum (2002, p140) urges us not to fear anxiety and to recognise it instead as an opportunity for growth and insight. Only by understanding our own feelings of being marginal and powerless do we understand the insecurities that drive staff to focus on targets. Only by understanding our own feelings do we connect with the feelings of service users in the face of the institution with its often inflexible rules and regulations.

If all this sounds a little grim, we don't have to go it alone. For a start, legislation in the form of the Equality Act 2010 means that it is now an offence for staff to give someone inferior treatment because of their religion or belief. What's more, the only way they can avoid this is by receiving appropriate training which can only sensibly be provided by someone who has thought deeply about these issues, engaging with them at both an intellectual and an emotional level.

Please don't be fooled into thinking that any tools or guidelines your trust may be using are gold standard, evidence-based and subject to peer review. The second author of this chapter, Julian Raffay's observations are that staff may be fumbling around with poor materials which may not even be fit for purpose. Many different tools are often in use within a single trust. There's plenty of scope here for development.

If this all still feels too hard, then let me offer you this tip. I restore my passion for the work by reflecting on the most painful points in my life and asking myself what I would have hoped for from the staff had I been admitted. I then ask myself the simple question: how might I help the staff to sustain this, in terms of both support and vision?

Reflection exercise

If you feel reasonably comfortable doing so, spend 10 minutes thinking what would matter to you if you were admitted to a mental health unit. (If you have been admitted in the past, ask yourself what would have made the difference.) Even better, put the same question to colleagues, friends, and service users.

You could draw encouragement from the significant number of staff in your trust who value either spirituality or the recovery approach or both. If you are part of a foundation trust, there will be service user and carer members and governors. Don't lose any time getting them on board. In Sheffield, I have benefited hugely from a spirituality strategy group that serves as a council of reference for the Chaplaincy and Spiritual Care Department. Every trust needs a spirituality strategy group.

I'm also allowing myself five years to complete what I am hoping to achieve. Though radicals will always welcome any kind of change, others find it far harder emotionally and some will only come kicking and screaming. The tide is turning within psychiatry as the technical medical model in its narrowest sense is increasingly being found insufficient. Having said that, it is helpful to understand something about the processes by which change takes place within organisations. I have found figure 1 (adapted from Leach, 1992, p247) most useful in understanding some of the surprising reactions we may observe when we seek to effect change.

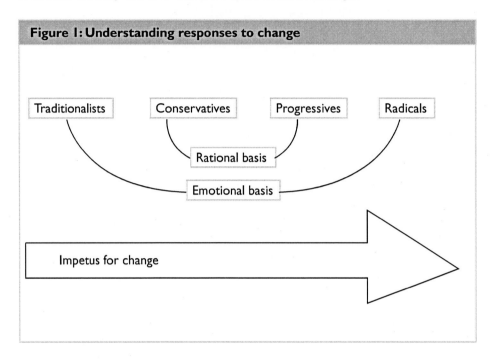

Figure 1: Understanding responses to change

If we imagine that the task involves nothing more than forcing staff to learn a few lists of religious practices and defining some basic principles on diversity, we will almost certainly fail. Some may be convinced by our arguments but others may hold the views they do because of a bad experience within a faith community or because a service user in their care went off the deep end on some spiritual issue. Clearly no amount of logical argument or frequency of e-learning is likely to bring about the desired change. Time needs to be given on any training course for mutual respect to develop and for emotional content to be engaged with as well. Clearly the work of the Janki Foundation offers precisely one such opportunity.

Embedding organisational change requires a willingness to use organisational tools. Here I have found that *Going Lean in the NHS* (Westwood, 2007) has helped me to focus, to clear out the clutter, and understand what I am trying to achieve. Remember, it's more important to be effective than efficient.

However slick we might be as managers, we will get nowhere unless the staff are confident that we care about them as well as the service users. Do give yourself time to build relationships with ward and unit staff. Unless you spend quality time with relevant staff, you can be certain that your task will take you a lot longer.

Don't hesitate to spend time with radicals, build up your confidence, and then venture onto harder ground. Do your best to understand the context and identify champions. In Sheffield, we have allocated chaplains to work on individual wards in collaboration with spirituality champions, ward staff whose role includes promoting spiritual healthcare on the ward. This model requires some working at but, if it's part of a sustained commitment over a number of years, will almost certainly pay off. Even better, if practical, bring champions together perhaps six times a year for mutual support and peer mentoring.

Finally, monitoring and evaluation should be built into the design of your training rather than be added at the end.

Course content

You may be thinking that this is all very well, but what about the practical aspects and content of a course on spiritual care? In Sheffield, we have already run three sets of courses and have a fourth in our sights; each of these seeks to bring about change in particular areas of care. See table 1 below.

Table 1: Staff training in Sheffield	
Course	**Target group**
Exploring spiritual and faith strengths and needs (1 hour)	For all staff, including housekeepers, ward clerks etc.
Assessing spiritual and faith strengths and needs (half day)	A crash course for those with limited time.
Mainstreaming spiritual and faith strengths and needs (1 day)	For qualified staff who wish to engage in more depth.
Championing spiritual and faith strengths and needs (2 days)	For spirituality champions and those wishing to exercise leadership in developing spiritual healthcare.

Over the months, we have engaged in reflective practice to refine the first three of these courses in the light of discussions and feedback from participants. We have found it particularly valuable to involve a service user (chaplaincy volunteer) in the training sessions. Even as I write this article, I am experimenting with delivering learning in hour-long modules rather than fixed courses.

One of the greatest frustrations we have experienced is the request from many staff for handbooks with guidance on different faiths which assumes that all adherents of a particular faith wish the same thing. Julian's response has always been to suggest that they consult the service user. Where staff are insistent, they are encouraged to visit a reputable website such as www.bbc.co.uk/religion.

Any course must help people to understand the difference between spirituality, faith, and religion and will ideally help staff address some of their own prejudices in these areas. It is well worth spending time on these matters as further progress is otherwise unlikely. Our preferred definition is from Murray and Zentner (1989, p259), not least because it comes from a nursing source:

'In every human being there seems to be a spiritual dimension, a quality that goes beyond religious affiliation, that strives for inspiration, reverence, awe, meaning and purpose... The spiritual dimension tries to be in harmony with the universe, strives for answers about the infinite, and comes especially into focus at times of emotional stress, physical (and mental) illness, loss, bereavement and death.'

The next section of our training involves explaining the rationale for spiritual care, picking up on work which was conducted by Julia Walsh, the transcultural team manager in our Trust. Here, we argue that quality spiritual care improves the staff–client relationship and reduces incidents, stress, absenteeism and burnout.

In all but the shortest of our courses, we then move on to consider the mechanics of how to conduct an assessment of spiritual strengths and needs. We encourage staff to work in groups pretending to assess each other, using the assessment tools that they actually have at their disposal. Where training is offered to staff from several directorates at a time, staff could be asked to bring their assessment tools with them. They could then work on this particular exercise with other members of their team. In teaching members of staff how to assess spiritual strengths and needs, we encourage them to provide worthwhile interventions through the nursing process rather than merely listing religions.

An invaluable perspective comes from Robinson *et al* (2003, p89):

'If authentic relationships are not developed, then both the nurse and the patient become part of a sterile, structured, systematic process which is devoid of integrity and meaning. If this position is taken, how can the nurse ever get near to the patient as a person?'

From there, we move on to consider the blocks to spiritual care using the excellent figure by Edwards and Gilbert (2007, p155)

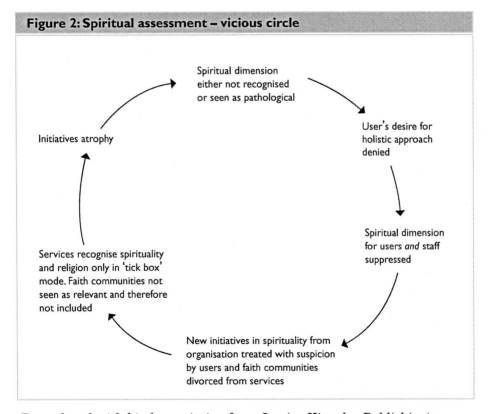

Figure 2: Spiritual assessment – vicious circle

Spiritual dimension either not recognised or seen as pathological

User's desire for holistic approach denied

Spiritual dimension for users *and* staff suppressed

New initiatives in spirituality from organisation treated with suspicion by users and faith communities divorced from services

Services recognise spirituality and religion only in 'tick box' mode. Faith communities not seen as relevant and therefore not included

Initiatives atrophy

(Reproduced with kind permission from Jessica Kingsley Publishing)

After what can be a slightly difficult part of the course, we then provide a chapter on resources available and seek to build people's confidence so that they aren't left with a sense that the task is simply too difficult.

With the longer courses, we include a section on differentiating between healthy and pathological spirituality as advocated by Crowley and Jenkinson (2009, p254). Here we can demonstrate our competence in addressing one of the more difficult issues in psychiatry. We also introduce the concept of resilience and encourage staff to recognise that, though not for all, many service users report that it is precisely their spirituality that enables them to survive years of psychiatric admissions, medication, and the effects of psychosis.

We also include a section on providing auditable spiritual care because we believe that spiritual care needs to be auditable if it is not to be sidelined by more supposedly important targets.

Throughout the courses, we are clear in our minds that respect lies at the heart of spiritual care, a matter that Joanna Barber (2010) has spoken about eloquently when drawing a distinction between implicit and explicit (my words) spiritual care.

Two ideas if you want to reach beyond 'death by PowerPoint' are (1) to use a wide range of photos as a warm-up to get people to explore what they understand by spirituality and (2) to show excerpts of the film 'The Soloist' which has much to say about the carer–service user relationship.

Leadership

Peter Gilbert's observation that *'when a healthcare organisation loses its way and concentrates on an inappropriate business model, while neglecting its primary function of treatment and care, the people suffer'*, demonstrates the importance of leadership (see chapter 1).

Leadership is not simply something for the chief executive. It is something that each of us is called on to exercise whether we are a student nurse, volunteer, or team leader. We exercise leadership when we demonstrate courage in the pursuit of excellence. We also exercise leadership when we arrive late and slope off early, albeit a rather negative form of leadership.

Reflection exercise

In what ways do you exercise leadership at work, in college, or in the community?

Overall, there seems to be an increasing recognition that leadership needs to be transformational and inspirational whereas a purely transactional management ethos can reduce morale. Basset and Repper (2005) stress the vital importance of hope among staff and this obviously underpins the work of the Janki Foundation. To state the obvious, hope has been central to the teaching of faith communities for centuries. It is also a vital component in training for spiritual care. Here we may see a number of interesting themes emerging which would benefit from further analysis. Clearly there is a link between the recovery approach with its origins in the Twelve Steps approach of Alcoholics Anonymous (which in turn has its origins in Christian theology) and spirituality. But a link might also be seen between these and the original model of servant leadership as demonstrated in John 13 where Jesus is recorded as washing his followers' feet. Here, he identified himself with the person at the very bottom of the organisational tree and encouraged other would-be leaders to do the same. If this account is connected with the rediscovery of servant leadership that is taking place in management today, it could yet prove to be a significant inspiration for future trends in effective nursing care (though of course others could be identified and may be preferred according to the faith position or spiritual standpoint of the reader).

For me (Julian), one of the key areas where we can demonstrate servant leadership is in respecting the autonomy of another person and helping them to achieve reasonable aspirations (Barker & Buchanan-Barker, 2005), especially when they conflict with our own. As mentioned earlier, we will almost certainly have our own values and prejudices but as healthcare workers, our task is to serve the client. As soon as we discriminate on the grounds of religion or belief, we may be in breach of the Equality Act 2010. If we really cannot get on the same wavelength as the client, we owe it to them to be honest about the matter and offer to put them in touch with another member of staff who may be better placed to help them. That too is leadership.

Clearly values, spirituality, recovery, and leadership are more than a set of ideas that fall neatly into bullet points. Instead, they shape who we are, how we affect the organisation in which we work, and how we lead our own lives. Spiritual care at its best is both profoundly human and technically proficient.

Conclusion

In this chapter we have considered the importance of valuing ourselves and training staff not only for effective spiritual care but for leadership in healthy and pioneering organisations. There is no doubt about the impact of staff stress levels and low morale in healthcare organisations, and the importance service users place on their beliefs, values, religion and spirituality in their recovery and well-being (see also *Taken Seriously: The Somerset Spirituality Project*, Mental Health Foundation, 2002). This chapter proposes that a key way to recognise and work with these priorities is through effective staff training which, in relation to spirituality, is still in its relative infancy of development. Some potential approaches, course content and methods for implementation have been discussed, as well as the importance of being aware of leadership, the system and the organisation within which we operate to promote and develop any change. Staff who are valued and trained appropriately will be in a far better position to offer hope and effective care to service users and carers and to work better within their teams, thus helping to transform the organisations they work for from primarily target-focused bodies to more evolved organisms with hearts that beat with health and vitality.

References

Alcoe J (2008) *Lifting Your Spirits*. London: Janki Foundation for Global Health Care.

Appleton K, House A & Dowell A (1998) A survey of job satisfaction, sources of stress and psychological symptoms among general practitioners in Leeds. *British Journal of General Practice* 48 1059–1063.

Barber J (2010) Launch of *Handbook of Spiritual Care in Mental Illness*. Birmingham: Birmingham and Solihull Mental Health NHS Foundation Trust.

Barker P & Buchanan-Barker P (2005) *The Tidal Model: A guide for mental health professionals*. London: Routledge.

Basset T & Repper J (2005) Travelling hopefully. *Mental Health Today* November 16–18.

Brown C (2003) Low morale and burnout: is the solution to teach a values-based spiritual approach? *Complementary Therapies in Nursing and Midwifery* **9** 57–61.

Brown C (2008) Doctors' health matters – learning to care for yourself. *Journal of Holistic Healthcare* **5** (2) 32–36.

Crowley N & Jenkinson G (2009) In: C Cooke et al. *Spirituality and Psychiatry*. London: Royal College of Psychiatrists.

Edwards W & Gilbert P (2007) In: ME Coyte *et al* (Eds). *Spirituality, Values and Mental Health: Jewels for the journey*. London: Jessica Kingsley.

Firth-Cozens J (1999) *Stress in Health Professionals: Psychological and organisational causes and interventions*. London: Wiley.

Hawton K, Clements A, Sakarovitch C, Simkin S & Decks J (2001) Suicide in doctors: a study of risk according to gender, seniority and speciality in medical practitioners in England and Wales, 1979–1995. *Journal of Epidemiology and Community Health* **55** 296–300.

Janki Foundation for Global Health Care (2004) *Values in Healthcare: A spiritual approach*. London: The Janki Foundation for Global Health Care.

Jones J, Barge B, Steffy B, Fay L, Kunz L & Wuebker J (1988) Stress and medical malpractice: organisational risk assessment and intervention. *Journal of Applied Psychology* **73** 727–735.

Koestenbaum P (2002) *Leadership: The inner side of greatness, a philosophy for leaders*. San Fransisco: Jossey-Bass.

Krasner M, Epstein R, Beckman H, Suchman A, Chapman B, Mooney CJ & Quill T (2009) Association of an educational programme in mindful communication with burnout, empathy, and attitudes among primary care physicians. *Journal of the American Medical Association* **302** 1284–1293.

Leach J (1992) *Liturgy and Liberty*. London: MARC.

Mental Health Foundation (2002) *Taken Seriously: The Somerset Spirituality Project*. London: Mental Health Foundation.

Murray & Zentner (1989) Nursing Concepts for Health Promotion. In:
L Culliford & Johnson S (2003) *Healing From Within: A guide for assessing the religious and spiritual aspects of people's lives*. London: Royal College of Psychiatrists.

Nishiuchi K, Tsutsumi A, Takao S, Mineyama S, Kawakami N (2007) Effects of an education program for stress reduction on supervisor knowledge, attitudes and behaviour in the workplace: a randomized controlled trail. *Journal of Occupational Health* **49** 190–198.

Oriah Mountain Dreamer (1999) *The Invitation*. San Francisco, CA: HarperONE.

Patani A, Constantinovici N & Williams S (2001) Who retires early from the NHS because of ill health, and what is the cost? A national cross-sectional study. *British Medical Journal* **322** 208–209.

Pines A & Aronson E (1998) *Career Burnout: Causes and cure*. New York: The Free Press.

Robinson S, Kendrick K & Brown A (2003) *Spirituality and the Practice of Healthcare*. Basingstoke: Palgrave Macmillan.

Seligman M (2003) *Authentic Happiness*. London: Nicholas Brealey Publishing.

Smith R (2001) 'Why are doctors so unhappy?' *British Medical Journal* **322** 1073–1074.

Westwood N (2007) *Going Lean in the NHS*. Coventry: NHS Institute for Innovation and Improvement.

Chapter 17

Equality and human rights approaches in the NHS: making spirituality in mental health care count?

Ranjit Senghera

Introduction

This chapter is for any individual and NHS organisation working to understand and apply the equality and human rights agenda within the NHS. Other chapters in this book provide an in-depth analysis of the concepts of 'spirituality' and 'religion' in mental healthcare. For the purposes of this chapter, I aim to provide an overview of the key drivers and leavers for change, both policy and legislative, and focus on some key examples and tools developed to effect change. At the time of writing this chapter there are many pending changes within the equalities legislative framework, which will impact on the policy drivers. It is for this reason that I have provided an overview and included references to websites to gain updates on the current developments.

This chapter will cover two areas:

▶ an overview of the equalities and human rights-based approaches for the NHS – legislative and policy drivers for change

▶ to focus on organisational frameworks and tools developed to support NHS organisations to effectively implement the equality and human rights-based approaches within healthcare.

Alongside each of the above I aim to highlight some areas of good practice and case studies that people may find useful.

Part 1: An overview of the equalities and human rights-based approaches for the NHS – legislative and policy drivers for change

Key legal and policy drivers on spiritual care in the NHS

Chapter 1 of this book provides a quick overview of the key policy drivers around spirituality and religious faith. As the legal and policy framework around equalities develops and the cultural make up of British society grows ever more diverse, there are a significant number of major policy imperatives set by government, and also expressed needs set out by people who use mental health services.

Equalities, spirituality and mental health issues

Spiritual interpretations of mental illness can play a crucial part in therapeutic success. A holistic approach to the patient, which takes account of their physical, cultural, social, mental and spiritual needs, would seem to have a particular significance within mental health services.

The National Service Framework for Mental Health set national standards and defined service models for promoting mental health and treating mental illness in key areas such as mental health promotion, primary care and access to effective services for people with severe mental ill health, caring for carers and preventing suicide. Building on this was the national mental health equalities programme, which focused in detail on all strands of equalities and social inclusion; it covered a range of approaches, tools and methods to mainstream the equalities and spirituality, religion and belief models and practices within mental health care services in England. For more information see www.nmhdu.org.uk/equalities.

The last decade has seen positive movements in the direction of travel for the equality and human rights-based approaches, both through legislative

Spirituality and Mental Health © Pavilion Publishing (Brighton) Ltd 2011 and policy imperatives, many which have been pioneered through the mental healthcare system. The approaches to engaging with one's spirituality and spiritual well-being has been driven by mental health survivors and their carers who have challenged the NHS to drive for changes to ensure that the spiritual well-being of a person is part of the core of who they are and will aid their continued recovery. The tools and frameworks that I address in this chapter are basic organisational tools and approaches that all people working in the NHS should work to embrace and implement. Swinton (2001) argues that we are all 'spiritual healers', he states:

'Spiritual healers have the ability to discern things of the spirit, to recognise the need for meaning, purpose, value and hope and to be able to work with these dimensions even in the midst of the most painful psychological distress. In order for this to happen there needs to be changes in the ways in which mental health carers are educated. We need to recognise these issues at an early stage ... that the language of the spirit can become our ... second, if not first language.' (p178)

I believe that this spiritual language works well with the understanding of human rights-based approaches, seeing the person first and not the illness. The Patient's Charter, 2001, stated that NHS staff will respect your privacy and dignity and to be inclusive, where services will be *'sensitive to and respect your religious, spiritual and cultural needs at all times'*. The recovery models in mental health care, mainly driven by the power of user voice, has been instrumental in ensuring that spirituality is at the heart of a person's care as well as at the heart of a person's continued recovery.

2008/9 saw the development of two important tools to support the NHS to ensure effective delivery of the equalities agenda around religion and belief through the development of *Religion or Belief – A practical guide for the NHS* (Department of Health, 2009) and *Human Rights in Healthcare – A framework for local action* (Department of Health, 2008a). I will be drawing on these tools in future sections, and addressing their applicability to improve the caring role.

More recently, the NHS Constitution and the Department of Health white paper, *Equity and Excellence: Liberating the NHS* (Department of Health, 2010b) speaks of a 'genuinely patient-centered approach' to care and in the consultations through 'nothing about me without me' reinforces the key messages of mental health services users and families/carers that we all want our care based on our person-centered approaches of dignity and respect, fairness and equality and our sense of spiritual being.

The Constitution's first principle stated:

'The NHS provides a comprehensive service, available to all irrespective of gender, "race", disability, age, sexual orientation, religion or belief. It has a duty to each and every individual that it serves and must respect their human rights. At the same time, it has a wider social duty to promote equality through the services it provides and to pay particular attention to groups or sections of society where improvements in health and life expectancy are not keeping pace with the rest of the population.'
(Department of Health, 2010a)

Equality Act (2010)

Over the last four decades, discrimination legislation has played an important role in helping to make Britain a more equal society. Why is equality important? The government recognises that equality is important for:

▶ individuals: fairness is a basic human right

▶ society: in unequal societies people feel excluded and communities lack cohesion

▶ the economy: in the current economic downturn, it is vital that everyone contributes and that employers can draw on the widest pool of talent.

Figure 1 provides an overview of the equality legislation over the last four decades. The Equality Act 2010 had two main aims.

▶ Streamline the law: previously there were nine major pieces of discrimination legislation, around 100 statutory instruments, and around 2,500 pages of guidance and codes of practice dealing with equality law. Understandably this body of law has become difficult for people to navigate.

▶ Accelerate progress: despite all this legislation over the last 40 years, we've seen only limited progress on equality issues. In fact, government figures show that the gender pay gap will not close until 2085; it will take almost 100 years before people from ethnic minorities will have the same job prospects as British white people; and disabled people will probably never have the same job prospects.

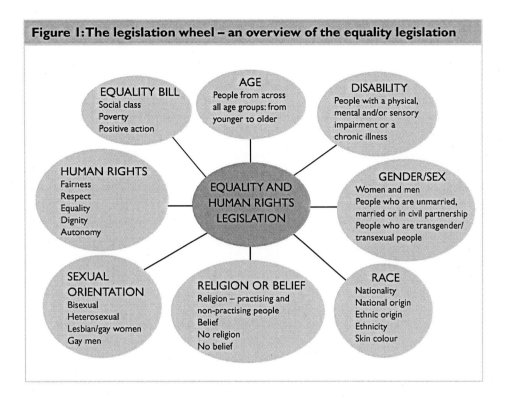

Figure 1: The legislation wheel – an overview of the equality legislation

Public bodies are bound by three general equality duties, relating to 'race', 'disability' and 'gender'. The duties require public bodies, in carrying out their functions, to have due regard to the need to:

▶ eliminate unlawful discrimination, harassment and victimisation

▶ advance equality of opportunity between different groups

▶ foster good relations between different groups (in the case of 'race') and promote positive attitudes (in case of 'disability').

Certain public bodies, from government departments to local authorities, schools, health bodies and police authorities, are also bound by specific equality duties; these are called Public Sector Equality Duty.

The new Public Sector Equality Duty (2010)

The Public Sector Equality Duty will replace three separate duties that require government departments, local authorities and other public bodies to take into account gender, race and disability equality both as employers and when making policy decisions and delivering services. The duty simplifies this requirement and also extends it to fully cover age, religion and belief, sexual orientation and gender reassignment.

The consultation is outlined in the *Equality Act (2010) The Public Sector Equality Duty: Promoting equality through transparency* (Government Equalities Office, 2010) and is the latest stage in the government's equalities programme, which so far has included enacting new rules to help tackle the gender pay gap and provide greater protection for the rights of disabled people, as well as work to improve equality for lesbian, gay, bisexual and transgender people. The Equality Duty could mean:

▶ in respect of age, a local council putting extra park benches in local parks so older people can enjoy public spaces as well as younger people

▶ in respect of sexual orientation, a school adapting its anti-bullying strategy to explicitly address bullying of gay and lesbian school children

▶ in respect of religion or belief, a local council looking for a provider of meals on wheels that delivers culturally diverse food including halal and kosher meals.

(Examples taken from Government Equalities Office, 2009)

The Equality Act (2010) became legislation in April 2010, however for public bodies working on the equalities agenda, this means building on existing single equalities schemes and action plans currently being implemented in the organisation. For more information on the Public Sector Equality Duty and an update on the provisions of the Equality Act see the Government Equalities Office website (www.equalities.gov.uk/equalityact2010).

All governments recognise that inequality does not just come from discrimination based on race, gender, disability or any other traditional equality group. Even today, the effects of class play a huge role in determining people's life chances. For example, a recent report found that people living in wealthier areas enjoy a significantly longer life expectancy than those living in deprived areas (people living in Hampstead, London can expect to live 11 years longer than those in nearby St Pancras). The government is currently considering the socio-economic duty on some public bodies.

The provisions in the Equality Act will come into force at different times, to allow time for the people and the organisations affected by the new laws to prepare for them. The government is considering how the different provisions will be commenced so that the act is implemented in an effective and proportionate way.

For more information please view *Equality Act 2010: The Public Sector Equality Duty: Promoting equality through transparency* (Government Equalities Office, 2010) on (www.equalities.gov.uk).

Equality on the grounds of religion or belief in the NHS

The UK now has a more diverse mix of religions, beliefs and wider forms of 'spiritual' support than ever before, and NHS organisations need to take this into account when developing services to the public and employment policies. *Religion or Belief – A practical guide for the NHS* (Department of Health, 2009) seeks to equip NHS staff at all levels to understand the importance of religious and cultural needs to:

▶ patients, service users and their families – in contributing to a person's well-being, improving experiences and satisfaction, and reducing lengths of stay and improving quality for individuals

▶ public sector equality duties by working to achieve person-centered services, redesign services and embedding equalities at the heart of all functions and structures and improving patient quality and informed care

▶ ensure that the NHS as an employer and provider of healthcare services inspires to be an exemplar of good practice in its delivery of services and employment practices.

Legal requirements for the NHS

Religion or Belief – A practical guide for the NHS (Department of Health, 2009) makes reference to key legislative directives and regulations on religion and belief and human rights, which are explored in more detail through the equality and human rights frameworks.

In 2003 the European Council Directive of 2000 establishing a general framework for equal treatment in employment and occupation came into force in the UK through the employment equality (religion or belief) regulations. These regulations made it unlawful to discriminate against people on the grounds of their religion and belief. The regulations apply to vocational training and all aspects of employment – recruitment, terms and conditions, promotions, transfers, dismissals and training.

Part 2 of the Equality Act (2006) (discrimination on the grounds of religion or belief) clarified the definition of religion to include 'any religion, or philosophical belief'; also made it unlawful to discriminate in the areas of goods, facilities and services on the grounds of religion and belief.

The Racial and Religious Hatred Act (2006), which came into force in 2007 as an amendment to the Public Order Act (1986), gives protection to people against hatred because of their religious beliefs or lack of religious beliefs and prohibits the stirring up of hatred against persons on racial or religious grounds.

While the legislation aims to protect people against discrimination on the grounds of their religion or belief (or lack of religion and belief), conversely the law does not entitle people to apply such beliefs in a way which impinges upon other people. The legislation is not intended in hinder people in the expression of their own religion or belief, but everyone has the right to be treated with respect whatever their views and beliefs and nobody should try to harass others because they do not agree with certain religious convictions.

Article 9 of the European Convention on Human Rights (Freedom of thought, conscience and religion) as given effect by the Human Rights Act (1998) states that:

'Everyone has the right to freedom of thought, conscience and religion; this right includes freedom to change his religion or belief and freedom, either alone or in the community with others and in public or private, to manifest his religion or belief, in worship, teaching, practice and observance.'

An overview of the human rights-based approaches within the NHS

In this section I aim to provide an overview of the human rights-based approaches within the NHS, and draw upon examples within mental health care provision.

The Universal Declaration of Human Rights (1947), the Human Rights Act (1998), and more recently, the NHS Constitution (2009), are key historical landmarks based on common values of fairness, respect, equality, dignity and autonomy (FREDA) for all. This is because healthcare and human rights are dependent upon each other – we simply cannot have good care without respect for human rights.

What are human rights?

'Human rights are about our basic needs as human beings. They capture the core rights we are all entitled to so that we may develop our potential and live our lives with dignity and respect.' (Human Rights in Healthcare: A Framework for local action (Department of Health, 2008a))

Human rights for NHS organisations are:

'Human rights are a set of recognisable principles on which NHS organisations can base their everyday work.' (Legal Advisor, NHS Trust in Department of Health, 2008b)

Human rights for individuals are:

'Basic rights to humane dignified treatment and things I should have access to simply because of the fact I am a human being.' (Mental health service user in Department of Health, 2008b)

Human rights belong to everyone; they are the basic rights we all have because we are human, regardless of who we are, where we live or what we do. Human rights represent all the things that are important to us as human beings, such as being able to choose how to live our life and being treated with dignity and respect. Human rights are based on a number of core values, also known as the FREDA principles: fairness, respect, equality, dignity and autonomy.

Why are human rights important in healthcare?

People come into contact with the NHS when they are most vulnerable. Putting human rights at the heart of the way healthcare services are designed and delivered can make for better services for everyone, with patient and staff experiences. This approach aims to improve experiences and outcomes for all by approaching decisions in a person-centred way.

You don't have to believe what I believe to give me spiritual care, but you have to have empathy and the understanding that this person requires this ... it's part of her. Carers need to be able to say "I may not believe it but because she needs it then we'll try and provide that for her."' (Swinton, 2001, p135)

This approach supports the delivery of wider NHS priorities and works to improve compliance with the Human Rights Act and reduces complaints/litigation. More information on the five national case studies working to implement the human rights-based approaches to equalities is outlined in *Human Rights in Healthcare – A framework for local action,* (Department of Health, 2008a) and *Human Rights in Healthcare: A short introduction* (Department of Health, 2008b).

What does the Human Rights Act mean for NHS organisations and staff?

'By valuing the human rights principles in relation to our staff and service users, we will demonstrate our effective commitment to quality outcomes which will improve the patient experience and provide satisfaction to our staff that they are undertaking a job that is valued.' (Heart of Birmingham Teaching PCT; outlined in *Human Rights in Healthcare – A framework for local action* (Department of Health, 2008a)

However, not all rights in the Human Rights Act are the same type. There are three main types of rights.

1. Absolute rights cannot be limited or interfered with in any way, by NHS organisations or by any other public authorities. An example of an absolute right that may be engaged in a healthcare setting is the right not to be tortured or treated in an inhuman or degrading way.

2. Limited rights can be limited only in specific and finite circumstances. These circumstances are set out in full in the Human Rights Act.

An example of a limited right is the right to liberty, which is often of relevance in mental health or residential care facilities. One of the circumstances in which the right to liberty can be limited is the legal detention of someone with mental health problems.

3. Qualified rights can be limited in a wider range of circumstances than limited rights and are the majority of the rights in the Human Rights Act. This is because the protection of qualified rights can affect the rights of others. For example, someone's right to freedom of expression may compete with another's right to respect for private life.

NHS organisations can take action that interferes with these rights when a number of general conditions are met.

Which human rights are most relevant to healthcare?

Some of the rights contained in the Human Rights Act are particularly relevant to healthcare. Table 1 (p326–327) introduces three rights that can come up most commonly for NHS staff in their day-to-day work.

Which human rights are most relevant to healthcare?

▶ The right to life

▶ The right not to be discriminated against

Key examples of NHS trusts taking forward the human rights approach are outlined in *Human Rights in Healthcare – A framework for local action* (Department of Health, 2008a) and *Human Rights in Healthcare: A short introduction* (Department of Health, 2008b).

The equality and human rights-based approaches are both innovative and ground breaking and as mentioned in the previous two sections are very real to the work of the NHS. In the next section I aim to provide an overview of useful tools and frameworks, useful to your organisation.

Table 1

Human right	Relevant issues in healthcare	Example
The right not to be tortured or treated in an inhuman or degrading way. • Inhuman treatment means treatment causing severe mental or physical suffering. • Degrading treatment means treatment that is grossly humiliating and undignified. This is an absolute right. Inhuman or degrading treatment does not have to be inflicted deliberately.	• Physical or mental abuse. • Soiled, unchanged sheets. • Leaving trays of food without helping patients to eat when they are too frail to feed themselves. • Excessive force used to restrain patients. • Staff not being protected from violent or abusive patients.	A man with learning disabilities was living in a residential care home. He was regularly tied to a bed or his wheelchair for 16 hours at a time to prevent him from hitting his head and face, causing him physical pain and mental anguish. This kind of situation could breach the right not to be treated in an inhuman or degrading way.
The right to respect for private and family life, home and correspondence. This right is very wide ranging. It protects four broad categories of interests: • Family life is interpreted broadly. It does not just cover blood or formalised relationships. • Private life is also interpreted broadly, including issues such as privacy, including personal choices, relationships, physical and mental well-being,	Privacy on wards and in care homes. • Family visits. • Sexual and other relationships. • Participation in social and recreational activities. • Personal records – including medical and financial. • Independent living. • Closure of residential care homes or hospitals. • Separation of families due to residential care placements.	A hospital had a mixed ward and promised to re-order it so that men were at one end, with women at the other. It did not do this, and an Orthodox Jewish woman was highly distressed about sharing a ward with men. This kind of situation could be a breach of the right to respect for private life.

Human right	Relevant issues in healthcare	Example
access to personal information and participation in community life. • The right to respect for home is not a right to housing, but a right to respect for the home someone already has. • Correspondence covers all forms of communication including phone, calls, letters, faxes, emails etc.		
The right to liberty. The right to liberty is not a right to be free to do whatever you want. The right to liberty is a right not to be deprived of liberty in an arbitrary fashion. The right to liberty is a limited right. It can be limited in a number of specific circumstances, for example, the lawful detention of someone who has mental health issues.	• Informal detention of patients who do not have the capacity to decide whether they would like to be admitted into hospital eg. those patients with learning disabilities or Alzheimer's disease. • Delays in reviewing whether mental health patients who are detained under the Mental Health Act should still be detained. • Delays in releasing mental health patients once they have been discharged by the Mental Health Review Tribunal. • Excessive restraint of patients eg. tying them to their beds or chairs for long periods.	A large number of patients throughout the UK who do not have capacity to make their own decisions but are not in a position to be detained under mental health legislation are informally admitted to and detained for treatment in hospital. This kind of admission and detention has been ruled to breach the right to liberty, as there are no clear rules and procedures governing who decides that someone should be detained, and for what reasons.

Part 2: Organisational frameworks and tools developed to support NHS organisations to effectively implement the equality and human rights-based approaches within healthcare

I aim to provide an overview of the useful tools and frameworks instrumental in ensuring that equality and human rights-based approaches are effective and instrumental in working to mainstream equalities – religion, belief and spiritual support within the NHS.

Single equality schemes and equality impact assessments

All public sector bodies are legally required under the 'general' duty of the equalities legislation to develop and implement a single equalities scheme and action plan aimed at working to mainstream the equalities agenda within the organisations, monitoring service delivery, outcomes and workforce issues.

Equality impact assessment (EqIA) is also a legal requirement. The Public Sector Equality Duty in the Equality Act (2010) will replace three separate duties that require government departments, local authorities and other public bodies to take into account gender, race and disability equality both as employers and when making policy decisions and delivering services. The duty simplifies this requirement and also extends it to fully cover age, religion and belief, sexual orientation and gender reassignment. The consultation is outlined in *Equality Act 2010: The Public Sector Equality Duty: Promoting equality through transparency* (Government Equalities Office, 2010).

The lever for EqIAs is to ensure organisational compliance and effectiveness with the equalities agenda, placing equalities and human rights-based approaches at the heart of the organisation. Moreover, as we are committed to best practice and not just legal requirements, organisations have to also intend to use the EqIA to review opportunities to promote and achieve the UK principles of human rights (fairness, respect, equality, dignity and autonomy), where possible. This is not currently a legislative duty, but it provides us with an opportunity to 'future-proof' our policies and functions, so we are better positioned to respond to the dynamic equalities environment – where new groups/issues soon become the focus of legislation and additional responsibilities for public bodies like ourselves.

Each organisation has a lead for the equalities programme – I suggest that you make contact with them and they can explain the process within your respective organisation.

For more information on EqIA and Single Equalities Schemes (SES) frameworks, read *Equality Impact Assessment: Summary tool and guidance for policy makers* (Department of Health, 2008d). In the guide you will be able to access templates for EqIA screening and full EqIA frameworks. For further guidance and access, see: http://www.dh.gov.uk/en/Publicationsandstatistics/Publications/PublicationsPolicyAndGuidance/DH_090396.

Religion or Belief – A practical guide for the NHS (Department of Health, 2009) provides NHS organisations with a range of resources and templates on working to implement the equality and human rights-based frameworks also known as single equalities schemes and action plans. This guide provides the reader with key questions in working to mainstream religion, belief and one's spiritual support, within any NHS organisation.

Further case studies and examples developed to complement EqIA framework are outlined below.

The National Mental Health Development Unit (NMHDU) in England

The National Mental Health Development Unit (NMHDU) currently supports both the Department of Health and strategic health authorities by advising on national and international best practice to improve mental health services and mental health. It does this by commissioning or providing:

▶ specialist expertise in priority areas of policy and delivery

▶ effective knowledge transfer on research, evidence and good practice

▶ support to translate national policies into practical deliverables which achieve the right outcomes

▶ co-ordination of national activity to help regional and local implementation.

The national mental health equalities programme focused on all strands of equalities and social inclusion and covered a range of approaches, tools and methods to mainstream the equalities and spirituality, religion and belief models and practices within mental health care services in England. For more information see: www.nmhdu.org.uk/equalities.

Case study 1: West Midlands Acute Care Programme – working to address equality and diversity issues in acute inpatient care

West Midlands Acute Care Programme of support developed a range of new resources, to help trusts bring about improvements in acute inpatient services, building upon the findings of the Healthcare Commission.

The Healthcare Commission review of Acute Inpatient Mental Health wards in 2007 audited and reported on the following points which need to be addressed in working to improve equality and diversity standards of care in acute inpatient mental health wards across the West Midlands.

▶ The proportion of all staff who report having received training in at least two types of diversity training from the following list: equal opportunities, racial awareness, gender awareness, disability awareness, religious awareness and assessing clients' spiritual and cultural needs.

▶ The level of support available for supporting clients' cultural and spiritual needs (including interpreters for care review meetings, therapies and activities, and access to pastoral and spiritual support).

Pathway Ethnicity Analysis Model: Excel-based example of analysing the ethnicity of the service user populations across referral pathways against local ethnic profiles to support rational analyses of access to acute inpatient services in relation to local population.

Source: National Acute Care Programme – www.nmhdu.org.uk

West Midlands Acute Care Programme – working to address equality and diversity issues in acute inpatient care.

(http://www.wmrdc.org.uk/mental-health/specialist-services-in-mental-health/acute-inpatient-care/equality-and-diversity-issues-in-acute-care/)

Case study 2: Enhancing pathways into care and recovery – from specialist services to healthy minds

This project aims to demonstrate how pathways to mental health care for black and minority ethnic (BME) groups can be improved. It takes the form of policy implementation, consultancy and service development for the appropriate and responsive services element of delivering race equality. We will document 'knowledge', 'skills', and the process of change for implementing improved pathways.

Ethnic minority groups in England and Wales have different pathways to and through mental health care when compared with their white British peers. There has been no concerted effort to collate evidence on how to improve pathways to care for ethnic minority groups. Providers have not been supplied with the information and advice they need to improve routes into and through their services. Local initiatives have offered different points of access to services and pathways to care, but such work needs to be synthesised and evaluated for the strength of evidence.

The EPIC project focuses on pathways to care in four NHS mental health trusts. We will demonstrate how these can be modified by informed statutory sector practitioners working in effective and balanced partnerships with non-statutory sector practitioners. We will document the strategies by which this is achieved, and obstacles to and facilitators of change so that other trusts can improve their pathways to care.

Source: *Delivering Race Equality in Mental Health Care* (Department of Health, 2005)

For more information on EPIC and work led by Professor Kamaldeep Bhui see: http://www.wolfson.qmul.ac.uk/psychiatry/epic

or: www.mentalhealthequalities.org.uk

The National Pacesetters Programme on Equality and Human Rights in healthcare in England

The National Pacesetters Programme, focusing on the wider health inequalities agenda, is also developing new and innovative methods to working to mainstream equalities into healthcare provision, with a range of examples on spirituality, religion and belief. For more information see: www.dh.gov.uk/publications/pacesetters for the publication a Dialogue of Equals (Department of Health, 2008c), which hosts tools for community engagement and service improvement on the equalities agenda.

> **Case study 3: A spiritual needs assessment tool developed by the Surrey and Borders Partnership Trust**
>
> Spirituality – religious and non-religious – plays a key role in the mental well-being of an individual and is increasingly recognised as being important in effective mental health assessment and treatment. The Surrey and Borders Partnership Trust is committed to ensuring that the quality of patient assessment, treatment and care is excellent, so it needs to ensure that patients' care plans address all their needs – an individual's spiritual needs are a key part of this process.
>
> A spiritual needs assessment tool was developed with the involvement of individuals who used the Trust's inpatient services from minority ethnic communities and representatives of the faith communities. It was then piloted in some inpatient settings in the east of the Trust. The tool helps staff to ensure that the spiritual needs of people who use services are assessed and addressed appropriately, regardless of their beliefs.
>
> Working in partnership with the Department of Health's Pacesetters Programme, the Trust has ensured that this spiritual needs assessment tool is available to all those who use its inpatient services across north west Surrey, whatever their religion or belief and regardless of whether these beliefs are religious or non-religious. Guidance notes on the key religions have been prepared, and all staff in inpatient services have been trained in spiritual needs assessment.
>
> The project aims to integrate spiritual needs assessments into the Care Programme Approach. Care co-ordinators undertake a spiritual needs assessment as soon as an individual is referred to the service. Over time, use of this tool will ensure that the quality of care and outcomes are improved.
>
> Source: *Religion or Belief: A practical guide for the NHS* (Department of Health, 2009, p33) and chapter 10 in this book.

Conclusion

I hope that this chapter is useful to you and your organisation. There are numerous models and examples I could have referred to in this chapter, however, I hope that I have provided enough key references and signposts to websites that will be useful in your quest. My challenge in this chapter was to help you as the reader to demystify an area that many people find very difficult, very hard to grasp and very complex. The equality and human rights approaches in the NHS are challenging, yet achievable. We all aim to provide a service that we would confidently use ourselves and recommend to our loved one. If we work on this premise, I believe that we can work to improve quality outcomes for all who work and access/ experience our NHS services.

References

Department of Health (2005) *Delivering Race Equality in Mental Health Care: An action plan for reform of inside and outside of mental health care.* London: DH.

Department of Health (2008a) *Human Rights in Healthcare – A framework for local action.* London: DH.

Department of Health (2008b) *Human Rights in Healthcare: A short introduction.* London: DH.

Department of Health (2008c) *Dialogue of Equals: Tools for community engagement on the equalities agenda in the NHS.* London: DH.

Department of Health (2008d) *Equality Impact Assessment: Summary tool and guidance for policy makers.* London: DH.

Department of Health (2009) *Religion or Belief – A practical guide for the NHS.* London: DH.

Department of Health (2010a) *NHS Constitution for England.* London: DH.

Department of Health (2010b) *Equity and Excellence: Liberating the NHS.* London: DH.

Government Equalities Office (2009) *A Fairer Future: The Equality Bill and other action to make equality a reality.* London: GEO.

Government Equalities Office (2010) *Equality Act 2010: The Public Sector Equality Duty. Promoting equality through transparency. A consultation.* London: GEO.

Swinton P (2001) *Spirituality and Mental Health Care – Rediscovering a 'forgotten' dimension'.* London: Jessica Kingsley.

Further reading and resources

BRAP – making equality work for everyone. Available at: www.brap.org.uk

Department of Health publications. Available at: www.dh.gov.uk/publications

Department of Health Pacesetters Programme hosts Dialogue of Equals (2008) alongside tools for community engagement and service improvement on the equalities agenda. Available at: http://westmidlands.nhs.uk/whatwedo/pacesetters.aspx.

Government Equalities Office – Promoting equality at the heart of government. Available at: www.equalities.gov.uk

Human Rights in Healthcare. Available at: www.dh.gov.uk/equalityandhumanrights

National Mental Health Development Unit (NMHDU) in England. Available at: www.nmhdu.org.uk/equalities

NHS Constitution for England (2009) Available at: www.dh.gov.uk/nhsconstitution

NHS West Midlands SHA – Equalities Agenda. Available at: www.westmidlands.nhs.uk

Public Sector Equality Duty and other updates on the Equality Act on the Government Equalities Office website www.www.equalities.gov.uk/equalityact2010

Chapter 18

Mental health and the sexual, religious and spiritual identities of lesbian, gay, bisexual and transgender (LGBT) people

Sarah Carr

Introduction

This chapter introduces lesbian, gay, bisexual and transgender (LGBT) perspectives on mental health and religious and spiritual identity. It will also outline some key facts about LGBT mental health and experience of mental health services and give an overview on practitioner training needs.

This message from experts at the Consortium of LGBT Voluntary and Community Organisations outlines some of the key starting points for this chapter:

Key message

'Lesbian, gay, bisexual and trans (LGBT) people do have unique health and social care needs. Unlike other minority communities, LGBT people often experience rejection and discrimination from their own families; this is more pronounced for individuals with composite identities, such as BME or religious LGBT people. Feelings of rejection and isolation have a profound effect on a person's mental health. Some change their behaviour and place their health at risk simply to gain acceptance and validation from within certain social contexts.'

(Consortium of LGBT Voluntary and Community Organisations, 2010, p33)

The final section of the chapter is given over to some personal stories of lesbian, gay and transgender people who describe their relationship with their religion, culture and spirituality. The idea is to provide real life accounts of marginalised identities and experiences in order to enhance practitioner awareness and understanding of the issues so cultural competency is improved. Research shows the value of learning from the personal experiences of LGBT people (Grove, 2009) and reflecting on personal assumptions and prejudices (Foreman & Quinlan, 2008) to develop LGBT affirmative practice.

From the outset it is important to remember that:

Key message

'LGBT people are diverse; they can be young, old, women, men, BME, disabled, of any class and any faith. LGBT people may be homeless, living in poverty, asylum seekers, refugees and/or prisoners. Their living situations may vary in terms of whether they are in civil partnerships and if they have children. Furthermore trans people may also be heterosexual as well as LGB.'

(Consortium of LGBT Voluntary and Community Organisations, 2010, p9)

Reflection exercise

Empathy and understanding are important qualities for mental health practitioners to possess, particularly when working with LGBT people. Below are the words of the American writer and academic, Bruce Bawer:

'Straight Americans need ... an education of the heart and soul. They must understand – to begin with – how it can feel to spend years denying your own deepest truths, to sit silently through classes, family meals, and church services while people you love toss off remarks that brutalize your soul.'

(Bawer, 1998)

How do his words make you feel?

Imagine yourself experiencing what he describes – how would you cope and what do you think the impact would be?

How do you think such experiences affect someone's identity, esteem and mental health?

Would these experiences affect a person's spirituality?

LGBT experience of mental health problems and services

There is clear evidence that because of experiences of fear and oppression, difficulties with identity and social discrimination, LGBT people are at greater risk of poorer mental health than their heterosexual peers, particularly in relation to suicide and self-harm (Meads *et al*, 2009; NIMHE, 2007; Department of Health, 2007a). For example, one research review suggested that 20–40% of LGB people had tried to commit suicide (over a lifetime) compared with 4.4% of the general population (Meads *et al*, 2009).

Despite the higher rate of mental health problems, LGBT people often experience inequalities when trying to access mental health services, with some staff behaving in a discriminatory, inappropriate or insensitive way, which can lead to mainstream services not being seen as 'safe' (Carr, 2010; Fish, 2009; Pennant *et al*, 2009; Bartlett *et al*, 2009). However, it is thought that one in two LGBT people will seek the services of a counsellor or therapist (LGF/UCLAN, 2008). This situation led the Department of Health and the former National Institute for Mental Health England (NIMHE) to conclude that:

Key message

'There is an urgent need for mental health services to develop LGB sensitive services and an obvious initial step would be the incorporation of LGB issues into diversity training for staff.'

(NIMHE, 2007, p3)

LGBT equality and diversity training

Equalities and diversity training in health and social care does not always include sexual orientation or account for the needs and experiences of LGBT people. This means that they often remain marginalised or even invisible in training designed to reduce discrimination and ensure services are accessible to all, something which needs to change, particularly in relation to the Equality Act 2010 (McNulty *et al*, 2010; Pennant *et al*, 2009; Fish, 2008; Carr, 2008; CSCI, 2008; Mule, 2006).

'Currently there is very little input about sexual orientation in the undergraduate medical curriculum, nursing training education and training of allied health professionals.'

(Consortium of LGBT Voluntary and Community Organisations, 2010, p10)

The Equality Act 2010 places a new duty on public bodies to take account of the needs of LGBT people when designing and delivering services and acknowledges that people can experience 'dual discrimination' (for example, a person may experience both racism and homophobia because they are black and gay). Mental health staff need to be able to provide appropriate care and support within this legal context.

Any training for mental health practitioners needs to account for the fact that LGBT people are very diverse and come from many different faith, cultural and ethnic backgrounds (Carr, 2010; McNulty *et al*, 2010; Department of Health, 2007b; Keogh *et al*, 2004). LGBT people may have multiple identities or experience complex forms of discrimination based on, for example, race and sexual identity. Mental health practitioners need to be able to offer support in a way that is led by the individual person rather than by professional or personal assumptions (Carr, 2010; Ross & Carr, 2010; Grove, 2009; Fish, 2008; Department of Health, 2007b).

Other experts warn against the tendency of public services, such as mental health, to categorise people for ease of administrative process, something which often forces people into inappropriate boxes that do not reflect the fullness of who they are (McNulty *et al*, 2010; Fanshawe & Sriskandarajah, 2010; Carr, 2010; Cocker & Hafford-Letchfield, 2009; Fish, 2008):

'Prejudice is almost always based on cruel reductionism; human beings are squeezed into rigid stereotypes. Though well-intentioned, the orthodox tick-box approach to equalities also risks reductionism.' (Fanshawe & Sriskandarajah, 2010, p8)

Key message

'We need to move away from fixed identities towards engaging with the more complex, multiple, fluid identities of LGB people, reflecting their individuality and their social and economic context.'

(Cocker & Hafford-Letchfield, 2009, p13)

Elsewhere in this book, this concept is explored as 'intersectionality' and is noted as being important for the understanding of a religious or spiritual identity alongside other identities an individual may have.

Training for good practice with LGBT people

The challenge is to design training to improve mental health practice with LGBT people and to enable staff to work with them holisticially and with due regard to their religious or spiritual needs as appropriate. Research suggests this means allowing practitioners a 'safe context' in which they can ask 'potentially difficult questions' (Peel, 2008). Some of the difficult questions may relate to practitioner views, moral or religious principles and social prejudice that could result in discriminatory practice towards LGBT people if not explored and addressed (Hancock, 2010; Carr, 2008).

General research has shown that the following practice points should be integrated into any health and social care training on LGBT equalities, and they are also relevant to training about mental health and spirituality:

▶ avoiding homophobia and heterosexism

▶ improving practitioner knowledge

▶ improving patient trust

▶ being perceptive about terminology used

▶ understanding embarrassment

▶ reducing over-cautiousness

▶ importance of positive affirmation of sexual identity.

(Adapted from Pennant *et al*, 2009)

Overall, it is important to remember that:

> **Key message**
>
> *'What is important to lesbians and gay men as service users and carers, is that [practitioners] have the ability to form effective relationships.'*
>
> (Cosis-Brown, 2008, p271)

LGBT identities, religion and spirituality

Spiritual identity formation

As noted earlier, LGBT people may be from faith communities or have been brought up as a member of a religion. Their religious and cultural background may be very important to their identity, and still part of who they are, whether they are still practising or not. As the testimonies and stories will show, like everyone, LGBT people will have different individual relationships to religion, culture and spirituality. It should not be assumed that because a person has same-sex relationships or identifies as gay or transgendered they cannot also be religious. Equally, as other chapters in this book suggest more broadly, you do not have to practise a formal or organised religion to have a spiritual identity and needs, which should to be accounted for as part of mental health and well-being (see Gilbert, 2008 for further exploration).

> **Key message**
>
> *'Everyone has the right to freedom of thought, conscience and religion, regardless of sexual orientation or gender identity.'*
>
> (Yogyakarta Principles, 2007)

LGBT people may express their spirituality through or with reference to a particular faith or belief, or their spirituality may be an individual, private matter. Some LGBT people will, perhaps because of negative experiences of faith-based discrimination and rejection, identify as atheist, humanist or secularist and not relate to the language of religion or spirituality. However, this does not mean they do not experience 'existential' dimensions to mental distress or live according to moral frameworks based on values such as humanity or compassion. LGBT people may find ways to reconcile their sexual identity with their birth or chosen faith or choose to be members of inclusive branches of larger world religions such as Judaism, Sikhism or Christianity. Some LGBT people find a sense of belonging and spiritual fulfillment in the neo-pagan or spiritualist traditions. Some of these different perspectives are illustrated in the personal accounts at the end of the chapter.

Research on the communities and identities of ethnic minority gay men outlines the complexities around sexual identity, religion, belonging and spirituality:

'Just as emerging gay identity implied a distancing from family and community structures, the role of the church also came into question as they came out as gay. That is, questioning or sometimes a rejection of the church often accompanied the development of a gay identity. Often however, respondents recognised the need for ongoing faith and spiritual sustenance in their lives. Some, despite a conflict regarding their church's attitudes towards their sexuality, still drew occasional comfort and social support from their religious movement.' (Keogh et al, 2004)

Sexual identity formation

LGBT people from religious backgrounds and faith communities often have an extra dimension to adolescent existential crises and identity struggles as described in an opening chapter because: *'At a time when other adolescents are discovering how to express themselves socially, those youth who identify as lesbian or gay, but wish to remain hidden, are learning to conceal large parts of themselves from their family and friends.'* (Rivers & Carragher, 2003, p382).

The threat and fear of rejection from family, friends and sometimes the faith community can result in long-term damage to the mental health, self-esteem and identity of many LGBT people:

'Young lesbian, gay and bisexual people may go through what is termed as the "isolation period"; a period of time when they are aware of their sexual

*orientation from as early as age **11**, but may not come out until [later]. This can be a very vulnerable time, and may lead to increased mental health issues, most commonly depression and an increased rate of suicide in comparison with heterosexual peers.'*

(Consortium of LGBT Voluntary and Community Organisations, 2010, p11)

Key message

'[Mental health] is an incredibly sensitive issue [for LGBT people] … because we fought so hard to say we're equal, we're happy with who we are. While that's true, we're also suffering from the trauma of the journey, the isolation, the secrecy and the shame, and the resulting effect on your mental health that is more likely to happen to you if you grow up gay than if you grow up straight.'

(Todd, 2010)

Although not all black and minority ethnic (BME) people have a religious background, LGBT people from BME communities and those from strong faith backgrounds *'can fear rejection by a family or community which is important for affirming an individual's ethnic, faith or cultural identity and protecting against racism'* (Carr, 2010, p18). Some people are afraid that coming out to family may lead to ostracism because of religious and cultural traditions (Keogh *et al*, 2004; Galop, 2001), while LBT Muslim women have been found to *'experience depression and some women contemplate or attempt suicide or self-harm'* because of unresolved internal conflicts with sexual identity, community and faith (Safra Project, 2003).

Rowland Jide Macaulay, director of an LGBT-affirmative African Christian ministry, recommended that:

'The actions required to support the journey for reconciliation of sexuality and spirituality will need a specific holistic approach that is tailored to the needs of African LGBTI [lesbian, gay, bisexual, transgender and intersex] people in the UK and that also brings an understanding of cultures and faith communities.'

(Macaulay, 2010, p9)

Mental health staff need to be aware of the potential support needs of LGBT people from strong faith communities and cultures, particularly those who are black or from a minority ethnic group, who may benefit from specialist cultural support to explore and affirm their sexual, racial, religious and spiritual identities. *'We need to examine the conditions that make separating spirituality from religion liberating or oppressive, and for whom'* (Wong & Vinsky, 2009, p1357). However, research suggests that generic faith-based organisations may not be inclusive for, or supportive of, LGBT people (Macaulay, 2010; Dinham & Shaw, 2009; Carr, 2008; Blakey *et al*, 2006).

Religious therapy

There are debates in the UK and the US about the practice of 'sexual orientation change therapy' by religious groups and therapists working within anti-gay faith-based practice (Forstein, 2004). Researchers recently discovered that 17% of the 1,400 UK mental health practitioners they surveyed had tried to help LGB patients reduce feelings of same sex attraction. They noted that *'therapists paid attention to religious, cultural and moral values causing internal conflict'* (Bartlett *et al*, 2009 p1). LGBT people have found attempts to change their sexual orientation damaging to their identity, mental health and well-being (Strudwick, 2010; Carr, 2005; Smith *et al*, 2004). Such therapy has now been declared discredited and harmful by the British Medical Association.

Therapy and counselling that enables a person to safely explore their identities, experiences and affirm their sexual orientation or gender identity is being promoted as best practice (Perlman, 2003; Pixton, 2003).

Key message
'Sexuality is such a fundamental part of who a person is, that attempts to change it just result in significant confusion, depression and even suicide.'
(British Medical Association, 2010)

Reflection exercise

Having read about some of the complexities LGBT people may experience with regard to their sexual, gender, religious, spiritual and cultural identities, now spend some time thinking about your own using the 'interplay model' below.

The idea is to reflect on how your gender and sexual identities and spirituality are part of what makes you a whole person.

▶ Gender identity – how do you see your gender role or behaviour? How do you present your gender identity to the world?

▶ Sexual identity – how do you identify? What are your attractions or expressions?

▶ Spirituality – how do you identify (this might be with a particular religion or belief or it might not)? How do you express your spirituality? Does this relate to your gender and sexual identities?

(Adapted from Beardsley et al, 2010)

(See http://www.lgbthealth.co.uk/wp-content/uploads/2010/09/Gender-Sexuality-Spirituality.pdf)

Where I am with religion and spirituality: some personal stories

Below are several people's stories of their faith, spiritual, sexual or gender identity. They are all true accounts, told in people's own words, of the types of struggle that can lead to mental distress. But the struggles can also eventually lead to confidence and certainty about one's sexual or gender identity and being reconciled to spirituality or a different personal relationship to religion which supports mental health.

HS's story: 'The way that I am is the way God intended me to be

I describe myself as a non-practicing Sikh. I have a strong belief in God. I go to the gurdwara when my heart tells me to, and I do listen to shabads, kirtans. I do pray occasionally. I don't have any overt symbols of Sikhism. I'm a British modern Sikh man.

I've never felt that my religious identity has been at odds with my sexual identity. My strong faith in God has helped my through some difficult times dealing with my sexuality whilst I was growing up. I've always felt my religion to be a great help.

My own personal understanding on Sikhism is that it is based on equality and that the scriptures contain no reference to homosexuality being a sin or unnatural. I've seen that as a sign that the way I am is the way that God intended me to be, and so I should accept myself and be at ease with myself.

I hope that there are lots of changes in Asian culture and in the Sikh community generally regarding attitudes towards sexuality. There needs to be greater education at large and people need to be more open minded. My identity is a fusion of being Sikh, British Asian, and being gay, and I feel like I have the benefit of the best bits of all of them.

From: http://www.sarbat.net/2010/06/being-gay-and-sikh-in-the-uk-testimony-of-hs-male-32-birmingham/

Laura's story: 'The words of Jesus the rebel'

I am a gay Christian. To many people these two identities are irreconcilable. You can be one or the other, but not both. One of these identities, my Christianity, I chose as an adult. The other, my sexual identity, is intrinsic to who I am.

I grew up in a typical liberal agnostic family. My parents were active in 60s politics and had not even the slightest interest in religion and belief. There were books about many things in my house when I grew up but none about religion. Neither my sister nor I were baptised as my parents believed that we should make our own choices about our beliefs. My grandmother, furthermore, described herself as an atheist and had no time whatsoever for religion; frequently trying to shock her more staid contemporaries with her dissenting views. My education was also devoid of any religious teaching. I can recall one morning assembly where 300 girls listened to our head teacher describe the scientific impossibility of many Christian teachings – in particular the virgin birth.

I first realised I was gay at about the same time that I developed a clear sense of being an individual; separate to my parents, with my own likes and dislikes. I have never doubted my sexuality; it has always been consistent and unchangeable, despite the immense social pressure to be 'normal' (ie. heterosexual). My sexuality was as much a natural aspect of who I was as my brown hair or blue eyes.

At 18, however, I chose to be baptised. I chose to be a Christian. Most importantly I did not do so with any sense of conflict with my sexuality. I began to develop an interest in Christianity as a teenager. Perhaps it was a fascination with something very alien to the non-religious, intellectual environment in which I had been brought up. I spent a considerable amount of time trying to understand what Christianity was and what kind of person it asked you to be. In fact, I ended up studying theology to Master's degree level. I was fascinated by the teachings of Jesus who seemed to be genuinely rebellious – not only in his time but would still be considered so now. This first century man taught us to reject strict religious codes in favour of a leap of conscience – to love your neighbour as yourself regardless of what religious teaching may say about that neighbour. That was certainly the message of the parable of the Good Samaritan and the woman taken in sin. I no longer attend church or even identify with any particular denomination (I was baptised into the Church of England but have been very disillusioned by its attitudes to the human rights of gay people). I find church structures and dogma frequently irreconcilable with the actual teachings of Jesus the man, who clearly rejected the frequent hypocrisy of the religious leaders of his day. I still consider myself a Christian and am certain that this does not conflict with my identity as a lesbian. And when I look at the words of Jesus himself, why should it?

Raza's story: 'An amicable divorce'?

The Pakistani Muslim community can sometimes be obsessed with respectability, and some Muslims seem more worried by what the neighbours might think than the censure of the Almighty.

My lovely socially gregarious extended family has covered both bases by committing sins against Allah and social respectability, in the eyes of the self-appointed community guardians. They have, by and large, eased up on the religiously inspired banishments. I say 'by and large', because some of the more devout members do pretend – during their endless round of social engagements – that an uncle is married to the non-Muslim English woman he has been living with for many years, and that one of my aunts is not in fact married to a Sikh (the fact he is only nominally Sikh and doesn't wear a turban helps).

My being gay and coming out on national TV made the perfect Muslim extended family routine slightly more difficult for my relatives to engineer.

You might say I should be grateful for the tolerance and recognition they show me and my partner, at least in the privacy of the family circle, like a woman allowed to take off her veil in front of close male relatives. I know violent homophobia exists within some parts of the Muslim community. This saddened me because, whilst I have never, since adolescence convincingly been a believing or practising Muslim, I did want to have an amicable divorce from the religion of my birth and early childhood, and find something good in the religion of my extended family.

But as a gay man, the more I found out, the more I understood how much the bad outweighed the good.

Sadly, much of my often painful research into the attitude of some imams impressed on me that while community institutions like certain mosques might not be directly responsible for homophobic assaults, they could foster attitudes which could lead to such actions. The high point of my investigations was an interview with a famous liberal imam who argued that homosexuals should not be subject to physical punishments but were guilty of a sin nevertheless – thanks but no thanks!

Surely my family asking me to deny my sexuality in public including at weddings counts as nothing besides such terrible intolerance? Maybe, but precisely because I have relative freedom to live a less secret life I feel a certain duty to make a stand. I may have experienced mental distress, partly as a result of the homophobia I have experienced, but I will not submit to the kind of cover up they want as it is oppressive: I will not be the wife relegated to the attic by their Mr Rochester.

Yve's story: 'God is infinitely more loving'

To me, spirituality is antithetical to materialism; the heart of human psyche and experience, where we find self-expression, life and sensation. It is ethereal, sacred, holy, divine, stimulates our senses. It is the cries of a newborn baby in a mother's arms or the bleats of a suckling lamb. It is the smell of freshly baked bread or ground coffee. That first mouthful of bacon and eggs or beef casserole with dumplings, banoffee pie or sticky toffee pudding! It is that sense of a life-giving force and presence greater than ourselves loving, guiding and inspiring us in all that we are and have; all that we can and will become. Spirituality is life, the fruit of which is 'love, joy, peace, patience, kindness, goodness, faithfulness, gentleness and self-control. Against such things there is no law' (Galatians 5:22–3 – N.I.V.)

Hope is the antithesis of fear and change is often a sign of life and hope. I believe God is architect of both and the spiritual heart of all things. Cardinal John Henry Newman once wrote: 'To live is to change, to be perfect is to have changed often'. Yet God is changeless and eternal, carrying and loving us among the ever changing scenes of life in whose hands I place my life, my soul and trust, for He has been merciful to me, strengthening me in all I do, asking only my love in return.

Spirituality makes time to be still to engage with and appreciate the beauty around us, to absorb the sounds and silence; stilling our restlessness and struggle maybe amid the candlelight and soft melodic music or sacred choirs; feeding our souls and renewing that life force within us. I've no doubt that God loves us all unconditionally; lesbian, gay, bisexual, transgender or straight commanding us only to love one another the same (John 13:34). If I did not believe this, I would not still be here. I always return to the belief that God gave Christ to us to do us good. He associated Himself with those whom society rejected, railed against the authorities of the day on a regular basis and ultimately tasted the pain of separation and rejection Himself because He wouldn't compromise His integrity or the will of His Father. This is why we can trust God because there is NOTHING we can experience that He hasn't already!

Galatians 3:27–28 'For all of you who were baptised into Christ have clothed yourselves with Christ. There is neither Jew nor Greek, slave nor free, male nor female, for you are all one in Christ Jesus' – is a very important passage in the bible for me which goes a long way towards reconciling my gender transition with my Christian faith. In the end it is God to whom we shall have to answer not some bigoted racist, homo/transphobe and God is infinitely more loving so we need not worry! Thank God He loves us just the way we are!

Sarah: 'Salvaging remnants'

When I heard Miriam Margolyes declare on the radio, 'I am a proud Jew and I am also an ashamed Jew', her sentiment resonated with the way I feel about the religion of my birth – Roman Catholicism. I am deeply ashamed of the Papal institution; by the appalling abuses of the Church; and by cruel and inhumane Vatican teachings. However, I am also proud of the good individuals who are at the front line demanding social justice alongside the sick, oppressed and the poor: people like the liberation theologian, Leonardo Boff who taught that the Church should always refer back to 'the preferential option for the poor' and who was excommunicated for doing so; of Sister Dorothy Stang who was murdered while working with impoverished Brazilian farmers to preserve their forests; of the openly gay priest Father Bernard Lynch who ministered to Catholic gay men who were dying from AIDS in spiritual despair. They were in despair because the Vatican had issued the encyclical On the Pastoral Care of Homosexual Persons, which said their sexual orientation 'is a more or less strong tendency ordered toward an intrinsic *moral evil'* (Ratzinger, 1986). It is the consequence of this teaching and other Catholic dogma on sexuality that have been intrinsic to my struggle with faith, family, spirituality and mental health – but never my sexuality.

Both my parents are converts to Catholicism and both had careers as teachers in Catholic schools. The majority of my schooling was Catholic and I grew up in what would now be called a sort of 'faith community'. For my mother the faith seems to be especially important – it provides her with a moral framework and she often seeks help from clergy if she is in crisis. One of these crises occurred when I came out to her at 17, and she took refuge in the confessional. Obviously, I have no idea what she said or what she was told but the outcome has been slowly devastating with her rejection and disgust unfolding over time. Because of her Catholic belief in the holiness of heterosexuality and divine primacy of reproduction within marriage, I don't think she can see her gay daughter as a full human being who is capable of real love – not just eros (erotic love), but because of my innate sexual orientation, I am also incapable of agape (love of God or friendship) and caritas (charity). I came away from one particularly painful confrontation thinking, '*So, Mum, no matter how much I love God or how many good works or acts of kindness I undertake, I will never tip the scales because the "sin" of my sexuality will always outweigh them?*'.

As a result of the influence of such Catholic morals in my family household, I became alienated and completely unanchored. I was without a place of belonging, something which has led at times to suicidal despair, self-harm and profound mental distress. When I came out, a time when I was very vulnerable, I was met with my mother's anger. My family and faith became dangerous. The impact was like a vast spiritual and emotional shipwreck. But I didn't drown because, ironically, I clung to some flotsam that Catholic spiritual culture, rather than dogma, gave me – a crucifix. I clung to the bloody body of a suffering, dying human who was killed for being different, who lived with the poor and rejected and spoke out against hypocrites and priests. Over the years I have returned to the wreck, now as a gay secularist, to salvage meaningful remnants of my Catholic culture in order to construct a sense of self and spiritual identity. The Church may reject me but the crucified human Jesus doesn't. To me, this says more about real love than any Papal doctrine.

Conclusion

This chapter has explored how diverse LGBT people relate to faith and spirituality and how this can influence mental health. As the personal stories and research findings here suggest LGBT people have done a lot of work on their identities, spirituality and mental health themselves, but may need sensitive and safe support at times of crisis, particularly if experiencing profound rejection from their family or faith community. The importance of mental health practitioners who have the capacity to work in an empathetic and affirming way with LGBT people is paramount and training which enables practitioners to examine their own values and prejudices will support good practice.

Acknowledgements

With grateful thanks to the people who generously shared their stories for this chapter: Raza Griffiths, Laura Hodgson and Yvonne Taylor. Thanks also to go to Dettie Gould and Parminder Sekhon.

This chapter is written in a personal capacity and does not necessarily represent the views of the Social Care Institute for Excellence.

References

Bartlett A, Smith G & King M (2009) The response of mental health professionals to clients seeking help to change or redirect same-sex sexual orientation. *BMC Psychiatry* **9** (11).

Bawer B (1998) Blessings or earnings? If David Geffen and Elton John are rich, isn't that a sign of God's favor? *The Advocat* 28 April.

Beardsley C, Ferguson S & Mitchell R (2010) *Gender, Sexuality and Spirituality: LGBT Health Summit workshop presentation 2010 Hertfordshire University 07/09/10* [online]. Available at: http://www.lgbthealth.co.uk/wp-content/uploads/2010/09/Gender-Sexuality-Spirituality.pdf (accessed November 2010).

Blakey H, Pearce J & Chesters G (2006) *Minorities Within Minorities: Beneath the surface of South Asian participation.* York: Joseph Rowntree Foundation.

British Medical Association (2010) In: S Cassidy. BMA declares that 'conversion therapy' for gays is harmful. *The Independent* Friday 2 July [online]. Available at: http://www.independent.co.uk/life-style/health-and-families/health-news/bma-declares-that-conversion-therapy-for-gays-is-harmful-2016391.html (accessed November 2010).

Carr S (2005) 'The sickness label infected everything we said': lesbian and gay perspectives on mental distress. In: J Tew (Ed) *Social Perspectives in Mental Health*, pp168–183. London: Jessica Kingsley.

Carr S (2008) Sexuality and religion: a challenge for diversity strategies in UK social care service development and delivery. *Diversity in Health and Social Care* **5** (2) 113–122.

Carr S (2010) Seldom heard or frequently ignored? Lesbian, gay and bisexual (LGB) perspectives on mental health services. *Ethnicity and Inequalities in Health and Social Care* **3** (3) 14–23.

Cocker C & Hafford-Letchfield P (2010) Out and Proud? Social work's relationship with lesbian and gay equality. *British Journal of Social Work Advance Access* 10/03/2010 1–13.

Consortium of LGBT Voluntary and Community Organisations (2010) *Building the Case for LGBT Health: Improving the health and social care experience for LGBT communities*. London: Consortium of LGBT Organisations.

Cosis-Brown H (2008) Social work and sexuality, working with lesbians and gay men: what remains the same and what is different? *Practice* **20** 265–275.

CSCI (2008) *Putting People First: Equality and diversity matters 1. Providing appropriate services for lesbian, gay, bisexual and transgender people*. London: Commission for Social Care Inspection.

Department of Health (2007a) *Briefing 9: Mental health issues within lesbian, gay and bisexual (LGB) communities* London: Department of Health.

Department of Health (2007b) *Briefing 12: Lesbian, gay and bisexual (LGB) people from black and minority ethnic communities*. London: Department of Health.

Dinham A & Shaw H (2009) *Faiths, Equalities and Sexual Orientation: An exploratory study*. London: Capacity Builders.

Fanshawe S & Sriskandarajah D (2010) *You Can't Put Me in a Box: Super-diversity and the end of identity politics in Britain* London: IPPR.

Fish J (2008) Navigating queer street: researching the intersections of lesbian, gay, bisexual and trans (LGBT) identities in health research. *Sociological Research Online* [online] **13** (1) Available at: http://www.socresonline.org.uk/13/1/12.html (accessed November 2010).

Fish J (2009) Invisible no more? Including lesbian, gay and bisexual people in social work and social care. *Practice* **21** (1) 47–64.

Foreman M & Quinlan M (2008) Increasing social work students' awareness of heterosexism and homophobia – a partnership between a community gay mental health project and a school of social work. *Social Work Education* **27** (2) 152–158.

Forstein M (2004) Pseudoscience of sexual orientation change therapy. *BMJ* **328** (7445).

Galop (2001) *The Low Down: Black lesbians, gay men and bisexual people talk about their experiences and needs*. London: Galop.

Gilbert P (2008) *Guidelines on Spirituality for Staff in Acute Care Services*. Staffordshire: Staffordshire University/NIMHE.

Grove J (2009) How competent are trainee and newly qualified counsellors to work with lesbian, gay and bisexual clients and what do they perceive as their most effective learning experiences? *Counselling and Psychotherapy Research* **9** (2) 78–85.

Hancock T (2010) Doing justice: a typology of helping attitudes toward sexual groups. *Affilia* **23** 349–362.

Keogh P, Henderson L & Dodds C (2004) *Ethnic minority gay men: Redefining community, restoring identity.* London: NHS/Sigma.

LGF/UCLAN (2008) *Something on Your Mind? What lesbian, gay and bisexual people want from the future of mental health services.* Manchester: LGF.

Macaulay RJ (2010) 'Just as I am, without one plea': a journey to reconcile sexuality and spirituality. *Ethnicity and Inequalities in Health and Social Care* **3** (3) 6–13.

McNulty A, Richardson D & Monro S (2010) *Lesbian, Gay, Bisexual and Trans (LGBT) Equalities and Local Governance: Research report for practitioners and policy makers.* Newcastle: University of Newcastle.

Meads C, Pennant M, McManus J & Bayliss S (2009) *A Systematic Review of UK Research on Lesbian, Gay, Bisexual and Transgender Health* [online]. Birmingham: Unit of Public Health, Epidemiology & Biostatistics, West Midlands Health Technology Assessment Group. Available at: http://www.wmhtac.bham.ac.uk/postersx/LGBTHealth.pdf (accessed November 2010).

Mule N (2006) Equity vs. invisibility: sexual orientation issues in social work ethics and curricula standards. *Social Work Education* **25** 608–622.

NIMHE (2007) *Mental Disorders, Suicide and Deliberate Self-harm in Lesbian, Gay and Bisexual People.* London: NIMHE.

Peel E (2008) Intergroup relations in action: questions asked about lesbian, gay and bisexual issues in diversity training. *Journal of Community and Applied Social Psychology* **19** 271–285.

Perlman G (2003) Gay affirmative practice. In: C Lago & B Smith (Eds) *Anti-Discriminatory Counselling Practice* [online]. London: Sage, pp50–61. Available at: http://www.pinktherapy. com/downloadables_new/theory/Gay_Affirmative_Therapy_Perlman.pdf (accessed November 2010).

Pennant M, Bayliss S & Meads C (2009) Improving lesbian, gay and bisexual healthcare: a systematic review of qualitative literature from the UK. *Diversity in Health and Care* **6** 193–203.

Pixton S (2003) Experiencing gay affirmative therapy: an exploration of clients' views of what is helpful. *Counselling and Psychotherapy Research* **3** (3) 211–215.

Ratzinger J (1986) *Letter to the Bishops of the Catholic Church on the Pastoral Care of Homosexual Persons.* Vatican: Congregation for the Doctrine of the Faith.

Rivers I & Carragher D (2003) Social-developmental factors affecting lesbians and gay youth: a review of cross-national research findings. *Children and Society* **17** 374–385.

Ross P & Carr S (2010) Practice Paper: 'It shouldn't be down to luck' – training for good practice with LGBT people: Social Care TV. *Diversity in Health and Care* **7** (3) 211–216.

Safra Project (2003) *Identifying the Difficulties Experienced by Muslim Lesbian, Bisexual and Transgender Women in Accessing Social and Legal Services.* London: Safra Project.

Smith G, Bartlett A & King M (2004) Treatments of homosexuality in Britain since the 1950s – an oral history: the experience of patients *British Medical Journal*, doi: 10.1136/ bmj.37984.442419.EE.

Strudwick P (2010) The ex-gay files: the bizarre world of gay-to-straight conversion. *The Independent* [online] 1 February. Available at: http://www.independent.co.uk/life-style/health-and-families/features/the-exgay-files-the-bizarre-world-of-gaytostraight-conversion-1884947. html (accessed November 2010).

Todd M (2010) In: T McVeigh. Breaking the taboo over the mental health crisis among Britain's gay men. *The Observer* [online]. Sunday 22 August. Available at: http://www.guardian.co.uk/theobserver/2010/aug/22/gay-attitude-depression-isolation (accessed November 2010).

Wong Y & Vinsky J (2009) Speaking from the margins: a critical reflection on the 'spiritual-but-not-religious' discourse in social work. *British Journal of Social Work* **39** 1343–1359.

Yogyakarta Principles (2007) *Principles on the Application of International Human Rights Law in Relation to Sexual Orientation and Gender Identity* [online]. Available at: http://www.yogyakartaprinciples.org/principles_en.pdf (accessed November 2010).

Further resources

Dinham A & Shaw M (2009) *Faiths, Equalities and Sexual Orientation: An exploratory study.* London: Capacity Builders.

Glidersleeve C & Platzer H (2003) *Creating a Safe Space: Good practice for mental health staff working with lesbians, gay men and bisexuals.* Brighton: Pavilion.

SHOUT! Centre for HIV and Sexual Health & Sheffield PCT (2010) *Different Strokes: A training tool for reducing health inequalities for lesbian, gay and bisexual people.* Sheffield: NHS Sheffield & Sheffield City Council.

Social Care TV films and resources on working with LGBT people: http://www.scie.org.uk/socialcaretv/default.asp

Chapter 19

Mindfulness-based stress reduction and mental health care practitioners

Julian Bowers

Clinical background

Mental health care professionals are subject to a unique range of stressors in their clinical work with service users. Stress arises from the ongoing demands of the therapeutic alliance and constant relating to disturbed and challenging patients, often in secure environments. Stress may also be felt in response to transferences and counter-transferences as well as from the sustaining of projections. Further stress may be experienced through over-identification with clinical roles and practice. Institutionalisation may lead to depersonalisation and a stressful 'siege mentality'.

Ask yourself
What causes me to feel stressed at work and at home?
What impact are these stressors having on me?

The disturbance within patients can transfer to staff. This may be either 'acted in' potentially leading to chaotic and overwhelming feelings of anger, low mood and depression or 'acted out', resulting in impaired social functioning in personal and professional relationships. Professional rivalry, omnipotence and perfectionism may all serve to heighten stress. In addition, there are often increasing organisational, workplace and career pressures with which to contend. 'Private life' pressures may further contribute to the practitioner's stress or be fed by it.

Such phenomena have been long recognised in healthcare settings and action has been taken to address them. Good professional management and support will include provision for group or individual clinical supervision. Supervision provides a 'safe place' to which difficult personal issues and emotional responses, arising or triggered in the course of the practitioner's clinical work, can be taken. In addition, the practice of mindfulness-based stress reduction (MBSR) has been found to be helpful to clinicians in the reduction of personal stress (Shapiro *et al*, 2005). There is recognition that the practitioner's own history, identity and vulnerability are not left outside the clinical environment.

Ask yourself

How do I respond to stress in my life?

Tom's story

Tom, aged 26, has been qualified as a registered mental health nurse for three years, having completed a degree course at a local university. He is seen as a highly committed and professional member of the ward-based clinical team who always 'goes the extra mile'. He radiates an idealism fuelled by perfectionist tendencies. His work on the admissions ward is demanding and sometimes he is involved in very challenging and potentially traumatising incidents. Outside work he feels socially isolated following the breakdown of a long-term relationship. Tom has lately been aware that his life both inside and outside work has become overwhelming and he has started drinking heavily. He feels unable to bring his personal issues to supervision or look to his manager and colleagues for support.

In this state of 'personal crisis' Tom's attention is drawn to the mindfulness-based stress reduction course (MBSR) which the trust is shortly to run over a period of eight weeks for clinical staff. He has read about MBSR in a professional journal and is aware that its practice enjoys a well-researched evidence base indicating its broad efficacy in reducing stress and increasing a sense of personal well-being. Tom decides to enrol.

Ask yourself

Could I experience improvement in the quality of my life if I managed my stress better?

The mindfulness-based stress reduction programme (MBSR)

The mindfulness-based stress reduction programme was developed by Jon Kabat-Zinn at the University of Massachusetts Medical Centre in the 1980s. Since those early days, MBSR has helped thousands of people worldwide to cope with anxiety, stress, pain and illness. MBSR training has been shown to clinically reduce symptoms of anxiety, psychological distress and secondary depression (Kabat-Zinn *et al*, 1992). This reduction in symptoms was seen to have been maintained when followed up after a three-year period (Miller *et al*, 1995). Furthermore, using skills learned in mindfulness training has been shown to be effective in a significant reduction of the recurrence of major depressive episodes in patients who have been treated for depression (Teasdale *et al*, 2000).

Kabat-Zinn brought mindfulness out of its original Eastern context and translated its psychological insights into Western culture and clinical practice. MBSR itself is not a religious activity so will usually sit comfortably with any faith tradition or none. It is essentially best understood as a 'mental technique'. However, the practitioner may come to attribute a spiritual quality and dimension to his MBSR practice.

Ask yourself
How do I feel about myself? Am I overly self-critical and judgemental? Do I enjoy a positive self-image?

The MBSR programme is usually taught across eight weekly two to two-and-a-half hour sessions with daily home practice of at least 45 minutes. Home practice is partly supported by a guided practice CD. The training programme is more than a taught course. Rather, in essence, it is a unique experiential process or personal journey for each trainee.

The programme is designed to help trainees to have an awareness of experience 'moment to moment' as it arises whether pleasant, neutral or otherwise. The arising and unfolding experience is held in awareness non-judgmentally with an attitudinal stance of self-compassion and kindness. Participants are introduced to techniques to help them become more aware of their thoughts and associated feelings and emotions, and observe them without judgment or criticism. MBSR helps enable the practitioner to be an impartial witness of his experience.

The programme also helps participants to foster an ability to choose whether or not to participate in their thoughts rather than allowing themselves to be caught up by them. It is a common human experience to be hijacked by a train of thought entirely unawares and to suddenly find one's self swept away – perhaps into an anxious state of mind.

The MBSR programme encourages participants to welcome, value and be nurtured by their experience of whatever kind, 'turning towards' it rather than 'pushing it away'. This 'pushing away' tends to happen when unpleasant thoughts or experiences arise. On the other hand, trainees are discouraged from 'clinging' to experience of whatever kind, even pleasant experience, as this 'holding on' to experience may distract attention from rich and fresh experience arising in each successive moment.

The programme is thus designed to teach participants how to become more aware of thoughts, feelings and emotions without necessarily being drawn into them or engaging with them (the MBSR practitioner is 'in charge' rather than the thoughts). Trainees learn to view their inner experience, thoughts and feelings, with an even-handedness from a detached observational viewpoint. There is consequently less potential attachment to thoughts and therefore rather less identification with them. Over time, there will develop a recognised sense of thoughts, feelings and emotions as being 'not me'. Consequently, they will tend to feel less personal or at least not so overly personal – particularly negative thoughts. This, in turn, can serve to lessen the 'hold' stressful thoughts, feelings and emotions can have on the practitioner. Furthermore, reference is frequently made during the programme to the 'Seven Pillars', which are fundamental to and undergird mindfulness practice (see appendix b).

'Responding' rather than 'reacting'

As the eight-week training progresses, participants may begin to notice that being mindful, and holding a detached observational view, grants a more balanced perspective to personal experience of whatever kind. Ongoing

MBSR practice facilitates what feels like the development of an 'inner spaciousness' with 'room to move', which allows the MBSR practitioner more emotional 'space' to respond appropriately rather than simply react 'knee jerk' style to experience – internal or external. Practice also helps develop a more expansive rather than contracted or narrow view of particular experience as if it were the whole story. It is often the case that when anxious thoughts, feelings and emotions arise, which are generated in our inner or outer worlds, such difficult experience becomes all consuming – the focus narrowed to the exclusion of all else. In the face of this very human reaction, MBSR practice helps inculcate a growing ability to stand back and to respond wisely and skilfully with greater internal 'poise' to stressful thoughts, feelings and emotions as well as to difficult situations, people and circumstances in life. In the process, being mindful may also afford a growing sense of personal reliable inner wisdom and trustworthy intuition.

Ask yourself

Do I sometimes find myself caught up unawares in negative thinking about my experience and life?

When does this tend to occur?

With practice, anxious thoughts and feelings, sometimes charged with negative emotional associations, may begin to be simply held in awareness and viewed impartially, 'given a good look at', and so to speak be 'rotated in the mind' and seen from all angles. This can put them into less threatening perspective and will enable a more skilful and potentially less anxious or overwhelming engagement with them if and when the practitioner should choose. They gradually occupy the 'driving seat' rather less frequently. Negative or anxious thoughts and feelings rarely tell us the complete truth about ourselves or our lives – indeed, sometimes they are very inaccurate representations. They are often tinted or deeply coloured with past negative experience. It is as if they are like 'old movies' still available for re-release. Ongoing MBSR practice also helps develop a level of awareness which alerts the practitioner to the arrival and seductive pull of negative automatic thinking which threatens to hold him captive. The practitioner is less often caught unawares.

Being 'open' even to difficult experience

Sustained practising of MBSR also helps the practitioner to 'soften' and 'open' and be less defensive in the face of more difficult and painful experience which may arise and view it more creatively (what can I learn from this?) as well as with self-compassion. This, as we have seen, is 'achieved' as anxious thoughts, feelings and emotions are held in awareness and viewed in a detached manner. It is as if 'I' am looking at the stream of thoughts, feelings and emotions as they come and go in my mind.

Ask yourself

Do I tend to 'nurse' negative thoughts, feelings and emotions so that they gain a greater hold on me?
Can I identify them?

MBSR encourages the practitioner to bring a spirit of gentle curiosity and inquiry about thoughts, feelings and emotional states as they arise and are held safely in the 'container' of awareness. Here they can be experienced, investigated non-judgmentally, as the practitioner chooses. However, this is done without 'nursing' them – particularly anxious thoughts – as like babies they will grow. If the practitioner avoids becoming personal with difficult thoughts, feelings and emotions they are much less likely in their turn to become particularly or painfully personal with him.

Ask yourself

Can I identify any unhelpful and 'stuck' type thinking patterns about myself and my life circumstances?

In being mindful and aware, the practitioner gains a measure of control over such thoughts, feelings, and emotions, which are now less likely to threaten, destabilise or have such a strong pull. Awareness affords control. The practitioner has a hold on his thoughts, feelings and emotions rather than vice-versa and begins to recognise 'stuck' patterns of thinking. As we have seen, MBSR trainees are encouraged to investigate difficult thoughts and feelings with gentle curiosity so as to learn from them. However, MBSR encourages the practitioner to investigate rather than to analyse or get too personal with negative thoughts and feelings, so as in the process, not to risk being drawn into them and associated past negative experience. This is key in MBSR practice.

Over time, the MBSR practitioner will begin to notice the presence of unhelpful habitual traits and attitudinal patterns in terms of thinking, feeling and emotional responses. These may prevent or inhibit full attending to 'being with' thoughts or feelings, whether pleasant, unpleasant or neutral, and in turn with the potential rich nurturing mixture of human experience of which they are part. MBSR practice encourages the welcoming and valuing of all experience as it arises.

Rumi's *The Guest House*, from an ever-growing mindfulness poetry anthology, articulates the MBSR non-avoiding stance of welcoming a whole mixture of experience in daily life.

The Guest House

'This being human is a guest house.
Every morning a new arrival.

A joy, a depression, a meanness,
some momentary awareness comes
as an unexpected visitor.

Welcome and entertain them all!
Even if they're a crowd of sorrows,
who violently sweep your house
empty of its furniture,
still, treat each guest honourably.
He may be clearing you out
for some new delight.

The dark thought, the shame, the malice,
meet them at the door laughing,
and invite them in.

Be grateful for whoever comes,
because each has been sent
as a guide from beyond'

(from *The Essential Rumi*, 1977. Quoted with permission from Coleman Barks.)

Being present – not 'miles away'

Throughout the MBSR programme, the accent remains on fostering ability to 'step out of clock time', as Kabat-Zinn describes it, and to be intentionally present in this moment right now. Trainees are encouraged to notice whatever experience there is in this moment right now and to be 'open' to it – in terms of physical sensation, or sounds and sights as well as in terms of thoughts, feelings and emotions – accepting them just as they are, not wanting to alter or change them, and without criticism or judgement. In MBSR practice or, as it is often termed 'meditation', focusing the attention on the breath helps to 'anchor' the practitioner in the present moment.

Ask yourself
Do I regularly catch unhelpful trains of thought?
Which are they?
Where do they take me?

Particularly in the first few weeks of the MBSR training programme, much time is spent in practising paying attention to a variety of bodily sensations (eg. sensation of the soles of the feet on the floor). This helps the practitioner to gain greater awareness of present moment experience including not only bodily sensations but also thoughts as they come and go (see appendix a – Mindful breathing practice). He begins to notice, is mindful, and consequently becomes more aware of his trains of thought. When perhaps he is 'whooshed' away from paying attention to the breath or body (or perhaps sound or sight) or distracted by a thought, feeling or emotion and has become aware that this has happened, he congratulates himself on being mindful and without criticism or judgement (for this is what minds naturally do) escorts the focus of his attention back to the breath, body, sound or whatever has been the focus of attention (eg. a flower). He practises this time and time again, informally, as he goes about his life.

Paying attention to the breath and associated bodily sensations and noting when the mind wanders (again, it's OK – that's what minds do) and then escorting the spotlight of attention back to bodily sensation produces a greater awareness not only of physical experience but also a greater awareness of thoughts, feelings and emotions. In time, this awareness of and noticing experience, becomes more spontaneous. Implicit in MBSR practice is choosing and practising where to direct (and redirect back) the focus of attention again and again. This ability to notice, be aware, that the mind has wandered (Aha! my mind has wandered) is the 'mindful moment'.

Ultimately, thoughts, feelings and emotions begin to be seen merely as 'mental events' – nothing more or less. This gives rise to recognition that such inner experience does not necessarily define the practitioner as a person. He also endeavours, as already noted, to take a detached view ('de-centred') of the experience whatever its quality. Furthermore, how he relates to experience, his attitude towards it, will determine how much potential 'stress impact' it holds. This 'detachment' or 'de-centring', as we have seen, helps prevent him from being caught up in a particular train of thought with associated emotion and feeling and being transported unawares to a destination 'miles away' in the past or to an imagined, potentially stressful, future. This being 'miles away' is an involuntary state known to every human being – not being with experience arising in the present moment. To help guard against being hauled unawares onboard a train of thought, usually with no advertised destination, the MBSR practitioner seeks to cultivate an awareness of just that moment when 'automatic pilot thinking' is kicking in and is taking him for a ride. There's time to jump off the train.

This ability to choose with which thoughts, feelings and emotions to engage affords insight, a personal discovery, that there is no need to get stuck in the same old 'mental ruts', going down the same old routes on the same old trains of thought. Such mental excursions, including rumination, and related negative thought cycles (including 'maintenance cycles'), may have been the source of all manner of personal difficulties and problems (including poor self-image) previously impeding life's journey. This is beautifully illustrated in lines from the poem 'Autobiography in Five Short Chapters' in which the writer, Portia Nelson, reflects something of the potential negative impact of always operating on 'autopilot' in life. In this poem she refers to constantly falling into the same deep hole in the pavement of a familiar street:

III
I walk down the same street.
There is a deep hole in the sidewalk.
I see it is there.
I still fall in ... it's a habit.
my eyes are open
I know where I am.

(Quoted with permission from Souvenir Press © Nelson P (1994) *Me in You*)

However, at long last and mindfully, there is a disengagement from 'autopilot' and the choice made to walk around the hole. Finally, exercising further inner wisdom, the decision is made to take a new route altogether down another street!

Ask yourself
Can I relate to this in some way in my life? How can I change my approach?

There is an innate tendency to operate on 'autopilot' which has had evolutionary benefit in terms of human beings learning to carry out complex activities 'without thinking'. However, the downside is that when a person is operating on 'autopilot' and engaging in habitual thinking, feeling and emotional responses, he is likely to be distracted from what is real and potentially nurturing and enriching in each moment and its experience. Simply reacting with conditioned responses will not be constructive, choiceful or helpful and will work against unlocking the fuller potential and richness of an individual's life. We can escape the *'chains of our robotic conditioning'* (Kabat-Zinn, 2005).

Ask yourself
What thinking, feeling and emotional responses have become habitual in me? Are they helpful or not?

Waking up

We have seen how MBSR practice helps develop a 'mindful way of being' with experience in contrast to 'mental doing', often losing ourselves in the activity of thinking (sometimes conditioned and inaccurate thinking) and how the trainee learns to be present and to be intentionally open in a non-judgmental manner to experience as it arises whether in body or mind by being 'anchored' in the present moment. Kabat-Zinn captures this in his definition of mindfulness:

'Mindfulness means paying attention in a particular way; on purpose in the present moment and non-judgmentally.' (Kabat-Zinn, 1990)

Furthermore, for the regular MBSR practitioner there is a 'waking up' to experience, even familiar experience, and finding a freshness in it. This is sometimes referred to in mindfulness as 'beginner's mind' or 'seeing differently'. Indeed, just as the experience may be seen and felt in a new way – nurturing in itself – it is, as we have seen, held in awareness with a gentle and compassionate curiosity. Such 'waking up' to familiar experience may lead to seeing one's self, other people, and situations in new ways, in a new light, rather than through a fog of pre-conceptions or past negative personal history, thus risking closing down on the new and fresh experience being offered in the present moment. A child in my garden will see the butterflies and the vivid summer colours while I may only see critically all the gardening that yet needs to be done. How easily inner critical thoughts can spoil good experience.

Ask yourself

How often do I try to see the people around me (or myself) with fresh eyes putting aside any preconceptions and prejudices?

The cradling of experience

Essentially, in MBSR practice the practitioner will find himself 'cradling' his thoughts, feelings and emotions, in awareness, as a mother cradles a child, holding them in the container of awareness. This *'provides a greater basket for tenderly holding and intimately knowing our suffering and that is transformative'*. (Kabat-Zinn, 2005). In this way painful experience becomes modified, more manageable. The changed experiential perspective afforded by MBSR is also well described by Rebecca Crane: *'We are no longer in the experience looking out onto the world through the filter of emotions created by it. Through seemingly subtle shifts in relationship with experience, radical new perspectives emerge'* (Crane, 2008). As already noted, the implied de-centering, or detached observation of thoughts, feeling and emotion creates a sense of a spacious 'interiority' in the mindfulness practitioner or 'room to move' emotionally in terms of response. As Kabat-Zinn has observed: *'Your awareness is a very big space in which to reside'* (Kabat-Zinn, 2005).

This detached inner state allows the MBSR meditator simply to view impartially the procession of thoughts, feelings and emotions that arise and to choose which ones to engage with. This detachment in itself guards against any sense of thoughts, feelings and emotions 'being me' and allows a sense of their being separate from me. So, I may feel anxious but know that I am not the anxiety. Rather, it is a case that 'there is anxiety' of which I am aware. However, mindfulness helps the practitioner take a very good look at the anxiety and see it for what it actually is (in proper perspective) rather than run away from it. Again, this reduces stress. It is also a bit like 'facing the pain' or 'facing down' personal demons. Besides which, they are not the whole story.

MBSR practice helps cultivate greater acceptance by taking each moment and each aspect of experience just as it is and simply being receptive to it without trying to change or alter it. Indeed, mindfulness practice encourages a disposition of acceptance of things as they are, myself as I am, other people as they are, with an observation which is gentle and compassionate. Nevertheless, it must be firmly stated that this is not resignation or an 'anything goes' attitude in any shape or form but rather a benefiting from mindfully choosing if and when to engage with personal issues and to learn from them. As we have seen, the practitioner may also begin to notice attitudinal patterns of thinking and behaviour, which are critical and lacking in self-compassion, and which inhibit experience, and hence personal growth.

Alongside, we see that MBSR practice involves the practitioner in a discovery that in not getting too personal with difficult thoughts, feelings and emotions they in turn become less persecutory. Moreover, if difficult or painful thoughts, feelings and emotions do not receive compulsive attention they will tend not to grow. In MBSR practice, it is simply a case of 'letting them be'. This 'letting be' happens through a process of 'letting go' (not attempting to change, suppress or avoid the experience) simply choosing to intentionally bring the focus of attention into present moment experience or during MBSR practice back to the breath, sensation, sight, or sound and so to being anchored in the present moment. 'Present moment' personal experience then occupies centre stage in awareness and other mental agendas seem to disappear into the wings. It is only possible to think about one thing at a time.

Thoughts are not facts

As we have seen, implicit in MBSR practice is developing a sense of being in the present moment, being directly aware of experience, observing thoughts, feelings and emotions rather than observing from them. MBSR enables the practitioner really to feel that 'my thoughts, feelings and emotions, are not me' but simply mental events. Indeed, the practitioner will discover that 'thoughts are not facts' (eg. *My boss criticised my performance yesterday so I will never get promotion in the future*'). Rather than feeling or seeing through a fog of conditioned pre-conceptions arising from past negative experiences, the MBSR practitioner is able to investigate such thoughts with a kindly curiosity and discover their lack of truth, thus enabling them to be disregarded more easily.

Ask yourself
What negative thoughts do I have about myself which I regard as fact? Are they factual – to what degree?

The mindful person will recognise and be aware of thoughts but see them solely as thoughts in the stream of consciousness and understand that they need to be tested for validity. As we saw earlier, he will be aware that he is not his thoughts neither are they he. He is exercising a 'non-attachment' and not identifying with them nor taking or finding his identity in them. His thoughts, feelings and emotions certainly do not define or accurately represent him. MBSR ongoing practice can help guard against his vulnerability perhaps to depressive thoughts of being useless or unlovable. Much of this is about the ability gained through MBSR training of mindfully disengaging from the autopilot or conditioned thinking in our heads. In addition, the MBSR practitioner will be more able to choose which trains of thought passing through the station of his mind to board and thereby be able to choose the destination. Thoughts, feelings and emotions no longer take on a life of their own setting unwanted agendas. MBSR practice helps him to be with difficult inner experience in a potentially radical and transformative new way opening up new possibilities and greater happiness. Thoughts, feelings, and emotions are less likely now to distort how he sees himself or hazard a true sense of connectedness with himself, with others, and the world around. Mindfulness can help him to gain a more balanced, less defensive, more open, more expansive and compassionate view and understanding of himself, other people and the world in which he finds himself.

> **Ask yourself**
>
> Are conditioned responses and preconceptions distorting my view of myself and the world? If so, can I identify them?

Start living here in each present moment

Williams *et al* (2007) describe the observational detachment in MBSR practice as an awareness allowing us to '*see our thoughts as mental events that come and go in the mind like clouds across the sky instead of taking them literally*'. In this way negative thoughts are seen as less personal and perhaps not so threatening, and they are far less likely to be felt as directly stressful. These may include depressing thoughts that may take us into a downwards mental spiral further into a depressed state of mind. Practising MBSR fosters greater awareness of such thoughts (or even thought fragments), which may build up and pull us into a downward spiral of depressive thinking and related stressful emotion. The brakes can be applied. Williams *et al* further describe mindfulness, being aware in the present moment, as enabling the practitioner to:

'*Start living right here in each present moment. When we stop dwelling on the past or worrying about the future, we open to rich sources of information we've been missing out on – information that can keep us out of the downward spiral and poised for a richer life.*' (Williams *et al*, 2007)

Ask yourself

Why don't I sign up for a mindfulness-based stress reduction programme?
What could be the benefits for me?

Tom's story transformed

Tom's attendance on the eight-week MBSR programme and his ongoing daily practice has made a radical difference to his life. There has been a shift of perception as he has noticed and become more aware of the negative patterns of thinking and feeling which have caused him to become 'stuck' in his life. He is much less in a state of 'craving' for a different set of life circumstances which in itself is a cause of suffering and stress. He has become far less judgemental and less self-critical. He is now viewing his life and circumstances with kindness and self-compassion as well as testing out the validity of his thoughts, feelings and emotions. Tom is more aware of his idealistic and perfectionist tendencies and particularly the stress that they impose. He notices a growing trust in the reliability of his intuitions. Tom has developed an ability to be present in the moment and not be buffeted so much by anxiety – past, present and future. In his work as a clinician he is more able to take a detached view, responding carefully rather than reacting to or being overwhelmed by difficult or stressful situations and people. Mindfulness-based practice rooted within a deep commitment and intention gives rise to an insightfulness which allows Tom to treat himself, friends, colleagues, patients and others with compassion. MBSR helps him to 'see differently'. He recognises a common mutuality and has a respect for that genius, which lies within each person. Yes, of course, there is still stress experienced in his clinical work but he now mindfully chooses how to relate to it. He is managing the stress in his life rather than it managing him. He is no longer a victim. A heightened awareness of living has brought him a richer and more rewarding life. MBSR practice is opening up an entirely different and more balanced approach to Tom's life.

References

Crane RS (2008) *Mindfulness-based Cognitive Therapy.* London: Routledge.

Kabat-Zinn J (1990) *Full Catastrophe Living: Using the wisdom of your body and mind to face stress, pain and illness.* New York: Delta.

Kabat-Zinn J, Massion AO, Kristeller J, Peterson LG, Fletcher KE, Pbert L, Lenderking WR & Santorelli SF (1992) Effectiveness of a meditation-based stress reduction program in the treatment of anxiety disorders. *American Journal of Psychiatry* **149** 936–943.

Kabat-Zinn J (2005) *Coming to Our Senses: Healing ourselves and the world through mindfulness.* London: Piatkus.

Miller JJ, Fletcher K & Kabat-Zinn J (1995) Three-year follow-up and clinical implications of a mindfulness-based stress reduction intervention in the treatment of anxiety disorders. *General Hospital Psychiatry* **17** 192–200.

Nelson P (1994) *There's a Hole in My Sidewalk: The romance of self-discovery*. London: Souvenir Press

Coleman B (trans) (1977) *The Essential Rumi*. San Francisco, CA: Harper.

Shapiro SL, Astin JA, Bishop SR & Cordova M (2005) Mindfulness-based stress reduction for health care professionals: results from a randomised trial. *International Journal of Stress Management* **12** 164–176.

Teasdale JD, Segal ZV, Williams JMG, Ridgeway VA, Soulsby JM & Lau MA (2000) Prevention of relapse/recurrence in major depression by mindfulness-based cognitive therapy. *Journal of Consulting and Clinical Psychology* **68** (4) 615–623.

Williams JMG, Segal ZV, Teasdale JD & Kabat-Zinn J (2007) *The Mindful Way through Depression*. London: Guilford Press.

Further reading

Baer RE (2005) *Mindfulness-Based Treatment Approaches: Clinician's guide to evidence-base and applications*. London: Academic Press.

Didonna F (2009) *Clinical Handbook of Mindfulness*. London: Springer.

Kabat-Zinn J (2001) *Mindfulness Meditation for Everyday Life*. London: Piatkus.

Santorelli S (1999) *Heal Thyself: Lessons on mindfulness in medicine*. London: Bell Tower.

Segal ZV, Williams JMG & Teasdale JD (2002) *Mindfulness–based Cognitive Therapy for Depression. A new approach to preventing relapse*. London: Guilford Press.

Appendix A

Mindfulness breathing practice

Sitting comfortably on a chair, feet flat on the floor, adopt a dignified and balanced posture with the spine erect and the eyes closed.

Bring awareness to the sensations of contact of the body with the chair or the floor. What sensations are there for you in this present moment? What is your experience right now? Spend time exploring this experience.

Next, bring your attention to your breathing, noticing bodily sensations especially around the nostrils, chest and abdomen. Bring awareness to the expansion and contraction of the abdominal wall.

Now maintain this awareness as you breathe allowing your body to do the breathing without attempting to change or alter your breathing, simply noticing the varying and changing sensations with each in breath and out breath.

Sooner or later you will notice that your mind has wandered. This is the 'aha! moment'. Now, without judgment or criticism that your mind wandered (that is what minds do) congratulate yourself on having noticed, having been mindful, and escort or refocus your attention back to your breath and bodily sensations. Note each time your mind wanders but do not be judgemental or self-critical. Simply, congratulate yourself on having noticed, having been mindful, and escort your attention repeatedly back to your breath and associated bodily sensations. This helps physical and mental awareness to grow – and in time, to develop a spontaneity.

Be very patient and kind to yourself.

After 10–15 minutes expand your awareness again to the whole of your body sitting wherever are.

Take something of this experience into the rest of your day.

Appendix B

The 'Seven Pillars' of mindfulness

1. Non-judging – Observing our thoughts, feelings and emotions as they happen and noting how often we habitually judge and react to our own experience.

2. Patience – Allowing an unfolding of experience while avoiding impatience with ourselves and our experience – impatience often compounds difficulty and distress 'pulling the knot tighter'. Patience helps us unravel the knots in our lives.

3. Beginner's mind – Seeing things freshly as if for the first time – like a child sees a world full of beauty and possibility. Try seeing yourself and the people around you with a beginner's mind.

4. Trust – Listening to yourself and trusting in your intuition and deeper wisdom. 'In there' you are a whole and complete person.

5. Non-striving – Not trying to succeed or achieve anything but simply being with your experience just as it is for you in the present moment.

6. Acceptance – Mindfulness practice helps cultivate greater acceptance by taking each moment and each aspect of our experience just as it is and simply being receptive to it without trying to change it.

7. Letting go – In mindfulness practice we simply acknowledge the experience that arises moment to moment, whatever its quality by 'letting it be' and 'letting it go'. We pay attention to our experiences as they arise and pass on in the successive moments of mindfulness practice.

Chapter 20

Reflective practice – the 'soul' of professional engagement in relationship work

Joy Gauci

This chapter considers the validity of spiritual and reflective compasses to guide professional engagements with people at points of emotional vulnerability in their lives. It takes the spiritual image of the journey of the soul, and explores its potential strength for service users engaged in narratives about their experiences. The soul journey is the individual's pursuit to identify and nurture the 'inner spirit' (see chapter 1) as it moves from inner search and contemplation to find a position of sufficient composure to meaningfully engage with others.

The chapter uses three voices – the main author, a social worker engaged in 20 years of community practice with adults, but also involved in a personal reflective journey due to experiences of transition. The two additional authors are people who have directly experienced transition or challenge in their personal lives and have accessed professional helping relationships at stages in their recovery. Each has considered the contribution of a spiritual and reflective consciousness in the move towards recovery.

In professional engagements the individual is invited to share his or her narrative, the expression of their search for meaning and the chapter considers the relevancy of a spiritual consciousness to this narrative approach. The professional helper engages with the narrative – the chapter promotes reflective practice as the 'soul' of professional practice which potentially prepares the professional for these highly sensitive personal encounters. Reflective practice is, then the preparatory 'soul journey' of the professional providing potential assurance for genuine, emotionally intuitive engagements.

The chapter makes a connection between spiritual imagery and reflective consciousness and promotes a combined model of spirituality and reflective practice. This model recognises complex truths and provides important messages about the construction of professional helping relationships. It suggests both service user and professional are engaged in a journey of self-discovery – a search for individual and professional composure. The professional relationship is a way of recognising the search for meaning, and honouring the insight and dignity of the service user as narrator. The relationship has the potential to acknowledge and nurture inner creativity and resourcefulness; it enables capacity building based on the consciousness of:

▶ reflective practice

  ▶ belief in the capacity of the individual (service user) to find his or her own meaning
  ▶ belief in the capacity of the professional to engender and support the person's construction of meaning.

▶ spirituality – the potential belief in capacity, the healing qualities in human, environmental and spiritual spheres.

As Andrew Powell puts it, those engaged in a therapeutic relationship are:

'in complementary roles – both need the other. Indeed, at heart we are far more alike than different, and as we meet on the path of life, there is one medicine constantly at our disposal that even comes free. This is the power of love, lending hope, giving comfort and helping bring peace to the troubled mind.' (Powell, 2009, pxviii)

The spiritual and intuitive aspects of practice

There are two languages in professional narrative – one of accountability, procedures, engagement and structured support and the other of fragmentation, search for meaning, and compassion. Both are valid – but the risk in procedural practice is that sensitivity to the inner spirit becomes diminished. The procedural has an agenda – the creative has a narrative, which recognises the need for dialogue or discourse to express and tease out complex truths rather than follow prescribed paths. Schön's influential work on reflective practice (1983) advocated the need to move from technical rationality to reflection, or 'reflection in action' (Schön, 2007, p48) which allows for spontaneity and intuition in professional engagements. Narrative, then, invites the exploration of alternative and individually owned planes of meaning.

For many people, this search for meaning will have an intuitive and spiritual circumference (section 1 & 2) although the interpretation and language to express it will be individually owned (section 3). The experience of cultural migration, redundancy, single parenthood, change of fostering placement, for example, might deeply challenge a person's sense of self-belief and location in the human landscape. The soul journey reflects the individual's striving to seek meaning and purpose in the face of life's complexities – it is a search for inner composure and connectedness in human, natural and, potentially, spiritual worlds.

Andy is a 49-year-old single man who has had experience of emotional vulnerability and depression throughout his adult life. This was triggered initially by experiences of bullying at school then being made redundant from a job in his 20s. He received little support through this experience of loss and has only since held casual work contracts. He has a strong sense of commitment and loyalty – cares for his parents and does casual voluntary work in his local community. The trauma of redundancy has shadowed his adult life and shaped his emotional health in terms of sensitivity to rejection, sense of self-worth and having to 'earn' his value. He has forged stability in life through engaging with others, giving deeply and having a strong sense of loyalty and integrity.

'It takes time to realise where you are going … it's about trying to find your true self and living up to that expectation without being too hard on yourself. It's about learning to trust others. Trusting others is very difficult to manage because it's having to show who you truly are inside. It is a real strength when you have people you can truly trust but it is a learnt strength. It is so difficult when the trust is broken.' (Andy)

Prag is a single woman of 49 who lived with her family in Uganda until sent to boarding school in England at the age of 12. She describes this is a time of personal dislocation from family and cultural bonds and a time of great sadness. Prag found the boarding school environment a further source of isolation. She never returned to Uganda and hence remained separated from her birth culture and family. A gifted, sensitive woman, Prag's adulthood has been a search to find her composure, emotional stability and social identity.

'I believe today that my past is my best asset because it has given me the grace to survive and make sense of its very challenging journey. I believe I was meant to go through the tragedies. I want to be able to use these experiences; they have given me a strong sense of purpose and a passion to live in a simple way without attachment to material things. They make me want to help others.' (Prag)

These are two very individual journeys which echo certain parallels – a sense of loss and dislocation which sets the path for adult life causing periods of social isolation and emotional vulnerability as well as deep strength. Each narrative conveys individual dignity and composure but provides glimpses into the challenge of the search for clear and accepted social identities and roles. Both narratives express an individual reflective spirit which has searched for meaning and through gaining composure found the ability to meaningfully engage with others.

Many people will need a helping professional – counsellor, social worker, GP, or teacher as they move through experiences of loss, change, or trauma. The process from inward reflection to acknowledgement of loss and search for renewal or acceptance cannot easily be taken alone. Within professional relationship work, there is an increasing focus on holistic assessment, which potentially engages body, mind and soul, hence recognising the need for professionals to be sensitive to, perhaps facilitate, the individual search for spiritual understanding. Tournier (1954, p13) suggested that... *'every illness calls for two diagnoses: one scientific, nosological and causal, and the other spiritual, a diagnosis of its meaning and purpose'.* McSherry (2000, p48) promotes an awareness of spiritual frames of meaning for healthcare practice and West (2000) explores the contribution of the religious, spiritual and mystical to models of psychotherapeutic engagement. Moss (2005b) highlights the increasing contemporary acknowledgement of spiritual perspectives in social work practice.

Whilst authors develop a convincing argument for spiritual consciousness in helping practice, this raises the complexity about how far the professional engages in or facilitates the spiritual debate. West's work considers specifically the line between psychotherapy and spirituality – a claim for the importance of a spiritual awareness in therapeutic engagements but a reminder of the need to respect the boundary between the appropriate and the intrusive. Within a model of narrative, the rules are clearer as the service user chooses the parameters. However, the important message for practitioners is the responsibility to be mindful that service users might choose to use a spiritual language to express their journeys.

What is distinct about spiritual perspectives in contemporary practice is the acknowledgement of individuality of interpretation; the emphasis on an intuitive spirit which forms meaning out of experience and reflective wisdom, alongside influences from established traditions of religion and faith communities. This is an interesting echo of the need for balance in professional engagement – between orthodox, scientific knowledge and an empirical knowledge receptive to individual experience and beliefs. Again, this need for promotion of individual expression and ownership is particularly suited to the narrative model of engagement.

The specific contribution of spirituality to the holistic recovery model

At the core of spiritual truth is the capacity for healing and restoration. Heron's work explores the concept of the 'self-transfiguring person' (Heron, 1992, p60) identifying the potential individual capacity for liberation from 'past conditioning and affliction'. An awareness of spirit, then, potentially holds the key to our psycho-emotional recovery enabling us to *access the life-giving currents that flow beneath a divided world, offering it an opportunity for healing and renewal'* (Tacey, 2003, p2).

> ### Box 1: The validity of the spiritual model of assessment
>
> It uses the image of the soul and journey to express the person's individual search for meaning.
>
> It recognises mystic traditions which allow for arenas beyond human understanding.
>
> It has a sense of authorship and 'divine purpose' beyond human planes of circumference.
>
> It explores the concept of personal ownership, responsibility, forgiveness and release.
>
> It validates human purpose in meaningful engagement.
>
> It allows for deeper questions and acknowledges complex truths.

McSherry's model of spirituality includes: hope, meaning, purpose, forgiveness, belief, morality, spiritual care, relationships, creativity, self-expression (McSherry, 2000, p171). This model suggests various facets of spiritual meaning which the service user might explore, hence choose to express. To reflect on a specific spiritual facet or image, for example, to consider the concept of purpose or of forgiveness, can potentially result in a significant step in the individual's search for composure.

> *'A single word can cause a release of energy because of its associations with aspects of your life – trigger words like love, forgiveness, trust.'* Andy

Three aspects of the individual capacity for recovery are – consciousness, understanding, and restoration.

Consciousness – A spiritual compass for professional relationship work is valid in engendering consciousness. A conscious spirit of enquiry will address the sense of meaningless that often comes from a deeply challenging personal experience. Meaninglessness risks a spirit of powerlessness – potentially resulting in a lack of self-composure, a fear of losing control or an anxiety that others will create our purpose for us. To reach a state where the individual can engage with the experience of loss of purpose is a significant step towards recovery and again, the narrative model invites the individual to take control of the journey's interpretation and expression.

Understanding – Consciousness invites a search for understanding, the exploration of our sense of purpose, self-belief, and self-worth. Moss identifies this as 'self-location' (2005a, p1). Self-location suggests a need for balance between an awareness of pain and an appreciation of restorative energy. It challenges a narrative which expresses lack of self-worth or individual composure. It highlights the need to recognise and accept our intrinsic worth rather than a worth that needs to be negotiated or justified.

'Not understanding to control it but to live with it.' Andy

'I do not know why I survived … what I have tried to do and tried to be ever since has been to give some sense of meaning to that survival.' Gryn, Auschwitz survivor.

Reflexivity and restoration

The spirituality model, then, promotes an exploration for self-worth, meaning and reflective composure. It also suggests a reflexive component – a responsibility to engage with and own the reflective state. It emphasises the potential for release, acceptance or restoration as a reaction to the reflective state.

Heron acknowledges the individual ability to engage with psychic and spiritual capacity (1992, p61). To acknowledge the reflective capacity is to hold the potential for release or renewal – the image of the phoenix with a resurgence of energy to release pain and disillusionment and to restore hope. The capacity for restoration presents a complex spiritual truth about embracing our individual reflective capacity for change. It is also about acceptance of the limitations of individual and human capacity. Restoration might therefore mean an acceptance of the mystical point beyond reasoning – a release of the burden of responsibility, anxiety, or guilt. This process echoes the spiritual image of faith: the recognition of the limitations of human capacity and potential belief in universal restorative powers.

Many of the journeys that helping professions engage with include experiences of transition and potential dislocation: the dislocation experienced by a child being placed in foster care; a young person exposed to the criminal justice system; an older person coming to terms with the diagnosis of dementia (see chapters 5 and 12). Reflective 'restoration' or composure might be an acknowledgement of the capacity to change or it might suggest a point of acceptance and search for peace. It means taking hold of the journey or...

'Being able to live life without it controlling you.' Andy

The use of narrative as reflective engagement in relationship-based work

Professionals need to engage with people in a way that is sensitive to the individual's awareness of the inner spirit. This requires a creative approach to a professional relationship which uses skills of reflection and critical reasoning to explore experience. It is important to recognise the sensitivity and complexity of engaging with individuals in a way that protects individuality of interpretation and expression:

▶ the challenge of restricting own beliefs in responding to another's interpretation of spirituality and intuition

▶ the vulnerability of the service user once his or her story has been shared

▶ the risk of professional 'conditioning' and control of the narrative

▶ the complexity of truly promoting anti-oppressive values in the interpretation of meaning, diversity of belief and individuality of expression.

Narrative work is a convincing model for genuine reflective engagement in helping relationships. It emphasises the individual construction, hence personal expression and ownership, of selfhood (Fook, 2008). Fook considers two aspects of narrative approaches in relationship work: use of language and critical discourse. Both forms of expression acknowledge the transient state of the construction of selfhood, the changing and relative aspects of identity (Sands, 1996, p76) and the use of the narrative to express and explore significant factors at a specific point in a person's reflective journey.

Language and the construction of selfhood

First, Fook's concept of language is significant as it authenticates the individual's version of their reality. It has the potential to create a radical form of engagement because it gives ownership of perspective to the service user; language is the individual expression of reflection and meaning.

Robinson, Kendrick and Brown (2003) promote a model of narrative that encompasses spiritual arenas of personal reflection:

'As the patient reflects on their narrative the spiritual meaning can emerge:

▶ *the experience of loss, disability etc. and how this changes the belief system*

▶ *the values critical to the person eg. love, care, duty, sacrifice*

▶ *the emerging beliefs about people who are valued, including what creates the structures of the individual's faith and hope.'*

In this model the individual's interpretation of experience includes the right to choose the moral circumference and the significant support structures that create meaning for the individual at that given time.

Critical discourse and anti-oppressive consciousness

Second, narrative is associated with the concept of critical discourse (Fook, 2008). Narrative has the potential to create a genuine anti-oppressive consciousness in professional relationship work. The individual might choose to explore the experience of isolation, marginalisation or victimhood with the use of critical discourse. A form of dialogue which encourages questioning, it has the potential to challenge domination in three spheres: external structures, social relations and personal constructions (Fook, 2008, p41). It acknowledges the need for emotionally engaged responses to challenge the template of individual achievement within economic rationalism. Dialogue, then, allows for a different type of knowledge construction. The individual is invited to explore their experience and potentially recognise a different but equally valid claim to citizenship status and social identity.

While the narrative model of engagement is valuable in emphasising the individuality of interpretation and control of the narrator, it is important to recognise that individual levels of capacity for reflexivity will vary. Heron's model of selfhood includes three stages: i. the creative person, with conscious awareness of their position in the world and a level of reflexive ability to question and challenge; ii. the self-creating person, who, *'through consciousness raising, can seek to dissociate their beliefs and behaviour from rigid and unjust social stereotypes'* and iii. the self-transfiguring person, able to *'deal with deeper tensions and cultivate a unique perception of the world'* (1992, pp59–61). The model is valuable in promoting the professional responsibility to gauge the individual level of capacity, potential support and hence, direction in engagement.

Beyond the narrative in relationship work

Relationship might be formed on the basis of communication but requires recognition that it has the capacity to extend beyond words, language, narrative and discourse. The use of silence is drawn from spiritual images of meditation and retreat – it recognises the importance of reflective searching as a mind state explored in the stillness beyond the expression of words. It invites the use of stillness and silence in the narrative to allow for deeper awareness and empathy in the relationship, to acknowledge the expression of a deep sentiment or to recognise the place of faith in the limitations of human understanding.

So far this chapter has demonstrated the validity of spiritual encompasses in professional helping relationships, and the complexities and challenges of appropriate responses to such sensitive, individual and emotionally charged expressions. The latter part of this chapter explores the reflective consciousness in helping relationships.

Reflective practice – the 'soul' of professional engagement in relationship work

At the core of social work and other aligned professions is a particular type of relationship work best described as sitting alongside people at times of challenge in their lives. Narrative work allows the individual expression of his or her perceived reality and recognition of the stage reached in the reflective journey. 'Narrative ... enables the person to both articulate, reflect on, critique and develop or affirm the life meaning' (Moss, 2005b, p2). Interpretative or interactionist (Howe, 1987), reflective practice invites knowledge creation through participation. Reflection is the pivotal point of this type of relationship based practice. Reflective practice promotes a type of depth consciousness at both professional and individual level. It is this depth consciousness which echoes the spiritual imagery of the soul, with associations of inner intuition, contemplation and restorative energy. It emphasises self-responsibility and self-discovery; coming to terms with self – both the personal self and the professional persona – in order to meaningfully engage with others.

The critical process of healing and recovery is potentially triggered by the individual's ability to critically reflect. Neimeyer's (2001) meaning reconstruction theory says that loss invites us to explore the realms of deeper understanding. A reflective consciousness promotes a critical awareness of the way we present ourselves, personality, beliefs and intentions, actions and interactions.

Distinct features of a relationship based on reflective consciousness are:

▶ a creative, intuitive self-awareness – the ability to explore new ways of being

▶ a sensitivity to people's search for meaning and emotional engagement.

The 'energy for consciousness raising' (Heron, 1992) has the potential to move from a functional engagement to a depth engagement in the relationship.

Reflective consciousness and identity/meaning reconstruction in relationship work

Reflection suggests a different type of knowledge construction through reflecting on experience, engaging in dialogue, and responding to the interaction. Schön describes this process as 'reflection on action' (2007). A reflective stance allows for critical awareness and recognition of alternative planes for meaning. Schön's emphasis on interpretative meaning is a reminder that the communication between the individual and professional changes. Erikson talked of the importance of 'testing interpretations' – the communication between patient and therapist *'keeps moving, leading to new and surprising insights and to the greater assumption of responsibility for … (the individual)'* (1958, p74).

The use of narrative in therapeutic relationship

First, narrative 'therapy' is based on the individual's engagement with inner reflection and self-awareness, with the potential, as already discussed, to move through a stage of awareness, to reconstruction and resolution or composure.

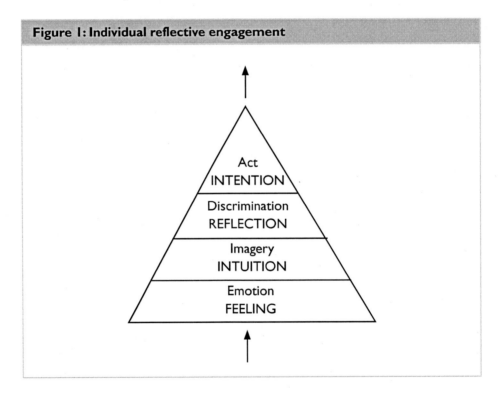

Figure 1: Individual reflective engagement

The professional as a reflective catalyst

The relationship between the professional and the individual has the potential to find a shared reflective state in which to consider new meanings. It is a 'transactional dialogue' (Brookfield, 1986) between participants who bring *experience, attitudinal sets and alternate ways of looking at their personal, professional, political and recreational worlds'.* This model, based on the image of dialogue, is a reminder that the state of reflective consciousness is in partnership. The shared responsibility for self-awareness and understanding has a powerful anti-oppressive message which potentially equalises the power basis of the relationship.

Reflective practice promotes the soul or inner spirit of professional practice. In order to achieve a genuine transactional dialogue the professional needs to develop a reflective consciousness. The reflective consciousness – in preparing for engagements, during engagement and after engagement (Schön, 1983) is a safeguard for authenticity on behalf of the professional.

Echoing the spirituality model of inner reflection to outward care or giving, reflection nurtures both self-awareness and social awareness. Reflective questions in the acknowledgement of complex truths allow for a questioning of practice, social and political realities with a recognition that such structures might be inflexible or oppressive to the individual's needs. It invites a thinking outside the box (Moss, 2005a) when social structures no longer respond to individual experience.

Reflective practice and professional discipline

An essential image taken from spirituality is the aspect of discipline. Having commenced with a challenge to a dominance in procedural objective approaches it is important to emphasise the need to organise professional relationship-based practice in a systematic way. The challenge is in needing to maintain a sense of our professional persona in an accountable objectivity while also being responsive to the individuality and creativity of the narrative.

A range of structured models of reflective practice provide guidance on achieving balance and objectivity in individual practitioner approaches.

Reflective preparation

First, in the preparatory stage, there is the need to develop precision in self-criticality, preparing for engagement and recognising any potential challenges to authenticity.

Reflection exercise
What personal life experiences have shaped my professional persona?   How do I deal with change in my own life?   What personal beliefs and values impact on my professional persona?   What are the stumbling blocks which might cause emotional challenge for me in engagements?

At the preparatory stage it is important to prepare both for depth of engagement and boundaries for an appropriate containment of the engagement.

Reflection in action

Second, a disciplined approach is required to recognise the various components of a reflective consciousness to ensure they are achieved in balance when applied to practice. Brechin *et al* (2000) emphasise three aspects of reflective practice – use of self, critical thinking and reflection.

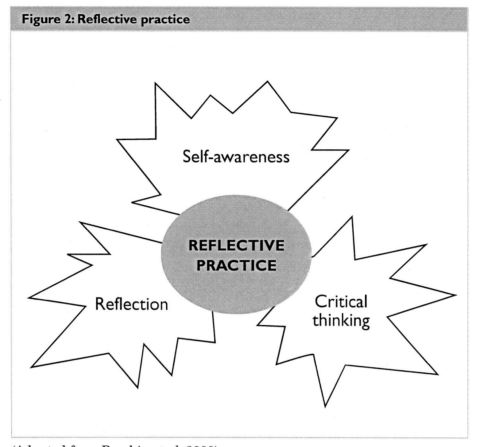

Figure 2: Reflective practice

Self-awareness

REFLECTIVE PRACTICE

Reflection

Critical thinking

(Adapted from Brechin *et al*, 2000)

This model creates the potential for balance in skills of intuition, creative energy and discipline during the engagement.

Reflection on action

Perhaps the greatest need for professional discipline is in protecting the reflective process after an engagement. This requires protected time and the discipline of a structured approach which allows the practitioner to reflect in a balanced way. The following model is just one approach which supports this reflective discipline.

Reflective contemplation – beyond the narrative in reflective practice

The author has advocated for a style of professional engagement which includes use of stillness and silence to allow the individual the facility for reflection and potentially for expression of depth emotions. This is equally important for the professional. The professional needs to acknowledge the energy required in depth engagement and the necessity of being able to withdraw to re-energise in the silence of reflection. Hence, within professional contexts there is an emphasis on the use of supervision as a means of protected reflective dialogue. But again, there is the need for a reflective space beyond dialogue – 'time out' to reflect on the authenticity of the professional and to protect the well-being of the professional.

Application for practice – the reflectively competent practitioner

In order for a practitioner to be reflectively competent they must apply the following:

▶ self-awareness – ensuring professional integrity, composure and validity of engagement

▶ response to narrative – recognition of a need to respond to the individual's story and interpretation

▶ composure – seeking a balance between acknowledgement of pain or loss and restoration

▶ respect for the individual's expression of a spiritual consciousness

▶ ensuring an authentic and appropriate contribution

▶ ensuring individual sustains ownership of the narrative

▶ discipline – use of structure and containment

▶ professional reflective space, supervision and retreat.

The spirit of reflective practice – the 'soul' of professional engagements

The value of seeking parallels between a spiritual and reflective consciousness is the potential validity of spiritual imagery to guide the professional in preparing for relationship-based practice with individuals. Of the images considered there are three distinct themes for the professional to consider: self-scrutiny, search for truth and transformational or restorative energy.

Box 2: The spirituality and reflective practice model

Key features of the spiritual and reflective consciousness model

▶ Image of the soul – recognition of deeply intuitive perceptive realms.

▶ Image of a journey or evolving state of consciousness.

▶ Search for meaning or composure and recognition of complex truths.

▶ Commitment to social justice – deep empathy with people whose life circumstances have caused them to challenge social structure.

▶ Openness to express anguish as process of release and change.

▶ Use of stillness and silence – the slow pace of reflective contemplation.

▶ Therapeutic forgiveness – the idea that pain and anger can be acknowledged, articulated and explored, and potentially then released.

▶ Transformative energy – for both individual and the professional helper.

▶ Continual process of reflection and review.

The combined spirituality and reflective practice model is a radical model which promotes:

1. deep questioning: *'we must change the myths and narratives that we live by'* (Moss, 2005b, p2)

2. a deep sense of personal responsibility. The individual is invited to take ownership of their capacity to change. Similarly, the professional is expected to be honest about the validity and quality of their engagement and to be prepared to be honest about reflecting on this and revisiting,

Figure 4: Spirituality and reflective practice model

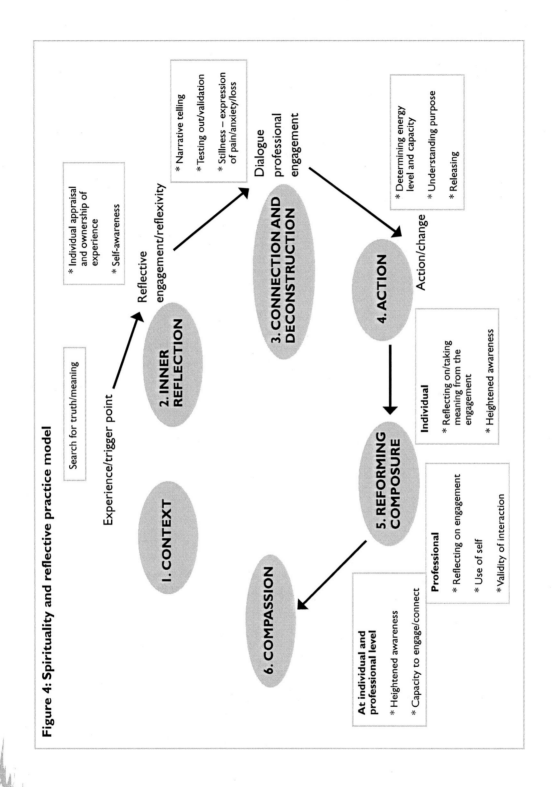

making changes where required. This requires skills of balance – an honest questioning approach but sufficient professional composure to provide reassurance to the individual.

In essence, it is a challenging but deeply meaningful form of practice. Nietzsche's work emphasised the changeability and rhythmic cycles of spiritual life. This image of spirituality is a reminder that professional practice always needs to be evaluated – it never completely finds its niche. Both at an individual level and agency level it is always evolving and developing just as the soul searches through life for glimpses of metaphysical truths.

The final spiritual image: compassion

The essential component in a helping relationship is the warmth of encouragement (Oriah Mountain Dreamer, 2003) – an acceptance that this is a stage in our journey and that we should be accepted in the expression of pain, distress and questioning. An acknowledgement of the need for compassion is the reminder that we need to be accepted in our teasing out of complex truths and life challenges – to believe in the expression of the 'fragile beauty of our humanness' and to be encouraged to recognise and celebrate our humanity and capacity.

Oriah uses the image of the dance in her expression of the soul journey – a dance being the expression of the search for a balance between individual expression and connectedness, echoing the soul's search for moments of inner reflection balanced by engagement.

We need to take responsibility for our reflective journey but acknowledge the value of genuine engagement along the way.

'Sit beside me in moments of shared solitude,

Knowing both our absolute aloneness and our undeniable belonging.
Dance with me in the silence and in the sound of small daily words,

Holding neither against me at the end of the day.

Dance with me in the infinite pause before the next great inhale of the breath that is breathing us all into being...

Don't say, "Yes!"

Just take my hand and dance with me.'

From *The Dance* © Oriah Mountain Dreamer (2001). All rights reserved. Printed with permission of the author. (www.oriah.org)

Acknowledgements

With grateful thanks to the people who generously shared their stories for this chapter: Andy Butler and Prag Shah.

References

Brechin A, Brown H & MA Eby (2000) *Critical Practice in Health and Social Care*. London: Sage.

Brookfield S (1986) *Understanding and Facilitating Adult Learning*. Milton Keynes; Open University Press.

Erikson E (1958) The nature of clinical evidence. In: D Lerner (Ed) *Evidence and Inference*. Glencoe, Ill: The Free Press.

Fook J (2008) *Social Work: Critical theory and practice* (2nd ed). London: Sage Publications Ltd.

Heron J (1992) *Feeling and Personhood: Psychology in another key*. London: Sage Publications Ltd.

Howe D (1987) *An Introduction to Social Work Theory* (2nd ed). Aldershot: Ashgate Publishing Ltd.

McSherry W (2000) *Making Sense of Spirituality in Nursing Practice: An interactive approach*. London: Harcourt Publishers.

Moss B (2005a) *Thinking Outside the Box: Religion and spirituality in social work, education and practice*. London: Equinox Publishing Ltd.

Moss B (2005b) *Religion and Spirituality*. Lyme Regis: Russell House Publishing.

Neimeyer R (Ed) (2001) *Meaning Reconstruction and the Experience of Loss*. Washington DC: American Psychological Association.

Nietzsche F (1872) The birth of tragedy from the spirit of music. In: W Kaufmann (Trans) (1967) *The Birth of Tragedy and the Case of Wagner*. New York: Random House.

Oriah Mountain Dreamer (2001) *The Dance* (2nd ed). San Francisco, CA: HarperONE.

Powell A (2009) Introduction. In: C Cook, A Powell, A Sims (Eds) (2009) *Spirituality and Psychiatry*. London: RCPsych.

Robinson, S Kendrick S & Brown A (2003) *Spirituality and the Practice of Healthcare*. Basingstoke: Palgrave Macmillan.

Sands R (1996) The elusiveness of identity in social work practice with women. *Clinical Social Work Journal* **24** (2)167–86.

Schön D (1983) *The Reflective Practitioner*. New York: Basic Books.

Schön D (2007) *The Reflective Practitioner: How professionals think in action*. Aldershot: Ashgate Publishing Ltd.

Tacey D (2003) *The Spirituality Revolution – the emergence of contemporary spirituality*. Sydney: Harper-Collins.

Tournier P (1954) *A Doctor's Casebook in the Light of the Bible*. London: SCM Press.

West W (2000) *Psychotherapy and Spirituality: Crossing the line between therapy and religion*. London: Sage.

Chapter 21

Chaplaincy and mental health

Andrew Wilson and Rob Merchant

Introduction: what is healthcare chaplaincy? (nature and context)

The background of healthcare chaplaincy in the United Kingdom is entwined with the history and development of the National Health Service (NHS). At its inception in 1948 the NHS appointed approximately 28 chaplains, mainly working in teaching hospitals, who became full-time NHS employees (see www.nhs-chaplaincy-spiritualcare.org.uk. At the start of 2010, there were around 425 full-time and 3,000 part-time chaplains employed by the NHS. About 75% of the full-time chaplains and approximately 50% of the part-time chaplains were members of the Anglican Church (HCC, 2010). In addition, volunteers, from all faith groups, now support chaplaincy services in the provision of spiritual care to patients and staff.

Healthcare Chaplaincy in the UK is represented by a number of different organisations, including the Hospital Chaplaincies Council (currently being revised), the Free Church Health Care Chaplaincy Steering Committee, the Healthcare Reference Group of the Roman Catholic Church, the Scottish Association of Chaplains in Healthcare, the Multi-Faith Group for Healthcare Chaplaincy, the College of Health Care Chaplains and the European Network of Healthcare Chaplaincy.

The work of chaplaincy has at its heart compassion and vocation. This compassion for the person who is in need, and experiencing suffering, is offered by a person of faith, answering the need, but also responding to their own inner sense of calling. It is important to recognise this motivation in the delivery of healthcare chaplaincy; and to acknowledge that chaplaincy is driven by this inner direction and is not simply a 'career choice'. This sense of vocation is shared by many other non-chaplaincy staff serving in healthcare environments, and this in itself can provide a powerful dynamic, enabling mutual support and collaborative practice. Healthcare chaplains bring a wealth of knowledge and experience into the multi-professional environment. A Department of Health report from the NHS, observes *'Healthcare chaplains are an invaluable resource of support for NHS managers and staff in providing advice, education and training on multi-faith issues'* (*Religion or Belief – A practical guide for the NHS* (Department of Health, 2009)).

Mental health chaplaincy has changed over recent years as chaplains have engaged more closely in community-based healthcare environments, working with voluntary sector groups like the Association for Pastoral Care in Mental Health (www.pastoral.org.uk) and MIND (www.mind.org.uk).

There has been an acknowledgement of the contribution that spirituality and religion can make towards well-being in the last few years. This has often been driven by the expressed needs of service users, identifying the centrality of belief in their lives. A significant review of literature exploring the impact of spirituality on mental health recommended that service users should be asked about their spiritual and religious needs upon entry to a service, and that they should have access to relevant spiritual and religious resources, and suggests that *'all service users, including those who do not regard themselves as spiritual or religious, are offered the opportunity to speak to a chaplain or other spiritual leader if desired'* (Cornah, 2006).

Mental health chaplains work within a secular system, and in settings where people's needs are often complex and confused. They need to discern carefully what support they offer. It would be all too easy to respond immediately in a pastoral encounter to what might appear, at first sight, to be a straightforward request for religious support. Such an immediate response may well by-pass the more profound spiritual and emotional issues which need to be addressed if effective recovery and healing is to take place.

Case study 1

Andrea Jones (53) was admitted to an acute care unit and, when there, she constantly asked to receive exorcism. She believed a doppelganger haunted her life, constantly following her. She began to feel that this situation could only be resolved through exorcism. Andrea asked her consultant psychiatrist for help, and he referred her to the mental health chaplain supporting the acute care unit. Refusing to opt for a 'quick fix', over a period of several months the chaplain listened as Andrea spoke about the rape she had endured as a student, the burden of care for her severely disabled daughter and the lack of support she had received from the rest of her family. Eventually Andrea's 'double' disappeared and she was able to begin a process of recovery. Andrea's consultant psychiatrist wrote to her referring GP to explain that the most effective intervention for Andrea had been her work with the mental health chaplain.

Is chaplaincy relevant? (sacred vs. secular agenda)

Religion continues to play an important role in the world globally. At the same time, spirituality has developed as an expression of an individualised belief system, particularly in western societies (Berger *et al*, 2008). The theory that secularism has in some way driven out religion and spirituality from society has received considerable critique (Brown, 2001; Davie, 2002, Parkes & Gilbert, 2010). However, some UK sociologists have observed a rise in spirituality linked to holistic activity as formal religious observance has declined (Heelas & Woodhead, 2005). This shift away from formal religious practice to a personally-based spirituality has proved challenging for chaplains in their understanding of their own role, but it can also limit the use others make of them. Despite being skilled in the provision of spiritual care to a broad range of people, they can be perceived by colleagues as only representing a limited and prescribed religious belief.

In preparation for the fifth Diagnostic and Statistical Manual of Mental Disorders (DSM-V), Peteet *et al* have edited *Religious and Spiritual Issues in Psychiatric Diagnosis – A research agenda* (2000). This volume explores the implications of religion and spirituality for the diagnosis, and outcomes of mental health care, and hopes to support all mental health practitioners who 'seek to practise in a more integrated, holistic fashion' and examines the charge that the DSM neglects this 'vital dimension of human experience'.

A document produced by the British Institute of Human Rights describes the five unalienable elements in human rights as fairness, respect, equality, dignity and autonomy (*Human Rights in Healthcare – A framework for local action* (Department of Health, 2008)) and the Mental Health Foundation (2008) observes that *'being able to express and explore our spirituality is a basic human need and a universal human right'* (p4). The duty of public bodies like NHS trusts is to ensure that patients experience care in an environment which actively encompasses their individual values, beliefs and personal relationships.

As a mental healthcare chaplain, Andrew Wilson received a thank you card from a service user, who had received ongoing support from him.

'To one who listens – from one who is finding himself, and is creating the person he wishes to be, thank you! Sweeping out the old ways, and bringing in emancipating new ways – watching, observing a new way of life I did not know even existed, (and it brings confidence) abandoning the 'inevitable' cruel destructive ways – destructive of me and destructive of others. (Perhaps this is the first chance, at the age of 67 that I have ever had.)'

Belief expressed through religious forms or spiritual values retains a vital role in the lives of many people. A healthcare chaplain is a skilled practitioner who is able to navigate a range of belief systems to benefit the service user.

Case study 2

'Bob' is in his 40s and has been under the care of the local forensic team for some years. His mother left his father when he was about six, after mistreating Bob physically and emotionally. Despite his demanding work as a long-distance lorry driver, Bob's father did all he could to support him, including paying for child-minders when he could not be at home. As a young man, Bob exhibited increasingly violent behaviour and eventually, after several spells in prison, was finally diagnosed as having bipolar disorder. Through all his trials, Bob's father was the one stable point in his life. Eventually, Bob began to manage his illness better and was moved to the care of a community team. However, his father suffered a severe stroke, and Bob became his main carer, while at the same time remaining emotionally dependent on him. When the father was diagnosed with terminal cancer, Bob told his mental health team that he would kill himself when his father died.

It was then that the team called for support from the chaplain. The chaplain worked closely with them, sometimes on a daily basis, as Bob's father's illness progressed. He continued to support Bob beyond the funeral, which Bob could not bear to attend. It was the chaplain's extended experience of bereavement which meant that Bob could express the full range of his emotions, while some other professionals would simply have attempted to 're-assure' him. While comforting at one level, such an approach failed to address his intense grief.

Chaplaincy in an evidence-based world

Harriet Mowat and John Swinton wrote a report that asked the question, 'What do chaplains do?' (Mowat & Swinton, 2005). They argued that, in order to answer the question, chaplains needed to engage in the evidence-based environment in which they were located.

The health and social care environment in the UK is now committed to the evidenced-based medicine model (Sackett *et al*, 2000). This expects each professional to support the clinical decisions they have reached with the best evidence available. Chaplaincy as a professional group has been slow to engage in the process of developing a substantial evidence base to support their work. This may be due to the small size of the chaplaincy workforce in comparison with other healthcare professionals and the failure of some policy makers and research funders to grasp the importance of belief in the lives of people. Chaplains have an important role to play within the NHS, but they do need to demonstrate more systematically and consistently the impact of their service upon service users. The call for an evidenced-based approach to chaplaincy has not been welcomed by all chaplains (Newell, 2005), some of whom see it as in conflict with their autonomy, values and sense of vocation and pastoral ministry.

In working towards a model of recovery, research from Newcastle University has explored the changes in mental health care, and recognises the need for a move towards a more pragmatic approach, which emphasises the central importance of the relationship between professionals and their clients, and the need to empower patients. The Tidal Model (Barker, 2001) reflects on the distress that patients and their carers experience. In his article presenting the Tidal Model, Barker likens this model of 'recovery' to the tradition of care provided over a thousand years ago by Celtic monks for people who would now be recognised as experiencing a mental illness. Barker cites research, particularly from the USA, which suggests that what some may diagnose as mental illness could equally be described as a 'spiritual crisis'. He observes that currently a significant number of health professionals are uncomfortable about acknowledging that the process of care may involve the spiritual. But Victor Frankl (2004), a survivor of the Holocaust, insisted on the necessity of finding meaning if a person is ever to 'recover' from pain and trauma. He believed that it is only when there has been an exploration of personal meaning that a person can make sense of their life in the present. Disturbance, whatever label we choose to apply to it, inevitably calls into question the meaning that someone attaches to their experience of being human.

Case study 3

Eva is in her 40s, and as the result of ongoing sexual, physical and emotional abuse within her parents' Satanist group, now exhibits a severely fragmented personality. Her therapist called for support from the chaplain because Eva wanted to explore whether she could be 'delivered' from the continuing 'spiritual assaults' she described in distressing details.

The chaplain had worked with similar patients in the past, in a supportive role, but what Eva wanted was a more explicitly religious approach. The chaplain was aware that in discussions in a similar situation previously, a consultant had vigorously dismissed any notion of a multiple personality disorder. She also understood that this was an area of work that could easily arouse quite powerful reactions and scepticism. In order to make an adequate assessment of her role, and review current thinking in this area, she examined the latest research in the field.

The chaplain also enrolled on a service user-led workshop on dissociative identity disorder, and together with the therapist, explored the literature and research being done in the field. She felt it was important to look into the likely neurological effect Eva's abusive childhood might have made. Each of these avenues, together with her own knowledge of the client's faith tradition, informed her collaboration with the therapist and Eva. Gradually, Eva has come to a deeper understanding of the enduring elements of her condition and what might trigger intense reactions. She now has a more realistic expectation of what her support team can offer. Eva has been able to empower herself in setting firmer boundaries in many of her relationships and the team, for their part, have been able to understand their often unconscious desire to distance themselves from the enormity of what Eva endured.

Chaplaincy in practice

Chaplains are required to provide regular acts of worship and reflection in times of distress and crisis in ways that address the spiritual, religious and cultural expectations of an increasingly diverse population. This can be within a group setting, or on an individual basis, not only on wards, but for example other NHS sites, in the community, in hostels, and private homes. Often this means organising celebrations to mark festivals and significant times for people who are isolated from their own faith communities. Experiences of illness and distress are precisely the times when people may wish to return to the practice of their faith. Many others, with no previous formal religious affiliation, will also experience a spiritual awakening in these marginal situations.

Chaplains work with clients to create individual rituals which process emotions and thoughts that might otherwise remain unexpressed and unresolved. In his work as a mental health chaplain Andrew Wilson has worked with many different clients to create rites that express this. These have included supporting a Hindu client wanting to perform a traditional Hindu funeral ritual, but with someone who knew her history well and who would be able to understand all the uniquely personal aspects of her grief for a sibling who had died. Another woman worked with Andrew to construct a memorial service for the daughter she still mourned. The child's life was terminated while she was sectioned as a young woman, at the direction of a consultant, because she was suffering a severe psychotic depression.

The skill of the mental health chaplain is expressed across an increasingly broad range of faith and spiritual perspectives. Chaplains have often undergone training as therapists to enhance their skills base, as they encounter this wide spectrum of clients.

Apart from short-term pastoral interventions on wards, mental health chaplains work in a more sustained way to support those who have ongoing needs. These include a wide range of conditions, spanning the age range from adolescence to old age. At any one time a chaplain may encounter patients suffering from psychotic illness, mood disorder or personality disorder, victims of sexual abuse, bullying or violence, and patients working with substance misuse issues. A noticeable proportion of these clients will also have significant physical illness in addition to their mental health diagnosis, including diabetes, ME, circulatory problems, and terminal conditions. Traditionally, it is the chaplain who works in the area of loss and bereavement. In some cases, this work unearths complex and unresolved grief, or supports families as they deal with the suicide of their loved ones.

A further expectation of mental health chaplaincy is to monitor and protect the rights of patients, staff and carers. Chaplains have the ability to challenge malpractice, and advocate for others, especially when people feel unsafe or unheard. Chaplains are often involved in the support of people who are fearful of the service, or who because of difficult experiences within the system have disengaged from it. Sometimes a chaplain may be the only professional in regular contact with an isolated or suicidal patient. There is sometimes the risk that because a team fails to understand the chaplain's contribution there is a significant failure of service to the client. From experience, chaplains know that their involvement can be dismissed by ill-informed staff.

Chaplains hope to act as consultants to colleagues on appropriate interventions, and endeavour to contact external help from other faith communities when they cannot provide particular religious or cultural needs from within their own team.

Case study 4

An increasing concern, not just within the chaplaincy, but also within the trust's educational team, is that the cultural, spiritual and religious needs of some client groups are not met adequately. As a result of discussions over several years, the trust has now allotted funding to enable the chaplaincy, in co-operation with a local voluntary sector organisation with similar concerns, to set up a training scheme which brings together trust staff and representatives of local faith groups. The course has gained university accreditation and requires students to create a project within their own work or community setting which puts into practice the learning assimilated in the course. The aims of the course are two-fold. First, it encourages staff within the trust to further a consistent assessment of patients' spiritual, religious and cultural needs; this is already an expectation in the on-line directions for the initial assessment of each patient. Second, it is designed to equip faith leaders to support members within their own communities suffering from mental health problems and to reduce stigma and ignorance.

Summary

▶ From its inception, the NHS has employed chaplains as part of its package of holistic care and recognises their unique contribution.

▶ Interest in the interface between religious belief, spiritual values and mental well-being has increased. Recent research reassesses the contribution that these factors can make to a patient's recovery.

▶ Chaplains and their colleagues need to exercise discernment as they offer appropriate care that answers psychological and emotional as well as religious and spiritual needs.

▶ Although formal religious practice has declined in some measure in the west and has partially been replaced by a personal concern for spiritual values, religion continues to play an important role in the world globally.

▶ The human rights agenda highlights the importance of respect for an individual's values, beliefs and personal relationships.

▶ Decisions in health care are expected to be based on evidence. Chaplaincy has often been slow to embrace this approach and needs to be more effective in monitoring and assessing its impact on the service.

▶ Chaplaincy in the mental health setting fulfils many roles, including advocacy, meeting ethical challenges, creating individual and corporate acts of worship, celebration and counsel and support for staff, patients and carers. The fact that chaplaincy plays an integral role with the life of a trust enhances the efficacy of its work.

References

Barker P (2001) The tidal model: the lived experience in person-centred mental health nursing care. *Nursing Philosophy* **2** 213–223.

Berger O, Davie G & Fokas E (2008) *Religious America, Secular Europe? A theme and variations.* Surrey: Ashgate.

Brown C (2001) *The Death of Christian Britain.* London: Routledge.

Cornah D (2006) *The Impact of Spirituality on Mental Health: A review of the literature.* London: The Mental Health Foundation, p5.

Davie G (2002) *Europe: The exceptional case.* London: Darton, Longman & Todd.

Department of Health (2008) *Human Rights in Health Care – A framework for local action – 2007*. London: Department of Health. Available at: http://www.dh.gov.uk/prod_consum_dh/groups/dh_digitalassets/@dh/@en/documents/digitalasset/dh_088972.pdf (accessed November 2010).

Department of Health (2009) *Religion or Belief: A practical guide for the NHS*. Available at: http://www.dh.gov.uk/prod_consum_dh/groups/dh_digitalassets/documents/digitalasset/dh_093132.pdf (accessed November 2010).

Frankl V (2004) *Man's Search for Meaning* (5th ed). London: Rider.

HCC (2010) *Health Care Chaplaincy and The Church of England: A review of the work of the Hospital Chaplaincies Council*. London: Hospital Chaplaincies Council. Available at: http://www.cofe.anglican.org/info/socialpublic/hccreview2010/hccreview2010.pdf (accessed November 2010).

Heelas P & Woodhead L (2005) *The Spiritual Revolution: Why religion is giving way to spirituality*. Oxford: Blackwell Publishing.

Mental Health Foundation (2008) *Executive Briefing: Spirituality and mental health*. Available at: http://www.mentalhealth.org.uk/publications/?EntryId5=61019 (accessed November 2010) p4.

Mowat H & Swinton J (2005) *What Do Chaplains Do?* Aberdeen: Mowat Research.

Newell C (2005) 'Whose side are we on anyway?' Professional standards, professionalisation and the nature of spiritual care in a mental health community. *The Journal of Health Care Chaplaincy* **6** (2) 37–42.

Parkes M & Gilbert P (2010) Gods and Gurdwaras: The spiritual care programme at the Birmingham and Solihull Foundation NHS Trust. *Mental Health, Religion and Culture* **13** (6) 569–583.

Peteet J, Lu,F & Narrow W (Eds) (2010) *Religious and Spiritual Issues in Psychiatric Diagnosis: A research agenda for DSM-V*. Arlington, VA: American Psychiatric Publishing.

Sackett D, Strauss SE, Richardson WS, Rosenberg W & Haynes RB (2000) *Evidenced-based Medicine: How to practice and teach EBM*. Edinburgh: Churchill Livingstone.

Chapter 22

Recovery and spirituality: aligning ourselves with ourselves

Tanya Kennard-Campbell

Introduction

The purpose of this chapter is to explore the deeper 'spiritual' aspect of recovery from mental distress/illness and to offer insights into 'what helps' from those who have suffered.

It will present how recovery is a spiritual journey of discovery, starting with a heartfelt decision, connection or insight. Recovery is a human journey, one that we have all experienced to a lesser or greater degree and therefore it is not unique to those who experience mental distress/illness, but unique to the human race.

This chapter is built around a dialogue with a young woman (Polly), who experienced a profound insight that transformed her journey, and the stories of those who have experienced recovery from mental distress or extreme states. The insights shared hold great wisdom for us all and echo the experience of many others who have found recovery where they had given up hope for themselves.

This chapter will also present a useful means of understanding the human experience, which has practical, yet profound, implications for the way we consider and support those in recovery. Points of reflection will be offered to deepen your understanding of spiritual recovery.

Recovery – listening in a new way

Before we move into the main body of this chapter, it is important to suggest ways in which you can get the most out of it, or indeed in understanding for yourself, the concepts of recovery and spirituality. I would suggest listening with an open heart and mind, trying not to compare or judge. By doing this, you are more likely to be touched by the deeper messages implicit in this chapter. Listening from the heart is a way of engaging our wisdom, or our ability to see beyond what we think we know about a given situation or person to what is really there.

Reflection exercise

How often do we listen or regard people, situations or information without the censor of our own thinking?

How often do we truly listen for what is being shared without judgement?

When listening to those who are finding the use of understandable language a problem, the ability to listen beyond the words, increases the likelihood of getting a 'feel' for the message. This is an important aspect of creating understanding when assisting with those in distress. It's not what we think of their words, but what they think of their words that creates their experience in any given moment and helps alert us to the cause of distress.

What is recovery?

'Revolutions begin when people, who are defined as problems, achieve the power to redefine the Problem.' (John McKnight)

Recovery has been a subject of much debate among providers, family members, ex-patients and policy makers over the past few decades, fuelled by the different views of those involved. However, 'Recovery is an idea whose time has come.' (Shepherd et al, 2008)

The debate about whether recovery is possible has been stilled as we move forward with transforming the way we consider and support those with mental distress. Whichever view you take on the origins of mental illness, or mental distress, recovery is a movement fuelled by stories of what it feels like to discover a way out of distress, limitations, hopelessness and despair, to recreate new concepts of self and one's place in the world.

One thing is certain, recovery involves more than the elimination of symptoms, it involves changes to the whole person as perceived by the self and others.

'The concept of recovery is rooted in the simple yet profound realisation that people who have been diagnosed with mental illness are human beings. The goal in recovery is not to become normal. The goal is to embrace our human vocation of becoming more deeply, more fully, human.' (Deegan, 1996)

Recovery is the natural process of healing, change and growth following significant threats to one's health, well-being and sense of self.

There are many ways to define what recovery is or means, but the most important definition is the one made by the individual experiencing the loss. For them, how they see their recovery depends greatly on what they believe is possible. The power behind recovery is fuelled by the power behind our thinking about it.

'When I was looking to be "fixed" I was "fed for a day" in daily "meds" and weekly "talk therapy" I was dependent on people, places and things outside of myself for my answers, my peace and my happiness. When I taught myself how to "fish for a lifetime" I became my own best resource and discovered the meaning behind that catchphrase "self-empowered". Knowledge is the beginning of the truth that empowered me to find this freedom. "Wisdom" was having the confidence to take the next step with the knowledge I had gained. As my friend Gianni Kali says ... I accept no label other than "human".' (Susan Smith)

Recovery is not merely for the lucky few, but a possibility for anyone who has lost something or someone, be that a heart's desire or dream, a loved one, a role, health or a sense of him or herself.

Reflection exercise

Think of something you have 'recovered from; this could be the loss of a loved one, an important role, relationship, or place of birth. Take a moment to remember how it felt and what it took to overcome this experience and begin to move on.

Recovery and spirituality

'Sometimes people get the mistaken notion that spirituality is a separate department of life, the penthouse of existence. But rightly understood, it is a vital awareness that pervades all realms of our being. Wherever we may come alive, that is the area in which we are spiritual.' (David Steindl-Rast)

According to the Collins English Dictionary, spirit means *'the non-physical aspect of a person concerned with profound thoughts and emotions'*.

Connecting to something bigger or greater than us leads to connecting to something bigger and greater inside of us. This 'thing', which I will call wisdom, is the thing that sustains and guides recovery. We are constantly drawing from this spiritual energy, via our ability to sense, experience and create, moment to moment to moment.

Our minds make forms of this creative spiritual process by creating a mental life that shifts and changes in content, quality, intensity and focus. It's always working. This is the spiritual, formless aspect of who we are, not necessarily the content of our minds but the creative force behind it.

What we make of our experiences becomes the forms of our thinking, beliefs, ideas, and opinions. These forms include the many forms of religion, created via human minds or human hands (through transcription), trying to point beyond to a spiritual truth or essence. Unfortunately, many listen to the form of the words and miss the true meaning, because the true meaning is spiritual, beyond word, or form.

How does this relate to recovery?

We have all experienced a 'spiritual spark' igniting when we have experienced hope, new love, wonder, gratitude, connection, understanding or insight. This spiritual spark cannot be described in words, but is felt and acknowledged within. These experiences have the power to transform our experiences, memories and lives.

This is the spiritual dimension I point to when I say that recovery is a spiritual journey, the intangible essence of us. True spiritual recovery occurs when there is a spiritual shift inside; when we 'know' that something needs to change and from now on, it's down to us, that the past no longer has to limit us, in any given moment we can choose what to listen to. Wisdom has the power to lead us out of the pain of our experiences or the stories created by our selves or others from the past.

Reflection exercise

How often do we choose to listen to what we make of the past, our thinking minds, or our wisdom?

For me, recovery is a deep spiritual commitment to honour and discover your true self, of following an inner wisdom that leads us into new understandings about ourselves and the world around us. It's also about no longer seeking comfort and acceptance in others' eyes, but inside our selves on a level that transcends the physical. As Polly put it:

'To me recovery is like a spiritual awakening, you step outside yourself, like connecting to a higher power, something that's greater than yourself, this higher power can restore you to sanity, because it's greater, or bigger than you and as you find your spiritual awakening you begin to grow. When my recovery first began, I used my higher power, was one other person. So instead of battling with everything in my own head, I shared it with another person, and then I went to group therapy and my higher power became a group, then I became more comfortable and that widened to everyone around me, it grew and increased into trusting in a God. The higher power was about the spirit of connection to something beyond, this could be anything that's outside of my own thinking, my personal world I create inside of my head.' (Polly Baker)

So things like nature, people, pets, art, meaning, God, ritual – it all involves letting go of what's currently occurring in our mind, in order to connect to something else. In this process, we let go and connect. It's not necessarily what the thing we connect to is, it's the spirit of connection that matters.

'I had a strong spirituality that really helped. And perhaps more importantly of all, when I got out of bed in the morning, I always knew the reason why I had a purpose in life, I had been called, I had a vocation, and I kept saying yes to it'. (Deegan, 1996)

'I also had a powerful spiritual experience of Christ consciousness and undiluted Grace at my lowest ebb. It was after this that I started to climb out of the claws of depression, and its grip loosened. Therein I discovered true hope.' (Grainne Humphrys)

All these experiences point towards the uniquely personal, yet spiritual nature of recovery, of connecting to something beyond us. Both Polly and I shared a similar experience where, we both reached a point in our recoveries, where we appealed to something beyond us for help, beyond our capabilities, beyond our thoughts, beyond our capacity to know what to do and at that point it became spiritual.

Spirituality in these cases is a faith and belief in more. That there's something beyond me and my thinking, which is also a part of me.

'I think we all have a little voice inside us that will guide us. It may be God, I don't know. But I think that if we shut out all the noise and clutter from our lives and listen to that voice, it will tell us the right thing to do.' (Christopher Reeve)

What initiates recovery and what maintains it?

'At first people refused to believe that a strange new thing can be done. Then they begin to hope it can be done. Then they see it can be done. Then it is done and all the world wonders why it was not done centuries ago.' (Francis Eliza Hodgson Burnett)

In the instant of connection we get to feel differently, see differently and be differently. This is part of the magic of life. When in one moment, we recover a connection to our true selves, or spiritual essence.

My approach to understanding and assisting those in their recovery is from a 'principle based perspective', as originated by Sydney Banks. This approach believes true change occurs from the inside, following a significant shift in awareness or insight. This occurs as a natural process of growth and change and is an inherent part of being human. It is based on knowing that there is an inbuilt wisdom or health behind our physical minds and bodies, available to us in any present moment, that when realised can create a form of personal guidance for life.

This perspective offers that we all suffer, we all get lost, we all lose our way, but our capacity for wisdom is never damaged. Our thinking can obscure our wisdom or clarity, but as our understanding increases, we make wiser choices about what to listen to.

As we begin to trust our own wisdom more than our own thinking, we begin to 'let go' of many of the limitations we have placed on ourselves and others. Sometimes this happens bit by bit, sometimes in moments of profound insight. This is spiritual recovery in action. We have all experienced this to one degree or another.

Reflection exercise

Think of a time when you knew you had to listen to what was true for you despite what others around you were telling you.

How difficult did you find it when others thought they knew what was best for you?

What did you learn from this?

I propose that there are two spiritual factors that create a sustained sense of personal well-being and recovery:

▶ connecting to a deeper feeling within

▶ understanding (the universal principle behind the human experience).

Connection to a deeper feeling wisdom/health within

Recovery occurs repeatedly in moments of insight or connection, when we momentarily leave the contents of our minds and connect to something beyond us. Connecting to one's purpose in life, connecting to others, to something beyond us; our children, pets, garden, vocation, all give us a deeper sense of purpose and access to a higher level of feelings, such as gratitude, love and compassion. These feelings have the power to bring us out of our distress and hopelessness and provide us the opportunity to see and feel differently, even if it is for a short time.

The single most important thing in recovery is beginning to connect to wisdom, or clarity of mind. These experiences provide the opportunity for temporary respite or a more permanent shift in awareness (recovery).

When insights occur, we experience the potential for a fundamental shift in the way we see our life and once experienced, these insights bring us closer to our wisdom, peace of mind, clarity and objectivity. Connecting to wisdom or the present moment, offers us moments of recovery, but any ground gained often can be lost when we don't understand how we got there or what takes us away from it. Understanding what creates good judgement or insight and what takes us away from it, offers us all a means of protection for the tough times, and allows us to gain ground.

Understanding the principles behind the human experience

'You've been guided by a spiritual force far far greater than you, you've always been guided, ever since day one you've been guided, but your own mind doesn't know that.' (Banks, 1998)

Understanding is the key to maintaining recovery. To begin to draw on an understanding based on fundamental principles that explain inclusively and exclusively how and why we experience life the way we do has the ability to revolutionise our world.

Prior to the discovery of the principles of flight, germ theory and gravity, there was a lot of guess work, mishaps and theories – sometimes by accident progress was made, but without understanding progress is hard to replicate or sustain.

When I first came across the principle-based approach, I was attracted by the implications for the recovery of those in distress. I was inspired by the way that 'health' or 'wisdom' within the individual was the focus of all interactions and that there was nothing damaged or broken about people, they had just moved away from their natural state, by innocently using the three principles against themselves.

It was important to me that this understanding was applicable for those experiencing psychosis or extreme states and also with those with low cognitive ability. Many of the approaches I had studied and applied before had limitations based on the person's state of mind or capacity. I believe that recovery is for everyone, not just for some – therefore I was not satisfied with limited applications.

The first time I consciously used this understanding in my work was on an intensive psychiatric inpatient unit, with a young man who was very agitated, hostile and was experiencing 'psychosis'. He wanted to engage in an angry debate about whether he had 'schizophrenia' or not and whether I and the other staff were part of a conspiracy he was aware of. I knew he was in a very low state of mind, yet I felt compassion for his distress and did not want to pursue the route my colleagues were suggesting (medication and seclusion) to calm his threatening behaviour. I wanted to help him understand why he was feeling so bad, so he could see how to protect himself from this in the future.

Case example

'You're part of this aren't you!'

'Matt, I know you're feeling angry and scared, I really wish there was something I could do to help.'

'It would help if you just owned up! You're part of this conspiracy aren't you?'

'What does your gut tell you?'

'My what?' (perplexed)

'Your gut, your instincts. I don't mean your thoughts, I mean your gut.'

'What's the difference?'

'One comes from here, (pointing to my head) from your thoughts, the other is in your gut instincts and it comes from here.' (pointing to solar plexus/tummy area)

(Confused look, pause. Silent reflection.) 'It says you're alright.'

'Great. You should always trust that Matt.'

(Suspicious look) 'Well, they must be part of it then?' (indicating the male nurses hovering around)

'Matt, they're just scared your gonna hurt someone.'

'Well I wanted to. (pause) They tell me I have schizophrenia, they're wrong aren't they?'

'Matt, that word is just a way of folk naming a bunch of experiences. It doesn't have to mean anything.'

'It means everything to me!' (angry again)

'Matt, with the greatest respect, I really want to help you work this out, but I just know it's not going to happen when you're not in your well-being.'

'What do you mean not in my well-being?' (sits down next to me; all the nurses on stand by, go off)

I then explained what well-being is, looks like and feels like and took the opportunity to help him see how lost we can all get – but by understanding how our thinking gets contaminated in these states, he can protect himself and others from his low quality thinking.

The next day Matt was allowed out on brief leave. On his return to the ward he ran up to me excited and shared what had happened in town.

He had been walking behind a couple in the town centre and he thought he heard them say 'the occult'. This triggered off powerful feelings of anger and he thought they were provoking him. He walked forward to confront them when, into his head popped 'what if it's just my thinking?'

He said he stepped back and checked in with his 'gut' and he realised how angry he felt. He remembered that I'd said powerful negative emotions contaminate thinking. So he realised he was not in a clear state to decide whether they were provoking him or not and decided to let it go.

He was so excited he said, because he was able to enjoy his trip into town and let go of a lot of the negative thoughts and voices that continued to enter his head. He was also able to return to the ward and not ask for 'PRN' medication, as he usually did to help him cope with his emotions. He also helped me realise that voices are externally experienced thoughts and can be understood in the same way as thought. We learnt a lot from each other.

This was one of many experiences of working with the principles in an acute psychiatric setting. This was when I truly began to discover the power of the principles in recovery and self-directed learning. To me, they explain how we access good judgement, wisdom and new insight and what takes us away from accessing this potential. They also help us all understand why we see the world or our realities the way we do and how recovery and resilience is created. This understanding has powerful implications for the way we consider and support people who experience mental distress.

The 'principle-based approach', also known in the past as 'health realisation' or 'innate health' was originated by Sydney Banks after a profound insight he experienced that changed his understanding of thought. Following this insight, pioneers such as Dr Roger Mills, Dr George Pransky, Dr Keith Blevens and colleagues, took this understanding into many fields including psychology, community resilience, mental health and business. From there it has grown to reach across America and Canada and now around the world.

The three principles that offer us the ability to relate to our experiences are:

▶ thought – our potential to create

▶ consciousness – our ability to be aware

▶ mind – the limitless formless potential, energy or intelligence behind life.

Thought

Thought is our formless capacity to create our moment-to-moment reality. It is available to us via a formless flow of potential constantly providing us with opportunities to create. Thought comes in limitless forms and qualities. It comes through in the form of memories, ideas, feelings, beliefs, opinions and personal truths, new, fresh, objective, insightful and wise or frightening, scary, distressing or bizarre. We have no power over what thoughts enter our heads, but we do have the free will to respond to them or see them as real, or for what they truly are; potential.

'I believe thought is the best-kept secret of all time. We just don't realise how powerful our thinking is to create our reality.' (Ezra Simonetti, 2009)

Consciousness (awareness)

Consciousness is our ability to be aware of our self, our worlds, our thinking and the realities we create. Our levels of awareness can fluctuate greatly, affecting our ability to be aware of what is real or what is a construction of our thinking. An example of this is if you are lost in a memory (a thought carried through time), you are not conscious of this current moment and what it has to offer.

Consciousness has the power to create an experience of your thinking through the use of your five senses. Where your thinking goes, energy flows.

'Thought is a creative agent we use to direct us through life. It is what we, as humans, put into our thoughts that dictate what we think of life. When you start to see the power of thought and its relationship to your way of observing life, you will better understand yourself and the world in which you live.' (Banks, 1998)

When I spoke to Matt, I shared with him how the principles of mind, thought and consciousness create our reality or experience in any given moment and how our feelings alert us to our state of mind or thought processes. The following insight points to this powerfully.

'This was my "aha" moment two-and-a-half years ago. If "mental" is thought. And "illness" is sick. That means that I can choose to learn how to recognise the thoughts that are making me feel sick ... and change. This was the turning point for me. This became my truth. For 15 years I had believed that I "felt bad" because I had some hidden, mysterious "disease" or "illness"

[...] even though the sun was shining, my kids were doing well, I had no life drama going on outside of me – I still felt like hell. I sat there in my car because I was so full of anxiety that I couldn't go anywhere near people and tried to think through this situation rationally. I had a new therapist who had set a clear boundary with me and had said very directly that as much as she wished she could "fix" me that she couldn't. It was up to me to make my life what I wanted it to be. Blast * yet awesome. For the first time in my career as a "consumer" of mental health services someone was telling me there was a solution besides more "meds". That I held the key to the life I wanted – within myself. And this was the moment I stood at the top of that mountain, tears streaming down my face, my body trembling in fear ... and leaned forward into the wind and knew that something would be there for me to stand on or that I would fly.' (Susan Smith)

Mind

Mind provides the limitless intelligence and energy behind our thinking, awareness and life – wisdom is found deep within our soul or being. For me, I have found it useful to know that within my wisdom, I have access to some of this divine intelligence as, limitless levels of awareness and potential accessible to me, when my personal thinking calms enough for me to hear it. In fact, part of my spiritual awakening, and for many others who have been touched by these principles, involved realising that we have a source of inner wisdom within us. This is the wisdom so many tap into in their recoveries, which offer insights that lead us out of the prisons of our minds. An insight is a sight from within, from beyond the limitations of the personal mind.

'My major learning was that everyone is born innately healthy and by understanding the principles of the structure of our minds we have access to all the wisdom and understanding that we will ever have to know and that through clarity of thought we can allow pure thought, which is coming from a higher source enter our mind this is what we call Siattoh Dishmayoh (Hebrew translation – to compare data, present data). So my illness gave me an opportunity to gain wisdom in understanding my own challenges and also gave me greater sensitivity in understanding other people's problems. Call this mental illness – I call it a blessing in disguise.' (Menucha Wilhelm)

These three principles work together to create our moment-to-moment experience, via thought and our senses. It's helpful to know that there is a logic or spiritual intelligence behind each person's psychological system that is designed to alert us of when we are moving away from our state of well-being or wisdom. Our feelings give us a direct experience of our thinking and alert us to the nature of our thinking. *'The feeling of the thought defines the meaning of the thought.'* (Blevens & Monroe, 2010)

When we believe the way we feel is separate from the way we think, we part with logic and immediately misplace power outside ourselves.

'We become distracted by and reactive to these imagined other reasons for the way we feel. We think about this other source as if it is real and we focus on it. We forget that thought and the feeling of thought cannot be separated. We get distracted by this thinking, we then take our focus off the power of thought as the source of why we feel the way we feel.' (Blevens & Monroe, 2010)

As we begin to grasp the implications of this, we can begin to free ourselves from the unnecessary distress caused by believing outside influences, be they people, places or experiences. Our thinking creates our experience. So allowing ourselves to resist reacting to our thinking and allowing a clearer feeling state to emerge, in its own good time, offers us the potential new thinking we need to take us out of our distress, or to bring new perspective to the situation. It's not the quality of our experiences that brings us good feeling, it's the quality of our thinking about our experiences.

'I find it completely mad how my thinking can turn around so quickly.'
(Polly Baker)

Reflection exercise

What do you believe recovery is, in your own experience?

From my perspective, recovery is a process of waking up, or gaining increasing insight into who and what we are. This leads to greater understanding and therefore an increased sense of control or peace of mind.

'Mental health lies within the consciousness of all human beings, but it is shrouded and held prisoner by our own erroneous thoughts.' (Sydney Banks)

The experience of recovery

'Like a procession, you walk together towards your God self. You are the way and the wayfarers. And, when one of you falls down, he falls for those behind him, a caution against the stumbling stone. Ay, and he falls for those ahead of him, who, though faster and surer of foot, yet removed not the stumbling stone.' (Gibran, 1919)

As highlighted by Pat Deegan (1996), the goal in recovery is to become more deeply and fully human. I would add the words 'warts and all'. Recovery is very much about becoming more accepting of ourselves completely, about reframing our experiences and finding acceptance as the people we truly are, as opposed to the people we thought we were.

'Each day, my story grows and changes in unpredictable ways, but one thing has become clear in my understanding: I am not, nor have I ever, been mentally ill.' (Steve Morgan)

For many of us, a big part of our distress has been in rejecting parts of our selves, or the experiences we have and seeing this as something that is bad or intolerable. Recovery is more than the elimination of symptoms, as for many, they continue to experience symptoms, it is just that now it no longer creates the distress and suffering it once did.

'So where does this leave me? Things come up, things go away, and when they do, there I am. The wind blows, but it never lies. When despair arrives, I am despair. When fired up arrives, I am fired up. If I choose to sink back into a witnessing state cultivated by meditative practice, I am witnessing. States of existence – dangerous to judge and painful to deny, rolling on and on and on, each one pushes toward the next by some force which I do not comprehend. It is the Great Mystery, and I feel utterly okay not having figured it out. And, thank God, for what a liberation it is to know that – just like you – I am plainly human: irreducible to theoretical constructs, unfathomable in my fullness … an imperfect being and a sliver of God's perfection.' (Steve Morgan)

How others can help

'Part of the reason I gave up so easily and returned to what I thought was my default place, my suffering, was because I innocently believed that it was inevitable.' (Polly Baker)

One of the essential elements in recovery is support, having someone who believes in you, and hope. *'I had someone who held my hope when I could not do it for myself.'* (Polly Baker)

All these things create a climate where recovery is fertilised. We cannot make someone recover, but we can create a climate that draws this out in a person. Creating healing environments does involve considering the physical environment, but more importantly the psychological or spiritual climate. There is nothing more damaging to a person's early recovery than being told, or feeling that they have little control over the course of their lives.

Below are a few examples of what I have found useful and have found reflected in others stories and in my conversation with Polly.

What helps?

▶ Being around people who understand what it takes to begin to find their own way because they have experienced it themselves. This is different from those who can tell you how they got into distress. Look for what the person has to teach you.

▶ By grounding distress in the reality of a shared human condition, rather than a pathological condition is essential. This support can come from your community, your friendships or those who support you.

▶ Having access to a 'talented pair of ears'. Someone who can allow you to share your feelings, fears and discoveries without having to 'do' anything about what you say. Sometimes talking helps us 'hear' what it is we need to do as it can release the build up of thoughts and emotions.

▶ Never giving up.

Reflection exercise

Think of times when you have been low or vulnerable, what helped create a healing environment for you?

How can you assist others to reclaim hope?

What would you add to the list?

Conclusion

The intent of this chapter was to suggest that recovery is a spiritual process of increasing awareness, sparked by listening to our own wisdom and sustained by understanding how and why that is possible. However, where one person's recovery starts and another stops is as unique as each person is, just as knowing how best to support a person is unique to the supporter.

I hope at the very least that this chapter has inspired some hope, or at least given food for thought. The greatest gift we were ever given is the gift of wisdom. It is not about age, or even experience, but an ability to connect and listen. If our systems of care, or our systems of education and punishment heard this message, then the environments in which they work would be very powerful environments of growth.

When reflecting on this conclusion with Polly, her words of wisdom were: *'I never see much point in conclusions, just like recovery, most things involve a journey that doesn't have a clear end.'*

A fantastic point to leave any process.

References

Banks S (1998) *The Missing Link: Reflections on philosophy and spirit.* Edmonton, Canada: Lone Pine Publishing.

Blevens K & Monroe V (2010) *How Our Thinking Works: Unpublished article.* Available from: www.freemindwellbeing.com

Deegan P (1996) Recovery as a journey of the heart. *Psychiatric Rehabilitation Journal* **19** (3).

Shepherd G, Boardman J & Slade M (2008) *Making Recovery a Reality.* London: Sainsbury Centre for Mental Health.

Personal stories and quotes

Polly Baker is a young woman who has experienced mental distress and recovery and now leads recovery support groups with the support of Freemind Well-being CIC.

Francis Eliza Hodgson Burnett quoted: www.iwise.com/gU4GI

Kahlil Gibran (1919) quoted: www.wisdomquotes.com

Grainne Humphrys (Blog spot) http://bipolarblast.wordpress.com/2009/11/16/hope-time-and-love/

John McKnight quoted in *Destination Recovery* (2008) New Zealand: Mental Health Foundation

Steve Morgan (Blog spot) http://bipolarblast.wordpress.com/2009/02/02/the-wind-never-lies-must-read/

Christopher Reeve quoted: www.wisdomquotes.com/002651.html

Ezra Simonetti (2009) To view presentation: http://www.threeprinciplesmovies.com/page10/page10.php

Susan Smith (Blog spot) http://www.zebraspolkadotsandplaids.blogspot.com/

David Steindl-Rast quoted: www.wisdomquotes.com/003424.html

Menucha Wilhelm is a young woman who has experienced mental distress and recovery, helped by an understanding of the three principles.

Chapter 23

Historical, spiritual and evolutionary approaches to suffering, compassion, caring and the caring professions

Paul Gilbert

Caring and compassion: evolution and the spiritual approach

This chapter explores concepts of compassion within both spiritual and evolutionary frameworks. We can begin by noting that the emergence of spirituality is clearly linked to 'religion' although many writers also want to clearly distinguish between them. Interestingly, however, the word religion comes from the Latin religare meaning 'to reconnect' and modern concepts of spirituality are also focused on issues of 'connection', empathy and relating. What makes a set of beliefs and practices religious or spiritual is rather complex. Not all religions are concerned with life after death or the supernatural (eg. Confucianism). Although many believe in the existence of deities who may control certain forces (eg. of nature), not all believe in a creator or God (eg. Buddhism). Many religions and ideas of God have been sculptured by socio-economic pressures and inter-group conflicts (Tiger & McGuire, 2010). The main monotheistic religions have a belief in a single, usually male God, and they gradually defeated and subordinated earlier Goddess figures and 'pagan' beliefs, which existed in places like early Crete. Religions such as Islam, Judaism and Christianity all originated in one small area on planet Earth – the Middle East – and formed in the midst of complex tribal conflicts. This says much about the power of history and traditions as shapers of social discourses, identities and conflicts that can shape the forms of spirituality they give rise to.

The problem of suffering

Concepts of religion, spirituality and compassion are often fused together – although they should be clearly separated. The cultivation of compassion has a long and venerable history, both as a path to well-being and happiness, and spiritual enlightenment (Ricard, 2007). Sometimes these are seen to run together, but not always. For example, Armstrong (2007) points out that in the early days of the Axial period that operated 800–200 BCE, religions were less focused on metaphysical propositions and rather more about developing codes of behaviour that facilitated good relationships and personal well-being. One of the reasons for this was that the nature of pain and suffering were all too obvious to our ancestors. They were the first species to become aware that our lives are relatively short (25,000 plus days, if we are lucky), we (and those we love) will all decay and die. With the evolutions of self-awareness, we became aware that we are victim to countless life disabling and shortening diseases and injuries, and natural disasters from famines to earthquakes and floods. Back then, and still in some parts of the world, child mortality was (is) high and starvation never far away. The reality of viruses, bacteria, ageing decay (the focus for the caring professions) and the sheer hardships of life, has always been something of a 'spiritual' challenge (Cupitt, 2005).

Trying to come to terms with the nature of suffering and the terrors of death is at the heart of many spiritual and philosophical quests in such a pain-filled world (Cupitt, 2005). Countless Gods have been invented, prayed to and sacrificed to in order to win favour over suffering and tragedy (Hinde, 1999; Tiger & McGuire, 2010). McMahon's (2006) excellent book on the history of the pursuit of happiness explores the Greek idea that, given the fickleness and impermanence of this life, the best approach is to simply enjoy the pleasures of possessions and wealth, good wine, friendship and parties – an idea still current for many, especially in capitalist circles. The caring professions are less keen because this lifestyle has a tendency towards obesity, and drug and alcohol problems. In contrast, Christian and other theistic ideas viewed happiness as only obtainable in the next life, subject to pleasing God in our stoical acceptance of suffering. Christianity stresses self-sacrifice and in the extreme compassionate courage (as symbolised by Christ's sacrifice and death).

Perhaps one of the most difficult experiences we have when something painful and unexpected arises – we become ill or in pain, or we lose somebody we love – is to ask the Job (from the Bible)-like question of 'Why me. Why now' (Jung, 1952/1998). We search desperately for meaning in the midst of suffering. Sadly, it has been this searching that many early religions have exploited in fearful ways, explaining pain and suffering as sins. Many cultures have beliefs about hellish realms where the 'bad people' go as punishment, and many also have beliefs that suffering in this world is somehow a punishment for the bad behaviour of our ancestors (as classically depicted in Genesis) or an earlier incarnation. At the time of the Indian Ocean tsunami in 2005, where over 300,000 died, some claimed this was God's punishment for decadence.

Mental health and illness are often situated in deep existential issues about the meaning of life and one's inner goodness or badness, and one's lovability (Gilbert, 2009). Spiritual approaches to suffering and healing have therefore a huge responsibility to address the historical, cultural creations of very intense existential terrors. Compassion is about becoming openhearted and being prepared to address that which creates terror. Although people like to claim that the heart of most religions is a compassionate heart (and there is much truth in this), it is a very one-sided view of religion. Some spiritual and religious beliefs create terrors, the subjugation of women, and compromise health care. For example, some religious people believe that stem cell research, that promises to bring huge benefits, is against the will of God and a step towards Doctor Frankenstein. Women's health has suffered enormously by the banning of contraception, and has done harm to HIV efforts in Africa. So the link between spiritualities and compassion is complex because people debate and are in dispute over what compassion is, depending on the situational context. Spiritual beliefs can conflict. For example, my 'spirituality' is that science has always been the way to address suffering, making me very pro birth control and stem cell research (Gilbert, 2009).

As we begin to think about spirituality in the context of health and illness we cannot ignore the historical and cultural context in which spiritualities arise. Part of the reason is because we are beginning to emerge into a new type of spirituality (Cupitt, 2005). Even in Buddhism, individuals are beginning to recognise that there is a core teaching, based upon how to engage with this life (eg. cultivating mindfulness and compassion), which does not require us to take on board any of the metaphysical speculations that go with it (Batchelor, 2010). The salient emerging spiritual psychology is compassion (Davidson & Harrington, 2002; Gilbert, 2005).

Science, medicine and the birth of health technologies

Humans did not put all their eggs in one basket waiting to find the right religion, prayer or incantation to heal the sick. If the Gods could not heal the sick and prevent the famines for us then maybe we had better help ourselves. Therefore, running parallel to spiritual approaches to suffering were more scientific approaches. From the shamanic healers through to modern medicine, diseases and suffering were believed to have causes that could be understood and rectified. This noble and highly successful approach to suffering has, however, always been divided. Even at the birth of modern Western medicine, a schism arose between the two major Greek schools of medicine founded over 2,000 years ago. The Hippocratic school believed in understanding diseases and illness in the context of a person's life, to see illness as a dimensional change from the ideal and relating to whole person patterns. The Hippocratic school focused on holistic medicine, the processes of becoming ill, personality, the contexts, life events and circumstances of an illness, and the therapeutic relationship as key to the art of healing – a basic biopsychosocial approach. In contrast, the Platonic school of medicine focused on the 'disease process' as an entity unto itself that could be studied separately from the person who was suffering (Kendell, 1975). The therapeutic relationship was less important as a healing agent.

Now Platonic medicine has been extraordinarily successful at identifying bacteria, viruses and genetic abnormalities in their thousands and developing drugs and surgery. It is a call to arms and we talk about 'battling' the disease, 'fighting' the infection. Taken to its logical conclusion, Platonic medicine would remove the physician completely from the process and hand diagnosis and treatment over to efficient computers. In some ways this may work better because at least patients would not be shamed and blamed.

The division between relation-based and technology-based medicine is also evident in cross-cultural approaches to illness. Cultures vary greatly on both counts. For example, Nisbett *et al* (2001) point out that collective societies focus on social relationships, and see the world in terms of patterns and the interconnected nature of things. Healing practices involve focusing on relationships between people, relationships of inner forces (eg. yin and yang) and restoring inner balance in 'energies/processes' as a holistic approach. This is in complete contrast to the more individualist

Platonic and western science-focused societies, with their concern for splitting, segregating and isolating things into individual categories and units, such as 'disease entities, specific genes or specific viruses or bacteria'. These 'units' are seen as having their own individual, autonomous characteristics, to be treated with the application of specific technologies (eg. drugs and surgery), and evaluated in research trials.

If we wanted to see compassionate medicine from a Platonic point of view we would simply note that today modern medicine has rid the world of smallpox, and many other (maiming and killing) diseases are well contained and easily treated. In the West, child mortality has fallen dramatically with a major increase in life expectancy. The invention of anaesthetics was a gift to the world of immense importance. We can even cheat death of its tortuous route out. When my father died in pain of lung cancer it was a relief for him to be rendered unconscious and heavily dosed with morphine at the end. One can only imagine the many millions of humans who have died without such relief. So it would be wrong to see this more Platonic impersonal approach as lacking in compassion because the whole drive of that science is to rid the world of major diseases and physical pain. Any spiritual approach to healing must confront these realities.

However, even as we celebrate these fantastic successes there are increasing concerns about the nature of healing, the nature of medicine, the nature of being a physician and clinician. Research has also pointed to a common theme in people's spiritualities – it is one of a caring relationship. It is doubtful whether spirituality would have any sense at all outside of the concept of relationship. In an exploration of the relationship between spirituality and social connectedness Cacioppo *et al* (2005) found that people who scored low for social connectedness are lonelier, have higher depression scores, are physiologically more stressed, more orientated to making threat interpretations and more vulnerable to a range of illnesses. Alternatively, research now shows that relationships affect many aspects of our bodies including our cardiovascular and immune system; we recover faster in the context of compassionate care; we are less vulnerable to viruses in the context of compassionate care; and our brains mature in different ways in the context of compassionate and affiliative relationships (Cozolino, 2007; Hamilton, 2010).

So a key message is that as we begin to understand more about genetic and social causes of illness and suffering, we are also learning about the power of human relationships to create the contexts for suffering, illness and healing, and also happiness. We now know that our early relationships can affect the expression of our genes and play a vital role in the way our brains and bodies mature. People from stressful and abusive backgrounds are now known to be vulnerable to a whole range of physical and mental conditions (Cozolino, 2007). Put simply, relationships regulate a whole range of processes, including pain thresholds, cardiovascular, neurohormonal and immune systems (Cacioppo *et al*, 2000). Not only this but relationships are the major source for our experiences of happiness and abilities to cope with things that are threatening and distressing to us. Even when we are facing death, doing so in the context of feeling valued, cared for and loved creates a hugely different experience than feeling uncared for and alone (Aldridge, 2000).

Compassion

Although tribal religions can stimulate very sadistic archetypes in us, fuelling desires to punish and inflict pain, there is also a recognition inside of us that somehow this is to go off track and that at the heart of the healing relationship is compassion. It is making an empathic connection to the other, and this empathic connection is more likely to flourish when we ourselves feel less threatened, safe and more openhearted (Gilbert, 2009). However, we can go further and recognise that compassion is something which is open to scientific study, refinement and improvement. Indeed, there are now foundations throughout the world that use science to study compassion and the applications of compassion. This includes the King's Fund (http://www.kingsfund.org.uk/current_projects/the_point_of_care/compassion/), Stanford University (http://compassion.stanford.edu/), The New Zealand movement of compassion in health care (http://www.compassioninhealthcare.org/) and my own foundation (www.compassionatemind.co.uk).

There are many definitions of compassion but its role in the healing professions cannot be underestimated (Fehr *et al*, 2009). One of the key codes for compassion made popular by Karen Armstrong's Charter for Compassion (http://charterforcompassion.org/) was the golden rule of '*do not do unto others what you would not wish done to yourself*'. Confucius was probably the first to propose this rule and it has subsequently appeared in different forms in many major religions. It is, of course, also (or should be) the golden rule in health care (Dossey, 2007; Cook *et al*, 2009). It is sad that many of us working in the health service can feel that we would not like either ourselves, our children or relatives to be cared for in the way we sometimes see our patients being cared for.

As many authors to this volume have pointed out, this simple rule is actually quite profound because it invites us to form an empathic relationship with others, not only to treat them as we would like ourselves treated but also to identify with them as 'beings just like us'. It runs against the intuitive sense we have of ourselves as separate and autonomous beings living inside our own skins, and points towards a sense of connectedness creating an empathic bridge between the self and the other (Dossey, 2007; Rifkin, 2009). Long before we had any science about the nature of empathy, and how it is we are able to have sympathy and empathy for other human beings with mechanisms in our brain such as mirror neurons – early humans were intuiting the importance of trying to form an empathic bridge to the minds of others. Indeed the word compassion comes from the Latin word compati, which means 'to suffer with'. More recently, the Dalai Lama (1995) has emphasised the key qualities of compassion by defining it as *'a sensitivity to the suffering of self and others with a deep commitment to try to relieve it'*. Here compassion arises from motivation and attentional sensitivity – adding different dimensions to the empathic intention of the golden rule.

In one of the major spiritual movements of the Axial period, Buddhism was to bring compassion to the very forefront of spiritual enlightenment and well-being. While most are familiar with the four noble truths relating to the arising and ending of suffering, there is commonly less recognition that the key to the ending of suffering was a harnessing and cultivation of compassion. The Buddha outlined the eight-fold pathway for compassion:

▶ right view: develop clear insight into the true causes of suffering linked to attachments and craving

▶ right concentration: related to focused attention in the form of mindfulness and compassion

▶ right intention: linked to the motivation for caring

▶ right speech: linked to interpersonal relating, saying kind rather than hurtful things

▶ right action: linked to behaviour that tries to heal rather than destroy

▶ right livelihood: linked to choice of career and how one conducts oneself at work

▶ right efforts: linked to the need to practise with effort/dedication

▶ right mindfulness: linked to paying attention 'in the moment' in a compassionate way.

Here compassion is seen as a multimodal process which has the power to organise and change our minds in particular ways. The practice of these increases our well-being and that of those with whom we relate.

Compassion and evolution

Some see our abilities to be compassionate as arising from a spiritual dimension to our being. We have the power to be compassionate because we carry something of God within us. However, modern science points to a different view, adding new textures and dimensions to our understanding of compassion. First, we can identify the evolutionary origins of compassion in the emergence of altruism and caring (Gilbert, 2005). It is well known that for many species that first emerged on our planet, caring for offspring was absent. Species survived because of the vast numbers parents could produce. Many have seen documentaries of young turtles hatching from the sandy nests and having to make a mad dash to the sea. Only one percent will survive long enough to reproduce themselves, and many will die in the first few days. That is what happens when offspring have no care and no protection. Then about 120 million years ago with the emergence of the mammals and live birth, a completely new reproductive strategy emerged in the world, which involved infant care. Rather than disperse, the infant stays close to the parent who provides protection and other resources such as food and comfort.

Caring then began as an emergent evolved reproduction strategy. With caring, adaptations occurred in brains and bodies to enable infants and parents to stay in close contact and be responsive to each other (MacLean, 1985; Porges, 2007). It is crucial that the parent is able to regulate and soothe the infant. For example, in the presence of the parent, mammalian infants tend to be calmer and more likely to sleep. Separation from the parent activates the infant's threat and alarm system. What emerges then is a whole set of emotional and physiological systems that are regulated through relationships.

Tracking back through history we can see that we are a species which is biologically adapted and functionally equipped to be highly social and, in particular, physiologically regulated by our relationships (Cozolino, 2007). From the day that we are born to the day that we die the kindness of others will have major impacts on our physiologies and mental states.

Key components of compassion

Compassion can be seen as a form of social mentality that organises different aspects of our minds (Gilbert, 1989, 2005, 2009, 2010). The model can be depicted in figure 1. Compassion can be distinguished between attributes and skills. The attributes of compassion operate as an integrated set of attributes that are mutually influencing and dependent. If we lose any one of them our capacity for compassion can be compromised.

Figure 1: The compassion circle

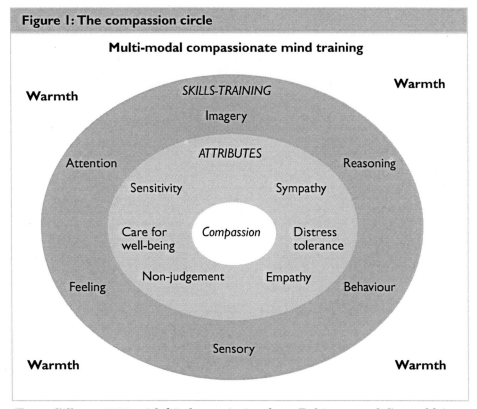

(From Gilbert, 2009 with kind permission from Robinson and Constable)

First, we begin by thinking about the motivation to be compassionate. Without a true and genuine desire to be compassionate to other people compassion probably fails to get off the ground. Harnessing compassionate motives therefore, understanding what facilitates them and blocks them, is key to creating compassion and caring services.

Next we can identify an attentional attribute, which is the sensitivity, the ability to notice, to make oneself aware of suffering. It is easy for us to lose that sensitivity. A third quality is one of sympathy, which is the ability to be emotionally moved by what we encounter. Sympathy is an automatic emotional connection that does not require us 'to think'. For example, we see a young child happily playing and then she falls over and badly hurts her head. That point of awareness can cause a stomach churning sense of anxiety and distress in us. This is a non-cognitive process. A fourth quality of compassion requires us to be able to tolerate distressing emotions and experiences. Research has shown that if we experience too much personal distress then we can be motivated to avoid that distress because we cannot tolerate it. Sometimes the psychotherapist can try to 'rescue patients who are tearful' because they find distress intolerable and want to turn it off – both for themselves and the person in distress. This may miss the opportunity of a person to learn how to work with their sadness. A fifth quality is empathy, which is our ability to imagine being that other person 'walking in their shoes'; it is key to the golden rule but it is also key to helping us think about 'mentalising' the situation of other people. For example, we may come to understand that the person who is angry is also frightened and feeling out of control. Empathy means we do not respond to the immediate external signal, we have a way of thinking about the situation from the other person's point of view. A sixth quality is non-judgement. When we enter into condemning, criticising, blaming and shaming we withdraw from compassion. Helping people take responsibility is of course vital to health care but condemning people for smoking and drinking or being obese does little to help them form a compassionate approach to self-care.

Compassionate skills are things that we can practise and work on by deliberately making choices. We can learn to pay compassionate attention, to think compassionately, to engage in compassionate behaviour and practise compassionate feeling. In developing compassionate feeling we can practise compassionate imagery and sensory focusing. We will explore these shortly.

A research focus on compassion means that once we have a model for compassion we can begin to think about the facilitators and inhibitors of compassion. For example, when we blame other people for their distress we tend to pull back from a compassionate approach to it. We might walk down the street and choose not to notice the beggars and those less fortunate than ourselves, we may switch TV channels when distressing news comes on. We also know that people can become burnt out or traumatised themselves by the process of caring for people in distress and pain (Figley, 1995; Rothschild, 2006). Research suggests that we are creating health care systems that have a higher risk of creating burnout in our caring professionals. It is also the case that if professionals themselves feel stressed and uncared for in their environments, it is more difficult to carry compassion into their workplace. As governments increasingly focus on targets and use threat-based strategies to pursue them, the recipe for squeezing out compassion is developing.

Compassion and the brain

However, the power of kindness and compassion no longer consists of just recommendations for the spiritually inclined but are actually supported by considerable research. For example, we can now identify specific brain systems that have been evolving over millions of years that are responsible and facilitate affiliative behaviour. Key to affiliative behaviour is a hormone called oxytocin.

Warm and affiliative interactions, however, are linked to social connectedness and safeness as conferred by the presence and support of others. Affiliative social relationships calm participants, alter pain thresholds, the immune and digestive systems, and operate via the oxytocin-opiate system (Depue & Morrone-Strupinsky, 2005). There is increasing evidence that oxytocin is linked to social support and buffers stress; those with lower oxytocin having higher stress responsiveness (Heinrichs *et al*, 2003). Oxytocin also impacts on threat processing in the amygdala (Kirsch *et al*, 2005). So social signals of affiliation and care have the qualities of soothing and involve neurohormones such as oxytocin and opiates (Carter, 1998; Depue & Morrone-Strupinsky, 2005; Panksepp, 1998; Uväns-Morberg, 1998). Signals and stimuli such as stroking, holding, voice tone, facial expressions, concerned interest/attentiveness and social support are natural stimuli that activate this system (Field, 2000; Gilbert, 1993, 2005; Uväns-Morberg, 1998; Wang, 2005). In a highly readable book, Hamilton (2010) traces the way in which kindness operates through oxytocin systems and produces a range of physiological benefits that can be measured on systems such as cardiovascular, immune and neurohormone.

Developing compassion

The development of personal compassion benefits greatly from personal practice. There is a wonderful story about a native American Indian chief who is talking to his grandson. As they walk along a river bank the grandson who is just entering adolescence is talking about his desires to be strong, fearless and to beat his opponents. The grandfather looks with understanding to his grandson and smiles, *'You know'*, he says, *'there have always been two wolves inside of me. One is aggressive and likes to fight, to win arguments and subdue others. The other seeks wisdom, kindness and justice'*. The grandson looks at his grandfather and eagerly asks *'So which one will win, grandfather?'* The grandfather responds, *'The one that I feed'*.

Our brains are designed with different types of emotion regulation systems (Gilbert, 2005, 2009). We have one that deals with threats and arouses us to anxiety and anger. We have another that focuses on achievement and resources and gives us feelings of excitement when we anticipate we will actually achieve them. If we win £1 million in the lottery we are likely to have a mild hypomania of excitement, racing thoughts and difficulty sleeping – at least for a day or two. This is related to a dopamine buzz. However, we have another type of positive emotion which is based on the endorphin and oxytocin system and gives rise to positive feelings of calmness and well-being. It is this system that needs training. We do not usually need to train ourselves to feel angry, irritable or anxious, these come naturally to us and can actually get in the way when we want to be calm. Equally, it is easy to get carried way with wanting more and more – to pursue the capitalist dream that more is better. We do not learn how to be content, how to be quiet and still within ourselves, able to appreciate and savour the small things in life. Developing compassion requires us to be more in touch with this aspect of ourselves, to be able to slow down, become more reflective, more open, sensitive and more tolerant – able to appreciate and to feel gratitude.

Developing mindful compassion

To do this there are various techniques that we can use. One is to pay attention to what goes on in our minds – the way our minds are full of worries and plans and things that need to be done next. We rush through the day on automatic pilot, and if we are thwarted this can arouse irritation or anxiety. However, there are practices such as mindfulness where we can learn to pay attention to the present moment without judgement (Siegel, 2010).

In addition, we can learn how to breathe in such a way that we slow ourselves down. This is called soothing breathing rhythm where we sit upright and focus on the breathing being slightly longer and slightly deeper than normal. We tune into the experience of body slowing. We notice how it feels when we tap into our own slower rhythms, especially the out breath that stimulates the parasympathetic system and calming (Gilbert, 2009, 2010).

Learning to become more mindful and taking time to focus on the breathing and slowing creates ideal conditions in which we can begin to think about and practise becoming more of a compassionate self (Germer, 2009). There are many ways one can do this. One of the easiest is to use a kind of method acting approach. In this approach we imagine ourselves to be a certain kind of person as if we are preparing to take on the role in a film or stage play. We want to get into the role in order to feel sufficiently acted and convince our audience. So for a short time we want to become the person we are acting.

To practice becoming the compassionate self means that we recognise the desire to be in touch with the compassionate circle within ourselves; to engage with our motivation to be compassionate. So, for example, you can sit or stand, engage in your soothing breathing rhythm and now imagine yourself to be a deeply compassionate person. This is you at your very best, as you would really like to be. Spend a moment imagining yourself to have the qualities of wisdom, an understanding about the nature of suffering. Imagine also that you are like an authority that has a calm confidence and strength about you. Imagine too that you have great kindness and warmth. You can aid this imagery by creating a compassionate facial expression. For example, allow your face to relax, starting at your forehead, moving through your cheeks and letting your jaw drop slightly in a relaxed way. Then begin to let your mouth turn upwards to create a smile. Keep going until you have created a smile that gives you the feeling of compassion and kindness. Next imagine how you live in the world – the kind of body postures and way you move and act that give you the 'air of a compassionate person'. Imagine how you act towards people – for example those in the caring professions can imagine how they would be with their patients if they were at their most compassionate. Finally, but most importantly, imagine how you talk as a compassionate person. Imagine the tone and textures of your voice; the kind of things you say and how you say them.

If you do these exercises regularly you are gradually becoming familiar with the feelings and ideas of the compassionate self. By practising these you become more familiar with them and gradually build them into the kind of person you want to be. We call this building compassionate capacity. There is no reason for this compassionate mind to develop and grow much unless you cultivate it. Our minds are like a garden – they will grow regardless of what we do, but we might not like the outcome. Making decisions about what to cultivate in one's mind, what to practise, creating in one's mind a clear view of what one wants to become, can be the first steps to developing into the kind of person you would like to be.

In compassion-focused therapy (CFT) we sometimes spend time imagining being the compassionate self before we begin therapy (Gilbert, 2010). Those working with CFT have found that this can be especially important when working with complex and difficult cases. By tuning into our compassionate self we are creating a mindset to be able to engage in the work we do – being with people in pain. It is stressed however that this does take practice.

Compassionate institutions and the costs of care

I want to end this chapter by emphasising that compassion is a way of addressing our social conditions, cultures and politics. If we wish for compassion in the health service then we will need to build alliances and work hard for them. The problem in our modern health service is partly due to medicine's success. We now have treatments for many different conditions and our population is living longer. We are dying less from heart disease and cancer in our 60s and more commonly from longer drawn out illnesses such as dementia in our 70s and 80s. From our science on infertility and body part replacements, to the extraordinary technical ability in helping people rehabilitate after serious injuries, including head injuries, our healthcare system has become increasingly expensive. These realities put pressure on governments who want to have themselves elected on low taxation platforms. Their argument here is that if you don't create wealth you can't spend it on health. So the rising costs of health send governments searching for efficiencies that focus on a need for better technologies and faster turnarounds, doing more for less.

In hurtling down this avenue we risk medicine becoming more and more 'factory like'. While understandable to those who worry about the accounts, the serious downside to this approach is that it squeezes out the time for compassionate relating and grossly underestimates the role of relationships in the healing and illness prevention process – not to mention facilitating well-being and more efficient working. Moreover, when compassion begins to go out of healing, and economic efficiency becomes the guide, even the technologies cannot work correctly. The way the Mid Stafford Hospital enquiry (http://www.midstaffsinquiry.com/) revealed how managers had corrupted the caring system in order to meet targets is a warning about what happens when compassion and the quality of relationships (the spiritual candle in us) is forgotten. These are not bad people – they are just bad systems. Blaming individuals makes it so much easier to turn a blind eye to the systems we are creating.

It is not that we do not know what inhibits compassion. Studies of institutionalisation have long shown that it is easy for compassion to be lost in large institutions. In 2008 the Royal College of Nursing published a report outlining a number of processes that interfere with compassionate care. These included: overcrowded and mixed sex wards; noisy and disruptive environments; resource and understaffing levels; excessive bureaucracy and paperwork; lack of leadership – to name but a few. There have also been many patient surveys on what they find helpful and what they do not. At the top of the list, they want to see clinicians who know them, rather than seeing a new doctor or nurse every visit. Patients always want trusting, caring and consistent, as well as competent care. In our own ongoing studies on the facilitators and inhibitors of compassion, care on acute psychiatric wards, lack of time to sit with and talk to patients and actually relate to people is the most common inhibitor. We have become obsessed with 'payment by results' while vast resources are increasingly tied up with accountability, with clinicians needing to record every minute of every working day, and with paid administrators somehow 'analysing' it all. The challenge therefore is to face the realities of financial constraints but for clinicians to insist there are compassionate ways of facing the challenge.

To keep to this importance of understanding and compassion in a social context, we must always keep in mind that we are deeply affected by the social context of our lives. In order to create compassionate institutions we need to sit down and think through what would create a compassionate institution. For example, supposing you are working on a ward – how often do you sit down with your team and patient representatives and work out what compassionate care looks like, explore it with your patients, think about how you or a loved relative would ideally like to be treated if you had this condition, and then think about how to make compassionate care happen? What gets in the way of doing this? Yet this type of exercise would be extremely helpful because our compassion can grow if it is supported and becomes not just a personal identity but an identity for the team we work in. Governments developing checklists to measure compassion show once again the fundamental misunderstanding about the psychology of compassion.

Compassion can cost individuals too. In fact the most compassionate, those most dedicated, are those most at risk of burnout (Figley, 1995; Rothschild, 2006), particularly in caring systems that are organised around accounts, economics and political targets. These problems have been well depicted by the research of the King's fund which has shown that compassion in our health service is increasingly difficult to sustain (http://www.kingsfund.org.uk/current_projects/the_point_of_care/compassion/).

There are many growing ideas and studies looking at how to facilitate compassion in the caring professions (Chambers & Ryder, 2009; Fehr *et al*, 2009; http://www.compassioninhealthcare.org/). Many of these tend to focus on individuals and individual skills and awareness. These are important but the social contexts in which individuals operate also have very powerful influences on feelings, thoughts and behaviours. Hence, we need to be more focused on 'building compassionate communities' that focus on the interactional and structural aspects of compassion. This means that we need to understand how we are creating systems that squeeze out compassion; for example, being overly concerned about outputs rather than inputs, supply and not demand (Seddon, 2008). At its simplest, there is too much threat with bureaucratic and autocratic solutions, so that we actually lose sight of what the systems are actually trying to provide (Lister, 2008).

Conclusion

We began this chapter by thinking about the origins of spirituality as linked to our searches to cope with the existential crises and terrors of suffering and death. Early religions focused on moral behaviours but also tribal boundaries and conflicts that recruit punitive psychologies; punishments for the disobedient, free riders and those who might loosen the cohesion of group identity. Compassion moves us in a different direction. When we have a compassionate mind our motives, feelings, attention, empathy and behaviours are totally different than when stressed or threat-focused. At the heart of medicine and the caring professions is the desire to reduce suffering – which is fundamental to compassion. The tragedy is that with the costs of health care spiralling upwards and governments unsure how to contain them we have moved back into fear-based psychologies with bureaucratic solutions. It is not God we now fear but the bureaucracies we work within. People operating in these systems will struggle to develop compassion even if they want to, because they will be time-limited and threat-focused.

Compassionate approaches to caring are not about metaphysical beliefs or simply tuning in or out mindfully. They are about a scientific understanding of the sources of our pain and suffering, the conditions that make us vulnerable to illnesses and those who help us heal and cope with them; it is concerned with what creates compassionate behaviours and the socially contextualised nature of human psychology. Compassionate approaches are about developing a genuine agreement about morals and ethics and the kinds of care we want to provide – after all, maybe we want to provide cheaper, technology focused, impersonal care? For some people it is not obvious that compassionate care – given that it is not cost free – is the choice. If we want our carers to behave compassionately, they need to be treated compassionately, and able to operate within compassion-facilitating systems. If not there will be various heroic efforts, well-meaning reports, but those will not change things on a grand scale. Compassion calls for political engagement as well as a personal cultivation of our compassionate mind.

References

Aldridge D (2000) *Spirituality, Healing and Medicine*. London: Jessica Kingsley.

Armstrong K (2007) *The Great Transformation. The world in the time of buddha, socrates, confucius and jeremiah*. London: Atlantic Book.

Batchelor S (2010) *Confessions of a Buddhist Atheist*. New York: Spiegel & Grau.

Cacioppo JT, Berston GG, Sheridan JF & McClintock MK (2000) Multilevel integrative analysis of human behavior: social neuroscience and the complementing nature of social and biological approaches. *Psychological Bulletin* **126** 829–843.

Cacioppo JT, Hawkley LC, Rickett EM & Masi CM (2005) Sociality, spirituality, and meaning making: Chicago health, aging, and social relations study. *Review of General Psychology* **9** 143–155.

Carter CS (1998) Neuroendocrine perspectives on social attachment and love. *Psychoneuroendocrinology* **23** 779–818.

Chambers C & Ryder E (2009) *Compassion and Caring in Nursing*. Abingdon: Radcliffe Publishing Ltd.

Cook C, Powell A & Sims A (2009) *Spirituality and Psychiatry*. London: Royal College of Psychology.

Cozolino L (2007) *The Neuroscience of Human Relationships: Attachment and the developing brain*. New York: Norton.

Cozolino L (2008) *The Healthy Aging Brain: Sustaining attachment, attaining wisdom*. New York: Norton.

Cupitt D (2005) *The Great Questions of Life*. London: Polebridge Press.

Dalai Lama (1995) *The Power of Compassion*. India: HarperCollins.

Davidson R & Harrington A (2002) *Visions of Compassion: Western scientists and Tibetan buddhists examine human nature*. New York: Oxford University Press.

Depue RA & Morrone-Strupinsky JV (2005) A neurobehavioral model of affiliative bonding. *Behavioral and Brain Sciences* **28** 313–395.

Dossey L (2007) Compassion. *Explore* January February **3** 1–5.

Field T (2000) *Touch Therapy*. New York: Churchill Livingstone.

Figley C (1995) *Compassion Fatigue: Coping with secondary traumatic stress disorder in those who treat the traumatized*. London: Routledge.

Fehr C, Sprecher S & Underwood LG (2009) *The Science of Compassionate Love: Theory research and application*. Chichester: Wiley.

Germer C (2009) *The Mindful Path to Self-Compassion: Freeing your self from destructive thoughts and emotions*. New York: Guilford.

Gilbert P (1989) *Human Nature and Suffering*. Hove: Lawrence Erlbaum Associates.

Gilbert P (1993) Defence and safety: their function in social behaviour and psychopathology. *British Journal of Clinical Psychology* **32** 131–153.

Gilbert P (2005) Compassion and cruelty: a biopsychosocial approach. In: P Gilbert (Ed) *Compassion: Conceptualisations, research and use in psychotherapy* (pp9–74). London: Routledge.

Gilbert P (2009) *The Compassionate Mind*. London: Constable.

Gilbert P (2010) *Compassion Focused Therapy: The CBT distinctive features series*. London: Routledge.

Hamilton DR (2010) *Why Kindness is Good for You*. London: Hay House.

Heinrichs M, Baumgartner T, Kirschbaum C & Ehlert U (2003) Social support and oxytocin interact to suppress cortisol and subjective response to psychosocial stress. *Biological Psychiatry* **54** 1389–1398.

Hinde RA (1999) *Why Gods Persist: A scientific approach to religion*. London: Routledge.

Jung CG (1952/1998) *Answer to Job*. London. Routledge.

Kendell RE (1975) *The Role of Diagnosis in Psychiatry*. London: Blackwell Scientific Publications.

Kirsch P, Esslinger C, Chen Q, Mier D, Lis S, Siddanti S, Gruppe H, Mattay VS, Gallhofer B & Meyer-Lindenberg A (2005) Oxytocin modulates neural circuitry for social cognition and fear in humans. *The Journal of Neuroscience* **25** 11489–11493.

Lister J (2008) *The NHS After 60 years*. London: Middlesex University Press.

MacLean P (1985) Brain evolution relating to family, play and the separation call. *Archives of General Psychiatry* **42** 405–417.

McMahon D (2006) *The Pursuit of Happiness: A history from the Greeks to the present*. London: Penguin.

Nisbett RE, Peng K, Choi I & Norenzayan A (2001) Culture and systems of thought: holistic versus analytic cognition. *Psychological Review* **108** 291–310.

Panksepp J (1998) *Affective Neuroscience*. New York: Oxford University Press.

Porges SW (2007) The polyvagal perspective. *Biological Psychology* **74** 116–143.

Ricard M (2007) *Happiness. A guide to developing life's most important skill*. London: Atlantic Books.

Rifkin J (2009) *The Empathic Civilization: The race to global consciousness in a world in crises*. Cambridge: Polity Press.

Rothschild B (2006) *Help for the Helper*. New York: Norton.

Seddon J (2008) *Systems Thinking in the Public Sector Failure of the Reform Regime and a Manifesto for a Better Way*. London: Triarchy Press.

Siegel RD (2010) *The Mindfulness Solution: Everyday practices for everyday problems*. New York: Guilford.

Tiger F & McGuire M (2010) *God's Brain*. New York: Prometheus Books.

Uväns-Morberg K (1998) Oxytocin may mediate the benefits of positive social interaction and emotions. *Psychoneuroendocrinology* **23** 819–835.

Wang S (2005) A conceptual framework for integrating research related to the physiology of compassion and the wisdom of Buddhist teachings. In: P Gilbert (Ed) *Compassion: Conceptualisations, research and use in psychotherapy* (p75–120). London: Brunner-Routledge.